THE FAR-FAMED WRITER of tales of the sea presents his own selection of the best stories of the ocean frontiers, chosen to give a more rounded picture of the subject than do most anthologies. As Mr. McFee himself has written to his publishers: "It is my idea to leave the beaten track of the yo-heave-ho school of sea fiction when possible, and include other facets of sea life besides the tough-guy fellows."

From this viewpoint, Mr. McFee has chosen seldom-collected stories by J. C. Bruce, "Bartimeus," Hanson W. Baldwin, Sir Ernest Shackleton, Captain E. V. Rickenbacker, Joseph Conrad, Eugene Burdick, James Norman Hall, John Kruse, George G. Toudouze, and others. Mr. McFee's own original contribution to the book consists of a new interpretation of the story of Captain Carlson of *The Flying Enterprise*.

A feature of the book is Mr. McFee's long introduction analyzing the lure of the sea story and showing its unbroken hold on those who travel only in the realms of the imagination.

GREAT
SEA STORIES OF
MODERN TIMES

EDITED WITH ORIGINAL MATERIAL
AND AN INTRODUCTION

By
William McFee

THE McBRIDE COMPANY
NEW YORK

Copyright 1953 by
THE McBRIDE COMPANY, INC.

First Edition

Library of Congress Catalog Card Number: 53–11945

Printed in the United States of America
Published Simultaneously in Canada by
McClelland & Stewart, Ltd.
Toronto

"They that go down to the sea in ships, that do business in great waters;

"These see the works of the Lord, and his wonders in the deep.

"For he commandeth, and raiseth the stormy wind, which lifteth up the waves thereof.

"They mount up to the heaven, they go down again to the depths."

Psalms: V, 107, 23–26.

CONTENTS

INTRODUCTION

WHY SEA STORIES? Why the classification? The question was raised by a professional writer irked by what he calls excessive regionalism in American writing. He could see no particular reason why there should be another region, a salt-water cult.

There are several reasons, all good, and it is the purpose of this Introduction to lay them on the line for all to see. It is not enough to retort that landsmen as well as seamen like to read stories about the sea. We must know why.

We must, in the first place, narrow the argument to what we call the West. All very well for Dr. Johnson to refer airily to ranging from China to Peru; he had never been to either place. The present remarks apply to Western Europe and North America. Natives of Hindustan, the Congo, and Central Asia, so far as we know, do not read sea stories, nor do they write them. It is true that Conrad, the greatest sea writer of all, came out of Poland and arrived in England by way of the French merchant marine. But Conrad is the dazzling exception that proves the rule. He is unique in many ways, and incomparable. Only seven of his two dozen volumes are about the sea, and it would be as rational to limit Turner by calling him a marine painter as to call Conrad a mere sea writer. He resented the title and, when he was breezily requested to turn out "a rattling sea story," he went berserk.

In the present case, moreover, the idea is to confine our anthology to modern literature, omitting such celebrated exhibits as "The Open Boat," by Stephen Crane, which have been anthologized to death. In place of Crane's masterpiece, we have the true story of Mr. Rickenbacker's open boat from his book, *Seven Came Through*. Perhaps even more revolutionary was the decision to include stories about passengers and passenger ships, stories about sea disasters, stories about submarines. In fact, the classification of sea literature, so far from being regional, has been greatly broadened in our time. Is not an airliner or a jet bomber called a ship? They have captains and pilots and navigators and engineers, and they sail over the ocean.

The true anthology, of course, would be marvelously comprehensive. We would have stories about all the seas. Not only the Seven Seas, but the Red Sea, the Black Sea, the White Sea and, in China, the Yellow Sea. Odd, by the way, that no one ever christened a Blue Sea or a Green Sea, although we have in popular parlance the Blue Mediterranean and the Blue Caribbean, which are often grey and menacing. There are the other seas which should be represented in this ideal anthology; the Adriatic, the Tyrrhenian, the Ionian and the Aegean, the Behring, the Barents, the Narrow Seas and the Coral Sea. Not to mention the Sargasso Sea, fabled to be full of ships locked forever in a silent, motionless sea of weed.

So far we have evaded the explanation of the lure the sea exerts on the landsman. In the first place, the land is always changing; the sea remains the same through the centuries. When the Athenian ships sailed for Syracuse, when the Roman grain ships left Africa for the Tiber, it was the same sea as when the Allied navies grappled with Mussolini's elusive squadrons. The sea Captain Bligh sailed on during his amazing voyage in an open boat was identical with that of Captain Rickenbacker's rugged adventure. Technological advances make yesterday's marvels obsolete, but man's emotions remain the same, century after century. He discovers an unconscious solace in the unchanging sea.

It is charged by those who write conventional verse that the public no longer appreciates "poetry." This is not so. A sea story, if it achieves its aim, corresponds to the ancient saga and ballad. It embodies a heroic, a desperate contest between men and the sea. It was no accident that Kipling used the ancient ballad form for many of his finest sea poems. The sea inspired the imaginations of writers, from Homer with his "wine-dark sea" to Tennyson's "summer isles of Eden, lying in dark purple spheres of sea," Kipling's "planet-powdered floors" of a tropic sea, and Masefield's enchantment with the sight of strange lands from under the "arched white sails of ships."

It is the baldest truth to say that, when sea literature rises to its supreme achievement, as in Conrad, it is pure poetry. When a reader turns to a sea story, what he seeks, and may sometimes find, is to be reassured of the bravery of the human spirit and the mystery and the fundamental integrity of the universe. He desires, in Conrad's phrase, to be awakened to that solidarity "which binds men to each other and all mankind to the visible world."

William McFee

Roxbury, Connecticut,
September 25, 1953.

Great Sea Stories of
Modern Times

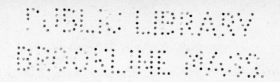
LOG THE MAN DEAD

By Eugene Burdick

"Log The Man Dead" is a story of the barbarous days of the British Navy, days of the press-gang, the cat o' nine tails, and the incredible practice of "flogging around the fleet," a punishment which often resulted in death before it was over. No one who has not delved into naval history can have any conception of the sadistic customs of the past. One of our early ambassadors, on his way to Russia in an American ship, commented with horror on the flogging he witnessed. A Southern aristocrat, he said he saw more flogging of white men on that voyage than would take place in years on his plantation.

Professor Eugene Burdick, of the University of California, who wrote "Log The Man Dead," took a tour of duty during World War II at the Newport, R.I., Naval College. He found many ideas for sea stories in the college library, and this is one we commend to those who look back nostalgically to the "good old days." A Rhodes Scholar at Oxford, where he obtained his doctorate, Professor Burdick is a specialist in political theory, but his real love is the sea. He has in mind a book on naval strategy, and he is completing a novel. In 1947 he won second prize in the O. Henry Competition with one of his short stories.

IN THE HARBOR of Plymouth, in England, the ship-building firm of Hawkins and Company was working day and night on the ship. During the day, men, naked to the waist, chipped at huge, raw logs, converting them into ribs and spars. At night, torches and cressets were lit and, in the fitful light, hot creosote and tallow were poured over the caulking which had been pounded into the seams. In the sail shops, yards of bright-red cloth were converted into sails. The great, gaunt ribs of the ship grew higher than the shops and were finally planked over and sanded into a slick surface. The masts were inserted into their locks and the long task of fitting the sails begun.

Crimping crews began to drive impressed crewmen aboard the ship. Among these was a tall, slim boy named Simon Jonson, from Devonshire. This was the first time he had ever seen salt water. As he filed aboard he looked up at the masts, their tips vanishing into the mist. The ship seemed enormous.

Finally a carpenter chiseled the letters T—I—G—E—R into the overhanging stern of the vessel. The next day the ship slid down the ways, heaved gently in the quiet waters and then rested, ready for the sea.

Four months later the ship was six hundred miles off Africa and becalmed in a great, dead circle of water. Occasionally a ground swell would bulge the gray, hot surface and the ship would creak. Under the steady blast of unrelieved brightness, the sea began to smell like iodine, quenched iron and dead fish.

But the *Tiger* was taut with excitement. For a man was on trial for his life and the man was Simon Jonson. He stood on the quarter-deck in front of a table over which the officers of a court-martial eyed him. Behind him the entire crew was drawn up in three straight lines.

The men stood stiffly and sweat streaked their clothes

black, poured down their faces, ran in trickles into their shoes. Simon Jonson, facing the sun, was almost blinded, so that the figures of the officers behind the table seemed to be tiny black figures, all identical and all very far away. Occasionally a salty drop of sweat ran into his eye, but he patiently blinked it away. He was thinking of an event that had occurred three weeks before. In exact and precise outlines, the memory came back to him. As the voice of the prosecutor droned on, endlessly and far away, Simon thought back to that rotten, irresistible memory.

It had started with a simple argument between Martin, the boatswain's mate, and Blake, the sailmaker. They had stood arguing by the hatch leading into the fo'c'sle and Simon had been listening. Suddenly, in one of those blinding seconds of action, the argument had grown heated and Blake had swung his sail needle at Martin. Quite by accident, the curved, ugly needle caught in Watson's shoulder muscle and jutted out, turning the shirt red as the blood seeped out. In a moment, Mr. Galbraith, the second mate, was on the scene, and had arrested Blake for attacking another man.

"He didn't mean anything, Mr. Galbraith," Martin said through his clenched teeth. As if to minimize his injury he reached up and jerked the needle out of his shoulder. The blood ran in a gush down his arm. "We was just fooling around."

"We'll let the captain decide that," Mr. Galbraith said coldly. "There are regulations to govern such matters."

Two days later the captain had called the crew together and read the verdict against Blake. The captain was a tall, thin, aristocratic man who wore immaculate white linen at his throat. He looked somehow like a preacher as his Adam's apple worked in his long neck. When he finished two men seized Blake and dragged him to a block situated in the middle of the quarter-deck. Blake screamed a long, quivering shriek and then stared with bulging eyes up at the sky.

One of the men forced the sail needle into Blake's open hand and then forced the hand down onto the block. At the same time another man stepped forward with a sharp hatchet. Simon had been standing numbly, hardly knowing what was happening. But as he saw the hatchet he guessed what was to come. With a quick, sliding jerk, he was out of the right ranks of the crew, had stepped across the deck and, tearing the hatchet from the man's hand, threw it over the side. Then, wheeling about, he swung accurately and powerfully at one of the men holding Blake's hand. The man fell and the other man let go. Blake stood frozen, staring up at the sky, paralyzed with fear, unable to move.

In a moment Simon was subdued by a brace of sea-men and was standing in front of the captain. He had not been excited when he left the ranks and he was not excited now, only impatient to explain to the captain the true story of the needle-stabbing episode.

"It was not a fight, sir," Simon started to say in a deliberate voice. "They were really only joking. It was not—"

The captain's already thin face had drawn sharp with anger. Two spots of color burned in his cheeks.

"It states in the Rules for the Regulation of the Navy that any man who draws the blood of another shall have the hand that inflicted the damage chopped off," the captain said in a crisp, rigidly controlled voice.

"But any rule that doesn't recognize that this was just

a joke between friends is a bad rule," Simon said. He could not conceive that the captain would not see the justice of this.

"The Regulations also state that anyone that interferes with the administrations of justice aboard a naval ship shall be confined to the bowsprit," the captain said. His narrow red tongue came out, flicked at the corners of his mouth, left his lips moist. "You shall stand court-martial for that offense."

And then, as the crew held Simon back, although he was calm and cool, the two men again held Blake's hand on the block. With a swish a new hatchet cut the air. A dark spray of blood shot over the deck, the severed hand opened with a jerk, and the gleaming, bright needle rolled out on the deck. Blake shrieked once, then groaned and fainted. Simon watched the proceedings coldly, his eyes moving from the hand to the captain's face.

"And Seaman Jonson was, to your best knowledge, not suffering from sunstroke, brain fever or other disease when he interfered with the administration of justice on last June fifteenth?" Lieutenant Galbraith, the prosecuting officer, was asking the ship's surgeon.

The surgeon, a squat fat man, with a red face, shook his head. "He was of sound mind and body." He turned his bloodshot drunkard's eyes toward Simon and then glanced quickly away.

Simon still could not believe that he would not be able to explain his actions. To his methodical, Devonshire mind it seemed a simple case of righting a wrong. He waited patiently for the moment when he would be asked to explain what had happened.

In a few more moments Lieutenant Galbraith finished

his interrogation. He turned to the captain saying, "Sir, I have finished the presentation of the case for His Majesty's Navy."

"In your opinion, Mr. Galbraith, does this offense fall under those crimes which call for automatic confinement to the bowsprit until dead?" the captain asked casually, although he was watching Simon while he spoke.

"Well, sir, it might be interpreted in another manner if extenuating circumstances were found." Lieutenant Galbraith hedged, unwilling to face the reality of such a sentence.

"What would such extenuating circumstances be?" the captain asked in an icy voice. Without waiting for an answer he stood up and announced, "Gentlemen, the court-martial shall retire to my cabin to reach a verdict."

So suddenly that he could scarcely comprehend what had happened, the officers had left the quarter deck and Simon realized that he would never have a chance to plead his case; that the decision would be reached on the basis of the evidence that the court-martial had now taken. For the first time he thought seriously of "bowspritting." It was one of the most dreaded words in the navy and Simon had heard endless stories of former "bowspritting" sentences in the crew's quarters.

This was the most hideous of punishments. A sailor sentenced to be "spitted" was led to the bow of the ship where the powerful jutting beak of the ship, reaching far out over the cut-water, constituted the bowsprit. At the foot of the bowsprit he was given a ration of beer, a half a loaf of bread and a sharp sail knife. Then two boatswain mates tied his body to the bowsprit, leaving his arms free. There, after finishing the bread and beer, he had three alternatives.

First, he could kill himself with the knife and have a speedy death. Or he could cut himself loose and fall into the ocean, where he would either drown or fall victim to the shark or the sharp slashing teeth of the barracuda. Or, finally, he could starve to death on the bowsprit. The thing he could not do is come back off the bowsprit onto the ship. Five yards behind the victim the ship was going about its normal life, but he could only eye that life as his own existence was slowly squeezed out.

If the man stayed on the bowsprit and died, his body was not removed, and for months there would be the thick, rotten odor of death about the bowsprit as the elements and the sharp, pecking beaks of sea birds reduced the body. Finally there would be nothing left but a jiggling, clean-picked skeleton, held to the spar by the few remaining lines. And no man would, or could, touch the lines on the skeleton. They must wait until the line rotted off and the skeleton slipped loose and fell into the sea.

"They won't spit you, Simon," one of the crew members murmured to him. "You did nothing wrong."

"Quiet there," the sergeant snarled.

The crew fell silent and then, after a pause, began to whisper among themselves. From the sound of their whispers Simon knew they thought he would get the bowsprit. He began to feel as if he were involved in a hot, steaming nightmare which had gripped him in some strange way, but which would release him before it was too late. The sun suddenly seemed to increase in size and warmth. His head felt empty and burned out. He knew he was afraid.

In ten minutes the officers filed back out of the cabin. The surgeon licked a smear of Demerera rum off his lips, the captain touched his hands to the linen at his neck,

Lieutenant Galbraith looked deliberately past Simon. They assembled quickly around the table and Lieutenant Galbraith stood up. He cleared his throat and spoke.

"We find Apprentice Seaman Jonson guilty of obstructing the administration of justice and under the Regulations of the Navy we order him confined to the bowsprit, never to return. God rest his soul. Ship's Clerk, strike his name from the record. Boatswain, carry out the sentence. All hands splice the main brace."

Simon heard the crew stiffen in anger behind him, even before he realized what the sentence was. Then Simon felt his cheeks burn hot; behind his eyes he felt blackness loom up; the table and officers angled before his eyes and then vanished. He had fainted.

The captain turned and walked into his cabin. The officers walked slowly toward the limp, unconscious body of the boy. They picked him up and carried him to the bowsprit and bound him to the long spar. It was a hot, sultry day and Simon did not regain consciousness for some time. An officer was stationed at the foot of the bowsprit to make sure that Jonson did not return to the ship. As far as the British Navy was concerned, Simon Jonson was already dead. The ship's clerk drew a line through his name on the roster and put these words after it: "Died at sea."

Simon had been on the bowsprit only a half hour when the whole aspect of the sea suddenly altered. The bottle-green color changed, a flat, black bank of clouds came bustling down out of the middle distance, and, with a sudden jerk, the sails filled, the frigate heeled over and began to scud across the ocean. The Canaries dropped away and the ship lurched swiftly toward the equatorial seas. The shock of the cool wind brought young Simon back to consciousness and as soon as he looked around he could see what happened. He glanced at the sea, down the bowsprit to where the officer stood. Then he glanced at the worsening sea. He tucked the bread, the bottle of beer and the knife into his shirt, tightened the ropes around his chest and waist and locked his arms around the bowsprit.

Simon was tough, intelligent and determined to live. When he looked over his shoulder at the men, who gathered at the foot of the bowsprit to shout encouragement to him, his eyes bulged slightly with fear, but his jaw was strong and tight. As the seas got higher the bowsprit would occasionally dip deep into the green water, lurch back, and Simon would come to the surface dripping water, his fingers biting into the smooth, tough wood of the bowsprit.

The storm lasted six days. During that time Simon drank and ate nothing. His only refreshment was the shock of the seas passing over his body as the bowsprit lunged into the tropical waters. When it rained, he turned his head toward the sky, stuck his tongue out and caught a pitiful few drops of water. With his hands, he scooped the thin, slick layer of rainwater off of the surface of the spar and obtained a few more drops. Meanwhile the *Tiger* pitched and wallowed down the length of Africa, passed Dakar, and finally began to head southeast to swing in under the great belly of Africa and to run along the Gold Coast.

On the seventh day the winds died and the sun came up hot and clear. The sails began to flap again, the ship rolled listlessly. They were within a hundred miles of the equator. The bowl of the sea and sky became brassy with heat, the ocean steamed. The sun burned the salt water off of Simon's skin, leaving streaks of pure-white salt behind. In the storm his cap and shoes had washed away, and now the exposed skin on his feet, hands and face turned pink, then red, and as blisters formed, a painful white.

By the tenth day the boy's tongue began to protrude from his mouth and he chewed on a small piece of the bread, trying to work up some saliva. On the eleventh day Martin advised him to take some of the beer, and for the first time the boy uncorked the bottle and took a mouthful of the rich bitter stuff. Martin was the boatswain of the *Tiger* and although he had spent twenty years at sea he was bitterly opposed to the navy method of discipline. A tough, wizened, sun-blackened man, he had much admired Simon's calm performance before the court-martial. The beer revived Simon at once and he waved a hand at the crew members who stood at the foot of the bowsprit. The crew roared support back to him.

"Just a mouthful, Simon. That's all you can have today," Martin called to him. "Cork up the bottle and put it back in your shirt."

The boy obeyed reluctantly, his bleary, bloodshot eyes fastened on the bottle of beer. Martin now spent his nights sleeping at the foot of the bowsprit, awakening throughout the night to give the boy encouragement and, occasionally, to pray with him.

On the thirteenth day two things happened. The lines holding Simon had become loose because of the weight he had lost. It took him six hours to untie the knots and tighten up the lines around his shrunken body. The second thing that happened was that he began to moan—an occasional desolate, low scream of pain that hung over the ship like a curse before the tropical winds swept it away.

By now the ship had swung under the great overhanging belly of Africa and was heading toward the tiny island of Sao Thomé, which was almost exactly on the equator. Each day the sun came up hot and clear and beat down on the boy on the unprotected bowsprit. During the hottest part of the day the helmsman tried to steer so that the sails made a shadow over Simon, but the captain insisted relentlessly that they hold to the true compass course.

By now the boy's tongue was black and swollen. The exposed skin of his feet and neck had formed into hard brown scabs of burnt flesh. He lay like a sack of rags, only his hands, clinging like claws to the bowsprit, seemed alive. He gave a cry of despair two or three times a day. Once a day he took a single mouthful of beer from the bottle. He could no longer chew the bread. Several times when the members of the crew were swabbing down decks they would throw a bucket of cool sea-water over his dry body. This would revive him and he would wave a thin hand in thanks. The crew members cheered wildly whenever this happened. The officer on watch would beat the offending crew member, but it went on despite this.

On the seventeenth day, Sao Thomé was sighted and the ship steadied on a direct course for the island. The boy had not stirred for a day now and the crew feared he was dead. As the ship threaded its way through the channel the crew stood watching him. The ship was finally warped alongside the dock.

"Boy, you've made it, you're safe," Martin said in a

low voice. "Come on, boy, wake up. Cut yourself loose. We've made a port."

Nothing happened, and a groan went up from the crew. Martin's voice went higher, a note of despair in it, as he repeated the words.

Then the bundle of rags stirred, the boy's head, now balancing on an incredibly thin neck, came up. Through the puffed and lacerated eyelids there was a gleam of light. Thick, swollen fingers laced with blood reached into his shirt, took out the knife. With weak, grotesque motions he sawed at the ropes, cutting through a thread at a time. He finished one rope and then collapsed, unconscious. In a half hour he revived and doggedly cut through the last rope. Then he turned and looked dully at the crew without speaking.

"You can't come back down the bowsprit," Martin shouted. "It's against the King's Regulations. Drop into the water."

The words slowly worked through to Simon's mind. He let go of the knife, half-turned on the bowsprit and fell into the still water alongside the dock with a loud splash.

The boatswain, Martin, and two other sailors dove over the side. They collared Simon and swam over to the pier with him. Two other sailors had sprinted off down the dock. They came back with oranges, sugar lumps and a beaker of water. They squeezed the juice of several oranges into his mouth, past the swollen, blackened tongue; then gradually and slowly they gave him water. By that afternoon the tough fiber of the boy's body was already knitting and he was asking for meat. He was going to live. But the seventeen days on the bowsprit had changed Simon Jonson. He was no longer a boy. He had become a hard and bitter man. Although he recovered quickly from the ravages of exposure, lines remained about his mouth and eyes. Whenever the *Tiger* was mentioned his face became a flat, implacable mask in which his eyes glittered with a cold hatred.

Martin explained that it had never been contemplated that a man would return alive from the trip to the bowsprit. In the eyes of the captain, Simon was now dead. In the eyes of the Navy and of England, Simon was also dead, and his family would be notified that he had died at sea. He was without passport, nationality, money, family or profession. Simon nodded grimly as Martin talked, his eyes occasionally wandering down the dock to the black, empty outline of the bowsprit on which he had lived for so many days.

"I'll live somehow," Simon said flatly. "Can you teach me how to build a boat before the *Tiger* sails? If you can, I'll have a trade that I can work at. Then I won't starve to death on this miserable island."

"I'll try, my boy," Martin said. "But it is a difficult craft. It takes time."

Eighteen hours a day, for the time the *Tiger* remained in port, Martin taught Simon the craft. Simon's gaunt hands were weak at first, but they were sure and deft. He learned quickly. In all that time, however, Simon did not once talk of England and he would not permit Martin to mention the Royal Navy or the humiliation of his bowspritting. Martin was disturbed by the steel-hard bitterness he found in Simon. Once he began to talk of Christian forgiveness, but Simon only stared at him with glazed and cynical eyes. Martin's voice trailed off inconclusively, disconcerted by the hardness in Simon's face which appeared to intensify.

Finally the *Tiger* sailed. Everyone on the island was on the docks to watch it leave—except Simon Jonson. He was on the far side of the island cutting a rosewood tree into spars for a sloop he had already started to build. He had his trade, and was hard at work.

During the next year Simon built furniture, homes, canoes—anything to keep alive. In his spare time he worked on his sloop. It took two years to finish it.

The day it was finished he took on a crew of four Gold Coast Negroes and began to roam the under part of Africa. He bought hard woods, spices, gold, pearls, and an occasional diamond. These goods he then resold to European merchants. He gained a reputation for being a fair and honest dealer and he worked at a grinding pace. He confided in no one, made no friends, was never known to smile. Within five years he was one of the richest men to be found along the Gold Coast.

Four times a year he wrote long letters to Martin. In these letters his furious, raging hatred of the British Navy was put into words. Martin, now retired to his cottage in Oxford, wrote Simon to soften his attitude, to let bygones be bygones. Each reply was the same: a restatement of Simon's quiet, deadly hatred for the men who had tortured him and whom he would never forget.

Finally, seven years after the bowspritting of Simon, Martin wrote a letter in which he offered to send his youngest daughter, Nancy, to Sao Thomé in the hopes that she and Simon would be married. The girl was eighteen, tall, clean-limbed and cheerful. Martin wrote that she was the only thing that could save Simon from the cancerous hate that was eating inside him.

For six months there was no response to his letter.

Then, suddenly and unexpectedly, Simon Jonson was given his revenge. He was in a dirty, hot anchorage north of Cape Lopez, negotiating for the purchase of six huge pearls that had been passed from one native hand to another halfway around the globe. He had almost completed the sale when a canoe with three natives in it came flying across the anchorage. They reported that they had seen an English man-of-war drifting hopelessly with the current, far out at sea. And, they reported, there was a man tied to the bowsprit.

Simon completed his sale, gathered his crew and set sail in the direction the natives indicated. After two days of sailing he located the ship. As soon as he saw it, he knew what had happened. It was the victim of what was called a line hurricane.

Line hurricanes are short-lived storms of a terrible intensity. The horizon is suddenly obscured by a black, solid line of clouds that is laced with lightning flashes around the surface of the sea, the sea in front of the storm becomes flat, the whole universe seems to stop and to wait dully for a few seconds. The hurricane strikes like a coiled snake. In a matter of seconds the wind rises to enormous velocities and pulls the tops of the waves after it, so that there is a flat, flying sheet of water a few feet off the surface. Beneath this, great combers of green and white water crash insanely against one another. For several minutes the whole ocean turns dark, and the hissing of water and wind is so great that normal voices are utterly lost. Then it is suddenly over. The sea falls flat, the sun reappears, a few wounded fish lie gasping and dying on the surface. But if a sailing vessel is caught in such a storm with sail on, either its sails will be ripped to shreds or its masts snapped. A poorly handled ship will simply vanish and a well-handled one will be badly damaged at the very best.

As Simon approached the ship, he saw it was a large man-of-war. It carried thirty-three guns and the name *India* was on its stern. All the masts had been broken, the decks were a tangle of broken spars and lines, there were gaping holes in the gun decks where the guns had come adrift and smashed their way overboard, the rails were slintered and torn, bits of sail, mattresses, shattered casks, wet powder were scattered over everything.

And the natives had been right . . . from the bow-sprit dangled the body of a man.

As Simon bore down on the *India*, the desultory activity of the men aboard the ship stopped. Men staggered to the rails, looked with bleary eyes at Simon's sloop. A hatch opened and the captain walked out on deck. Simon hove-to a hundred feet from the damaged ship.

"What happened to you?" he shouted to the captain.

"Hit by a line hurricane," the captain said in a rasping voice. "No time to batten down or secure. Our guns came adrift and smashed half the crew before they went overboard. Compass ruined. All our water kegs smashed into pieces."

The captain ran a dry tongue over even dryer lips. Simon realized that all of the men along the rail were half dead with thirst.

"You are a hundred and fifteen miles southwest of Calbar. I advise you to make for it at once," Simon said. He motioned for his black crew to set sail and he began to veer away from the *India*.

"Wait, man," the captain cried. "Do you have water?

My God, we are dying of thirst. We can never make land in this condition. If you have water, in the name of mercy give it to us."

"Yes, I have five large casks of fresh water," Simon said.

"Look, you talk English; you must be an Englishman," the captain croaked. "I order you to come alongside and give us water and supplies. I further order you—"

"I am no English subject," Simon said coldly. "I am a citizen of the seas. I am under no obligation to obey your orders."

He ran back alongside the ship, but carefully stayed out of gunshot. The captain, reeling slightly under the impact of the tropical sun, stared down at him unbelievingly.

"Then I request you to aid us in the name of common humanity," the captain said.

"Ah, common humanity, that is another thing," Simon said, but his voice was colder and more deadly than before. "Then, in the name of common humanity, I order you to take that man down from the bowsprit."

"That is impossible," the captain said. "That man was sentenced to the bowsprit several days ago under the authority of His Majesty's Regulations for the Government of the Royal Navy. It is impossible for me or anyone else to order him cut loose."

The men on the rail, the captain and Simon all looked down the ship toward the bowsprit. The poor wretch tied there raised his head, his eyes glittering with hope. The captain turned and looked down at Simon.

There was a long silence while all the vast and massive authority of the British Navy matched wills with a single individual in a small sloop.

"It is impossible for me to aid you as long as that man is tied to the bowsprit," Simon said deliberately and slowly. He gestured to his crew and the sails of his sloop went up. As the canvas ballooned slowly, the sloop picked up way and began to move away from the *India*.

"No man was ever allowed to come down off the bowsprit to the ship," the captain screamed.

Simon did not reply. He merely glanced once at the captain, then at the man on the bowsprit. Then he turned his back to the ship.

The captain's tongue came out, his hot, dry breath whistled out through the dry passages of his nose. Then he threw back his head and shouted after Simon, suddenly afraid that he could not be heard.

"Cut the man loose from the bowsprit. I pardon him unconditionally."

The crew began a ragged cheer. Men stumbled down the deck toward the bowsprit, clambered over the debris to set their shipmate free. The man on the bowsprit waved his hands feebly, unable to realize fully what had happened.

Simon heard the command and put his tiller hard over. The sloop bore down on the shattered hulk of the *India*. As lines came from the ship and were tied to huge water casks in the sloop, Simon did something he had not done in seven years. He put his head back and smiled up at the crew. As the men stove in the end of the first cask and stuck their dry heads into the fresh water he continued to smile at them.

Two weeks later when he returned to Sao Thomé, after aiding the *India* to make port, he sat down to answer the last letter of his friend Martin.

"My dear and only friend Martin," he began. "Since

you wrote, something has happened which has much changed my former attitude. You will now find that I am more kindly disposed toward His Majesty's Navy in particular and the English people in general. I would now be most grateful if you would send your youngest daughter Nancy to Sao Thomé as you proposed in your last letter. She will not have an easy life here, but she can be assured that I shall give her all the love and care and devotion of which I am capable . . ."

R. M. S. TITANIC

By Hanson W. Baldwin

Like "Bartimeus", Hanson W. Baldwin is a former naval officer turned writer. Unlike "Bartimeus," however, he is more the naval historian and analyst than popularizer. His articles in The New York Times *are regarded as authoritative commentary on sea affairs, and his researches into American seapower are satisfyingly documented.*

The horror of the Titanic *tragedy is enduring. Survivors, both British and American, wrote books about it; American law courts wrangled over the liabilities of the owners. For our purpose it was necessary to pass all that, and find a succinct, authentic report of what happened. This Hanson Baldwin has done in a masterly manner, without emotional asides or rhetorical denunciations. As he writes it, the tale is as bare as Defoe's story of the London Plague Year. Having read it, the reader finds the horror still there, like a huge black shadow . . . a ship that took three years to build and sank in two hours and a half in a calm sea; a ship with two thousand souls on board, and only sixteen boats.*

THE White Star liner, *Titanic*, largest ship the world had ever known, sailed from Southampton on her maiden voyage to New York on April 10, 1912. The paint on her strakes was fair and bright; she was fresh from Harland and Wolff's Belfast yards, strong in the strength of her forty-six thousand tons of steel, bent, hammered, shaped and riveted through the three years of her slow birth.

There was little fuss and fanfare at her sailing; her sister-ship, the *Olympic*—slightly smaller than the *Titanic*—had been in service for some months and to her had gone the thunder of the cheers.

But the *Titanic* needed no whistling steamers or shouting crowds to call attention to her superlative qualities. Her bulk dwarfed the ships near her as long-shoremen singled up her mooring lines and cast off the turns of heavy rope from the dock bollards. She was not only the largest ship afloat, but was believed to be the safest. Carlisle, her builder, had given her double bottoms and had divided her hull into sixteen water-tight compartments, which made her, men thought, unsinkable. She had been built to be and had been described as a gigantic lifeboat. Her designers' dreams of a triple-screw giant, a luxurious, floating hotel, which could speed to New York at twenty-three knots, had been carefully translated from blue prints and mold loft lines at the Belfast yards into a living reality.

The *Titanic's* sailing from Southampton, though quiet, was not wholly uneventful. As the liner moved slowly toward the end of her dock that April day, the surge of her passing sucked away from the quay the steamer *New York*, moored just to seaward of the *Titanic's* berth. There were sharp cracks as the manila mooring lines of the *New York* parted under the strain. The frayed ropes writhed and whistled through the air and snapped down among the waving crowd on the pier; the *New York* swung toward the *Titanic's* bow, was checked and dragged back to the dock barely in time to avert a collision. Seamen muttered, thought it an ominous start.

Past Spithead and the Isle of Wight the *Titanic* steamed. She called at Cherbourg at dusk and then laid her course for Queenstown. At 1.30 P.M. on Thursday, April 11, she stood out of Queenstown harbor, screaming gulls soaring in her wake, with 2,201 persons—men, women, and children—aboard.

Occupying the Empire bedrooms and Georgian suites of the first-class accommodations were many well-known men and women—Colonel John Jacob Astor and his young bride; Major Archibald Butt, military aide to President Taft, and his friend, Frank D. Millet, the painter; John B. Thayer, vice-president of the Pennsylvania Railroad, and Charles M. Hays, president of the Grand Trunk Railway of Canada; W. T. Stead, the English journalist; Jacques Futrelle, French novelist; H. B. Harris, theatrical manager, and Mrs. Harris; Mr. and Mrs. Isidor Straus; and J. Bruce Ismay, chairman and managing director of the White Star line.

Down in the plain wooden cabins of the steerage class were 706 immigrants to the land of promise, and trimly stowed in the great holds was a cargo valued at $420,-000: oak beams, sponges, wine, calabashes, and an odd miscellany of the common and the rare.

The *Titanic* took her departure on Fastnet Light and, heading into the night, laid her course for New York. She was due at Quarantine the following Wednesday morning.

Sunday dawned fair and clear. The *Titanic* steamed smoothly toward the west, faint streamers of brownish smoke trailing from her funnels. The purser held services in the saloon in the morning; on the steerage deck aft the immigrants were playing games and a Scotsman

was puffing "The Campbells Are Coming" on his bag-
pipes in the midst of the uproar.

At 9 A.M. a message from the steamer *Caronia* sput-
tered into the wireless shack:

Captain, *Titanic*—Westbound steamers report bergs
growlers and field ice in 42 degrees N. from 49 degrees to
51 degrees W. 12th April.

Compliments—

Barr.

It was cold in the afternoon; the sun was brilliant, but
the *Titanic*, her screws turning over at 75 revolutions
per minute, was approaching the Banks.

In the Marconi cabin Second Operator Harold Bride,
ear-phones clamped on his head, was figuring accounts;
he did not stop to answer when he heard *MWL*, Continental Morse for the nearby Leyland liner, *Californian*, calling the *Titanic*. The *Californian* had some message about three icebergs; he didn't bother then to take
it down. About 1.42 P.M. the rasping spark of those days
spoke again across the water. It was the *Baltic*, calling
the *Titanic*, warning her of ice on the steamer track.
Bride took the message down and sent it up to the bridge.
The officer-of-the-deck glanced at it; sent it to the
bearded master of the *Titanic*, Captain E. C. Smith, a
veteran of the White Star service. It was lunch time
then; the Captain, walking along the promenade deck,
saw Mr. Ismay, stopped, and handed him the message
without comment. Ismay read it, stuffed it in his pocket,
told two ladies about the icebergs, and resumed his
walk. Later, about 7.15 P.M., the Captain requested the
return of the message in order to post it in the chart
room for the information of officers.

Dinner that night in the Jacobean dining room was

gay. It was bitter on deck, but the night was calm and fine; the sky was moonless but studded with stars twinkling coldly in the clear air.

After dinner some of the second-class passengers gathered in the saloon, where the Reverend Mr. Carter conducted a "hymn sing-song." It was almost ten o'clock and the stewards were waiting with biscuits and coffee as the group sang:

> "O, hear us when we cry to Thee
> For those in peril on the sea."

On the bridge Second Officer Lightoller—short, stocky, efficient—was relieved at ten o'clock by First Officer Murdoch. Lightoller had talked with other officers about the proximity of ice; at least five wireless ice warnings had reached the ship; lookouts had been cautioned to be alert; captains and officers expected to reach the field at any time after 9.30 P.M. At 22 knots, its speed unslackened, the *Titanic* plowed on through the night.

Lightoller left the darkened bridge to his relief and turned in. Captain Smith went to his cabin. The steerage was long since quiet; in the first and second cabins lights were going out; voices were growing still, people were asleep. Murdoch paced back and forth on the bridge, peering out over the dark water, glancing now and then at the compass in front of Quartermaster Hichens at the wheel.

In the crow's nest, Lookout Frederick Fleet and his partner, Leigh, gazed down at the water, still and unruffled in the dim, starlit darkness. Behind and below them the ship, a white shadow with here and there a last winking light; ahead of them a dark and silent and cold ocean.

There was a sudden clang. "Dong-dong. Dong-dong. Dong-dong. Dong!" The metal clapper of the great ship's bell struck out 11.30. Mindful of the warnings, Fleet strained his eyes, searching the darkness for the dreaded ice. But there were only the stars and the sea.

In the wireless room, where Phillips, first operator, had relieved Bride, the buzz of the *Californian's* set again crackled into the ear-phones:

Californian: "Say, old man, we are stuck here, surrounded by ice."

Titanic: "Shut up, shut up; keep out. I am talking to Cape Race; you are jamming my signals."

Then, a few minutes later—about 11.40 . . .

II

Out of the dark she came, a vast, dim, white, monstrous shape, directly in the *Titanic's* path. For a moment Fleet doubted his eyes. But she was a deadly reality, this ghastly *thing*. Frantically, Fleet struck three bells—*something dead ahead*. He snatched the telephone and called the bridge:

"Iceberg! Right ahead!"

The First Officer heard but did not stop to acknowledge the message.

"Hard-a-starboard!"

Hichens strained at the wheel; the bow swung slowly to port. The monster was almost upon them now.

Murdoch leaped to the engine-room telegraph. Bells clanged. Far below in the engine-room those bells struck the first warning. Danger! The indicators on the dial faces swung round to "Stop!" Then "Full speed astern!" Frantically the engineers turned great valve wheels; answered the bridge bells . . .

There was a slight shock, a brief scraping, a small list to port. Shell ice—slabs and chunks of it—fell on the foredeck. Slowly the *Titanic* stopped.

Captain Smith hurried out of his cabin.

"What has the ship struck?"

Murdoch answered, "An iceberg, sir. I hard-a-starboarded and reversed the engines, and I was going to hard-a-port around it, but she was too close. I could not do any more. I have closed the water-tight doors."

Fourth Officer Boxhall, other officers, the carpenter, came to the bridge. The Captain sent Boxhall and the carpenter below to ascertain the damage.

A few lights switched on in the first and second cabins; sleepy passengers peered through porthole glass; some casually asked the stewards:

"Why have we stopped?"

"I don't know, sir, but I don't suppose it is anything much."

In the smoking room a quorum of gamblers and their prey were still sitting round a poker table; the usual crowd of kibitzers looked on. They had felt the slight jar of the collision and had seen an eighty-foot ice mountain glide by the smoking room windows, but the night was calm and clear, the *Titanic* was "unsinkable"; they hadn't bothered to go on deck.

But far below, in the warren of passages on the starboard side forward, in the forward holds and boiler rooms, men could see that the *Titanic's* hurt was mortal. In No. 6 boiler room, where the red glow from the furnaces lighted up the naked, sweaty chests of coal-blackened firemen, water was pouring through a great gash about two feet above the floor plates. This was no slow leak; the ship was open to the sea; in ten minutes there were eight feet of water in No. 6. Long before then the stokers had raked the flaming fires out of the furnaces and had scrambled through the watertight doors into No. 5 or had climbed up the long steel ladders to safety. When Boxhall looked at the mailroom in No. 3 hold, twenty-four feet above the keel, the mailbags were already floating about in the slushing water. In No. 5 boiler room a stream of water spurted into an empty bunker. All six compartments forward of No. 4 were open to the sea; in ten seconds the iceberg's jagged claw had ripped a three-hundred-foot slash in the bottom of the great *Titanic*.

Reports came to the bridge; Ismay in dressing gown ran out on deck in the cold, still, starlit night, climbed up the bridge ladder.

"What has happened?"

Captain Smith: "We have struck ice."

"Do you think she is seriously damaged?"

Captain Smith: "I'm afraid she is."

Ismay went below and passed Chief Engineer William Bell fresh from an inspection of the damaged compartments. Bell corroborated the Captain's statement; hurried back down the glistening steel ladders to his duty. Man after man followed him—Thomas Andrews, one of the ship's designers, Archie Frost, the builder's chief engineer, and his twenty assistants—men who had no posts of duty in the engine-room but whose traditions called them there.

On deck, in corridor and stateroom, life flowed again. Men, women and children awoke and questioned; orders were given to uncover the lifeboats; water rose into the firemen's quarters; half-dressed stokers streamed up on deck. But the passengers—most of them—did not know that the *Titanic* was sinking. The shock of the collision had been so slight that some were not awakened by it; the *Titanic* was so huge that she must be unsinkable; the night was too calm, too beautiful, to think of death at sea.

Captain Smith half ran to the door of the radio shack. Bride, partly dressed, eyes dulled with sleep, was standing behind Phillips, waiting.

"Send the call for assistance."

The blue spark danced: "CQD—CQD—CQD—CQ—"

Miles away Marconi men heard. Cape Race heard it, and the steamships *La Provence* and *Mt. Temple*.

The sea was surging into the *Titanic's* hold. At 12.20 the water burst into the seamen's quarters through a collapsed fore and aft wooden bulkhead. Pumps strained in the engine-rooms—men and machinery making a futile fight against the sea. Steadily the water rose.

The boats were swung out—slowly; for the deckhands were late in reaching their stations, there had been no boat drill, and many of the crew did not know to what boats they were assigned. Orders were shouted; the safety valves had lifted, and steam was blowing off in a great rushing roar. In the chart house Fourth Officer Boxhall bent above a chart, working rapidly with pencil and dividers.

12.25 A.M. Boxhall's position is sent out to a fleet of vessels: "Come at once; we have struck a berg."

To the Cunarder *Carpathia* (Arthur Henry Rostron, Master, New York to Liverpool, fifty-eight miles away): "It's a CQD, old man. Position 41–46 N.; 50–14 W."

The blue spark dancing: "Sinking; cannot hear for noise of steam."

12.30 A.M. The word is passed: "Women and children in the boats." Stewards finish waking their passengers below; life-preservers are tied on; some men smile at the precaution. "The *Titanic* is unsinkable." The *Mt. Temple* starts for the *Titanic*; the *Carpathia,* with a double-watch in her stokeholds, radios, "Coming hard." The CQD changes the course of many ships—but not of one; the operator of the *Californian,* nearby, has just put down his ear-phones and turned in.

The CQD flashes over land and sea from Cape Race to New York; newspaper city rooms leap to life and presses whir.

On the *Titanic,* water creeps over the bulkhead between Nos. 5 and 6 firerooms. She is going down by the head; the engineers—fighting a losing battle—are forced back foot by foot by the rising water. Down the promenade deck, Happy Jock Hume, the bandsman, runs with his instrument.

12.45 A.M. Murdoch, in charge on the starboard side, eyes tragic, but calm and cool, orders boat No. 7 lowered. The women hang back; they want no boat-ride on an ice-strewn sea; the *Titanic* is unsinkable. The men encourage them, explain that this is just a precautionary measure: "We'll see you again at breakfast." There is little confusion; passengers stream slowly to the boat deck. In the steerage the immigrants chatter excitedly.

A sudden sharp hiss—a streaked flare against the night; Boxhall sends a rocket toward the sky. It explodes, and a parachute of white stars lights up the icy sea. "God! Rockets!" The band plays ragtime.

No. 8 is lowered, and No. 5. Ismay, still in dressing gown, calls for women and children, handles lines, stumbles in the way of an officer, is told to "get the hell out of here." Third Officer Pitman takes charge of No. 5; as he swings into the boat Murdoch grasps his hand. "Good-by and good luck, old man."

No. 6 goes over the side. There are only twenty-eight people in a lifeboat with a capacity of sixty-five.

A light stabs from the bridge; Boxhall is calling in Morse flashes; again and again, to a strange ship stopped in the ice jam five to ten miles away. Another rocket drops its shower of sparks above the ice-strewn sea and the dying ship.

1.00 A.M. Slowly the water creeps higher; the fore ports of the *Titanic* are dipping into the sea. Rope squeaks through blocks; lifeboats drop jerkily seaward. Through the shouting on the decks comes the sound of the band playing ragtime.

The "Millionaires' Special" leaves the ship—boat No. 1, with a capacity of forty people, carries only Sir Cosmo and Lady Duff Gordon and ten others. Aft, the frightened immigrants mill and jostle and rush for a boat. An officer's fist flies out; three shots are fired in the air, and the panic is quelled. . . . Four Chinese sneak unseen into a boat and hide in its bottom.

1.20 A.M. Water is coming into No. 4 boiler room. Stokers slice and shovel as water laps about their ankles —steam for the dynamos, steam for the dancing spark! As the water rises, great ash hoes rake the flaming coals from the furnaces. Safety valves pop; the stokers retreat aft, and the water-tight doors clang shut behind them.

The rockets fling their splendor toward the stars. The boats are more heavily loaded now, for the passengers know the *Titanic* is sinking. Women cling and sob. The great screws aft are rising clear of the sea. Half-filled boats are ordered to come alongside the cargo ports and take on more passengers, but the ports are never opened —and the boats are never filled. Others pull for the steamer's light miles away but never reach it; the lights disappear, the unknown ship steams off.

The water rises and the band plays ragtime.

1.30 A.M. Lightoller is getting the port boats off; Murdoch the starboard. As one boat is lowered into the sea a boat officer fires his gun along the ship's side to stop a rush from the lower decks. A woman tries to take her Great Dane into a boat with her; she is refused and steps out of the boat to die with her dog. Millet's "little smile which played on his lips all through the voyage" plays no more; his lips are grim, but he waves good-by and brings wraps for the women.

Benjamin Guggenheim, in evening clothes, smiles and says, "We've dressed up in our best and are prepared to go down like gentlemen."

1.40 A.M. Boat 14 is clear, and then 13, 16, 15 and C. The lights still shine, but the *Baltic* hears the blue spark say, "Engine-room getting flooded."

The *Olympic* signals, "Am lighting up all possible boilers as fast as can."

Major Butt helps women into the last boats and waves good-by to them. Mrs. Straus puts her foot on the gunwale of a lifeboat, then she draws back and goes to her husband: "We have been together many years; where you go I will go." Colonel John Jacob Astor puts his young wife in a lifeboat, steps back, taps cigarette on fingernail: "Good-by, dearie; I'll join you later."

1.45 A.M. The foredeck is under water, the fo'c'sle head almost awash; the great stern is lifted high toward the bright stars; and still the band plays. Mr. and Mrs. Harris approach a lifeboat arm in arm.

Officer: "Ladies first, please."

Harris bows, smiles, steps back: "Of course, certainly; ladies first."

Boxhall fires the last rocket, then leaves in charge of boat No. 2.

2.00 A.M. She is dying now; her bow goes deeper, her stern higher. But there must be steam. Below in the stokeholds the sweaty firemen keep steam up for the flaring lights and the dancing spark. The glowing coals slide and tumble over the slanted grate bars; the sea pounds behind that yielding bulkhead. But the spark dances on.

The *Asian* hears Phillips try the new signals—SOS.

Boat No. 4 has left now; boat D leaves ten minutes later. Jacques Futrelle clasps his wife: "For God's sake, go! It's your last chance; go!" Madame Futrelle is half-forced into the boat. It clears the side.

There are about 660 people in the boats, and 1,500 still on the sinking *Titanic*.

On top of the officers' quarters men work frantically to get the two collapsibles stowed there over the side. Water is over the forward part of A deck now; it surges up the companionways toward the boat deck. In the radio shack, Bride has slipped a coat and lifejacket about Phillips as the first operator sits hunched over his key, sending—still sending—"41–46 N.; 50–14 W. CQD—CQD—SOS—SOS—"

The captain's tired white face appears at the radio-room door: "Men, you have done your full duty. You can do no more. Now, it's every man for himself." The captain disappears—back to his sinking bridge, where Painter, his personal steward, stands quietly waiting for orders. The spark dances on. Bride turns his back and goes into the inner cabin. As he does so, a stoker, grimed with coal, mad with fear, steals into the shack and reaches for the lifejacket on Phillips' back. Bride wheels about and brains him with a wrench.

2.10 A.M. Below decks the steam is still holding, though the pressure is falling—rapidly. In the gymnasium on the boat deck the athletic instructor watches quietly as two gentlemen ride the bicycles and another swings casually at the punching bag. Mail clerks stagger up the boat-deck stairways, dragging soaked mail sacks. The spark still dances. The band still plays—but not ragtime:

> "Nearer my God to Thee,
> Nearer to Thee . . ."

A few men take up the refrain, others kneel on the slanting decks to pray. Many run and scramble aft, where hundreds are clinging above the silent screws on the great uptilted stern. The spark still dances and the lights still flare; the engineers are on the job. The hymn comes to its close, Bandmaster Hartley, Yorkshireman violinist, taps his bow against a bulkhead, calls for "Autumn" as the water curls about his feet, and the eight musicians brace themselves against the ship's slant. People are leaping from the decks into the nearby water—the icy water. A woman cries, "Oh, save me, save me!" A man answers, "Good lady, save yourself. Only God can save you now." The band plays "Autumn":

> "God of Mercy and Compassion!
> Look with pity on my pain . . ."

The water creeps over the bridge where the *Titanic's* master stands; heavily he steps out to meet it.

2.17 A.M. "CQ—" The *Virginian* hears a ragged, blurred CQ, then an abrupt stop. The blue spark dances no more. The lights flicker out; the engineers have lost their battle.

2.18 A.M. Men run about blackened decks; leap into the night; are swept into the sea by the curling wave which licks up the *Titanic's* length. Lightoller does not leave the ship; the ship leaves him; there are hundreds like him, but only a few who live to tell of it. The funnels still swim above the water, but the ship is climbing to the perpendicular; the bridge is under and most of the foremast; the great stern rises like a squat leviathan. Men swim away from the sinking ship; others drop from the stern.

The band plays in the darkness, the water lapping upwards:

> "Hold me up in mighty waters,
> Keep my eyes on things above,
> Righteousness, divine atonement,
> Peace and everlas . . ."

The forward funnel snaps and crashes into the sea; its steel tons hammer out of existence swimmers struggling in the freezing water. Streams of sparks, of smoke and steam, burst from the after funnels. The ship upends to 50—to 60 degrees.

Down in the black abyss of the stokeholds, of the engine-rooms, where the dynamos have whirred at long last to a stop, the stokers and the engineers are reeling against hot metal, the rising water clutching at their knees. The boilers, the engine cylinders, rip from their bed plates; crash through bulkheads; rumble—steel against steel.

The *Titanic* stands on end, poised briefly for the

plunge. Slowly she slides to her grave—slowly at first, and then more quickly—quickly—quickly.

2.20 A.M. The greatest ship in the world has sunk. From the calm, dark waters, where the floating lifeboats move, there goes up, in the white wake of her passing, "one long continuous moan."

III

The boats that the *Titanic* had launched pulled safely away from the slight suction of the sinking ship, pulled away from the screams that came from the lips of the freezing men and women in the water. The boats were poorly manned and badly equipped, and they had been unevenly loaded. Some carried so few seamen that women bent to the oars. Mrs. Astor tugged at an oar handle; the Countess of Rothes took a tiller. Shivering stokers in sweaty, coal-blackened singlets and light trousers steered in some boats; stewards in white coats rowed in others. Ismay was in the last boat that left the ship from the starboard side; with Mr. Carter of Philadelphia and two seamen he tugged at the oars. In one of the lifeboats an Italian with a broken wrist—disguised in a woman's shawl and hat—huddled on the floor boards, ashamed now that fear had left him. In another rode the only baggage saved from the *Titanic*—the carry-all of Samuel L. Goldenberg, one of the rescued passengers.

There were only a few boats that were heavily loaded; most of those that were half empty made but perfunctory efforts to pick up the moaning swimmers, their officers and crew fearing they would endanger the living if they pulled back into the midst of the dying. Some boats beat off the freezing victims; fear-crazed men and women struck with oars at the heads of swimmers. One woman drove her fist into the face of a half-dead man as he tried feebly to climb over the gunwale. Two other women helped him in and stanched the flow of blood from the ring-cuts on his face.

One of the collapsible boats, which had floated off the top of the officers' quarters when the *Titanic* sank, was an icy haven for thirty or forty men. The boat had capsized as the ship sank; men swam to it, clung to it, climbed upon its slippery bottom, stood knee-deep in water in the freezing air. Chunks of ice swirled about their legs; their soaked clothing clutched their bodies in icy folds. Colonel Archibald Gracie was cast up there, Gracie who had leaped from the stern as the *Titanic* sank; young Thayer who had seen his father die; Lightoller who had twice been sucked down with the ship and twice blown to the surface by a belch of air; Bride, the second operator, and Phillips, the first. There were many stokers, half-naked; it was a shivering company. They stood there in the icy sea, under the far stars, and sang and prayed—the Lord's Prayer. After a while a lifeboat came and picked them off, but Phillips was dead then or died soon afterward in the boat.

Only a few of the boats had lights; only one—No. 2— had a light that was of any use to the *Carpathia*, twisting through the ice-field to the rescue. Other ships were "coming hard" too; one, the *Californian*, was still dead to opportunity.

The blue sparks still danced, but not the *Titanic*'s. *La Provence* to *Celtic*: "Nobody has heard the *Titanic* for about two hours."

It was 2.40 when the *Carpathia* first sighted the green light from No. 2 boat; it was 4.10 when she picked up the first boat and learned that the *Titanic* had foundered.

The last of the moaning cries had just died away then.

Captain Rostron took the survivors aboard, boatload by boatload. He was ready for them, but only a small minority of them required much medical attention. Bride's feet were twisted and frozen; others were suffering from exposure; one died, and seven were dead when taken from the boats, and were buried at sea.

It was then that the fleet of racing ships learned they were too late; the *Parisian* heard the weak signals of *MPA*, the *Carpathia*, report the death of the *Titanic*. It was then—or soon afterward, when her radio operator put on his ear-phones—that the *Californian*, the ship that had been within sight as the *Titanic* was sinking, first learned of the disaster.

And it was then, in all its white-green majesty, that the *Titanic's* survivors saw the iceberg, tinted with the sunrise, floating idly, pack-ice jammed about its base, other bergs heaving slowly nearby on the blue breast of the sea.

IV

But it was not until later that the world knew, for wireless then was not what wireless is to-day, and garbled messages had nourished a hope that all of the *Titanic's* company were safe. Not until Monday evening, when P. A. S. Franklin, Vice-President of the International Mercantile Marine Company, received relayed messages in New York that left little hope, did the full extent of the disaster begin to be known. Partial and garbled lists of the survivors; rumors of heroism and cowardice; stories spun out of newspaper imagination, based on a few bare facts and many false reports, misled the world, terrified and frightened it. It was not until Thursday night, when the *Carpathia* steamed into the North River, that the full truth was pieced together.

Flashlights flared on the black river when the *Carpathia* stood up to her dock. Tugs nosed about her; shunted her toward Pier 54. Thirty thousand people jammed the streets; ambulances and stretchers stood on the pier; coroners and physicians waited.

In mid-stream the Cunarder dropped over the *Titanic's* lifeboats; then she headed toward the dock. Beneath the customs letters on the pier stood relatives of the 711 survivors, relatives of the missing—hoping against hope. The *Carpathia* cast her lines ashore; stevedores looped them over bollards. The dense throngs stood quiet as the first survivor stepped down the gangway. The woman half-staggered—led by customs guards—beneath her letter. A "low wailing" moan came from the crowd; fell, grew in volume, and dropped again.

Thus ended the maiden voyage of the *Titanic*. The lifeboats brought to New York by the *Carpathia*, a few deck chairs and gratings awash in the icefield off the Grand Banks 800 miles from shore, were all that was left of the world's greatest ship.

V

The aftermath of weeping and regret, of recriminations and investigations, dragged on for weeks. Charges and countercharges were hurled about; the White Star line was bitterly criticized; Ismay was denounced on the floor of the Senate as a coward, but was defended by those who had been with him on the sinking *Titanic* and by the Board of Trade investigation in England.

It was not until weeks later, when the hastily convened Senate investigation in the United States and the

Board of Trade report in England had been completed, that the whole story was told. The Senate investigating committee, under the chairmanship of Senator Smith, who was attacked in both the American and British press as a "backwoods politician," brought out numerous pertinent facts, though its proceedings verged at times on the farcical. Senator Smith was ridiculed for his lack of knowledge of the sea when he asked witnesses, "Of what is an iceberg composed?" and "Did any of the passengers take refuge in the water-tight compartments?" The Senator seemed particularly interested in the marital status of Fleet, the lookout, who was saved. Fleet, puzzled, growled aside, "Wot questions they're arskin' me!"

The report of Lord Mersey, Wreck Commissioner in the British Board of Trade's investigation, was tersely damning.

The *Titanic* had carried boats enough for 1,178 persons, only one-third of her capacity. Her sixteen boats and four collapsibles had saved but 711 persons; 400 people had needlessly lost their lives. The boats had been but partly loaded; officers in charge of launching them had been afraid the falls would break or the boat buckle under their rated loads; boat crews had been slow in reaching their stations; launching arrangements were confused because no boat drill had been held; passengers were loaded into the boats haphazardly because no boat assignments had been made.

But that was not all. Lord Mersey found that sufficient warnings of ice on the steamer track had reached the *Titanic*, that her speed of 22 knots was "excessive under the circumstances," that "in view of the high speed at which the vessel was running it is not considered that the lookout was sufficient," and that her master made "a very grievous mistake"—but should not be blamed for negligence. Captain Rostron of the *Carpathia* was highly praised. "He did the very best that could be done." The *Californian* was damned. The testimony of her master, officers, and crew showed that she was not, at the most, more than nineteen miles away from the sinking *Titanic* and probably no more than five to ten miles distant. She had seen the *Titanic's* lights; she had seen the rockets; she had not received the CQD calls because her radio operator was asleep. She had attempted to get in communication with the ship she had sighted by flashing a light, but vainly.

"The night was clear," reported Lord Mersey, "and the sea was smooth. When she first saw the rockets the *Californian* could have pushed through the ice to the open water without any serious risk and so have come to the assistance of the *Titanic*. Had she done so she might have saved many if not all of the lives that were lost.

"She made no attempt."

THE RAFT

By Captain Edward V. Rickenbacker

*Captain Rickenbacker has been successful in several fields.
Although he has never been charged with literary ambitions,
he wrote a very good book, a very honest book. "The Raft" is
an excerpt from that book. It deals with something that
should never have happened at all, yet did occur. It will
probably happen again. It resembles the wicked chances the
sea packs against the cunning, the skill, and the fortitude of
man. It is very like the sort of chance which sank the Titanic.
A great airliner gets lost in the immense distances of the
Pacific, seeking an infinitesimal speck of an island, and passing it through a tiny miscalculation. And nobody can give her
a position. She calls in vain. Like the lifeboats of the Titanic,
Rickenbacker's raft sets out, by inconceivable bad fortune,
without the food and drink they had ready for it. They had no
luck at all, except the intangible asset of the Rickenbacker
personality. He took command, and seven of them came
through. It is a thrilling tale.*

THE LINE AROUND MY WAIST was now put to good use.
Because the wind and seas were fast sweeping the rafts
apart, I called the others in and, fastening the rope to the
hand lines around the rafts, we formed a line astern,
twenty feet or so apart. Cherry being captain, his raft
was first, mine was second, and the two-man raft brought
up the rear. The arrangement had its drawbacks. In the

heavy swell, as the rafts rose and fell at their different intervals, the interminable, uneven shocks on the line made rest impossible. But I shall always believe that had we separated, few if any of us would now be alive. A strong man may last a long time alone but men together somehow manage to last longer.

My memory of that afternoon is not wholly clear. The spray and the green water coming over the roll of the raft kept us soaked, and I bailed for hours with my hat— my wonderful old hat. This gave me exercise, besides keeping me from thinking too much.

Some time during the afternoon we totted up our possessions. The only food was four oranges that Cherry had stuffed in his pocket just before the crash, together with the chocolate bar that I had and half a dozen more that Alex had, which an Army doctor had given him the day before. The chocolate was never eaten. Alex' was ruined by his thrashing around in the water and he had to throw it away. Next day, when I felt in the pocket for mine, it had become a green mush, which neither I nor my companions would touch.

So, except for the oranges, we started with nothing. But knowing that a man can live a long time without food or water, I was more worried over the shortage of clothing. Only Adamson and I were fully dressed. He had his uniform and cap and I had on a blue summer-weight business suit, complete with necktie, pocket handkerchief, and refillable pencil. The others, expecting to swim, had taken off their shoes and hats before abandoning ship. None had hats or sweaters, but the two pilots had their leather jackets. Several had even thrown their socks away. Bartek, in fact, was naked except for a one-piece jumper.

I may have forgotten an item or two, but these were our total possessions: a first-aid kit, eighteen flares, and one Very pistol for firing them; two hand pumps for both bailing and renewing the air in the rafts; two service sheath knives; a pair of pliers; a small pocket compass; two revolvers belonging to Cherry and Adamson; two collapsible rubber bailing buckets; three sets of patching gear, one for each raft; several pencils; and my map of the Pacific. We all had cigarettes, but the salt water got to these immediately, and they were thrown away. And, finally, Reynolds produced two fish lines, with hooks attached, which he had snatched from a parachute bag after the crash. But there was no bait, and unless we managed to shoot down a gull, our chances of "living off the country" were decidedly thin.

But that first afternoon no one was conscious of our poverty; we were too exhausted to care. Three or four of the boys were violently seasick and I didn't feel any too comfortable myself, although I never reached the point of vomiting. Adamson was in agony from his wrenched back; every jerk of the boat, he said, felt as if someone was kicking him in the kidneys. But I was more worried about Sergeant Alex, in the little raft astern. Long after the others had stopped, he continued to retch. "What's the matter with him?" I called to De Angelis. "I don't know," answered De Angelis, "he must have swallowed a lot of salt water when we tipped over."

The sun went down swiftly, a cold mist gathering on the sea, and the moon came up—a three-quarter moon—beautiful to see. The wisecracks and the small talk, which sounded pretty silly in the immensity of the night, petered out and we were beginning to realize that we were in for hard times.

Naturally, one of the first things we had to do was to work out some organization of habits. Keeping a continuous watch—what we called an alert—was an obvious necessity. That first night we arranged to stand two-hour watches, relieving each other in turn. It seems pretty silly now, but I offered $100 to the first man to see land, a ship, or an airplane. But nobody slept that night. We were wet and miserable. Although the swell moderated just before midnight, the waves kept slopping into the rafts. Both air and water were warm, yet with each splash I felt as if I was being doused with buckets of ice water. Bartek and I changed positions every hour or so, to share the comfort of the other's lee. But I was never warm, and put in most of the night bailing. Sharks followed us from the plane; the water seemed full of them.

The second day came on slowly, first a gray mist and then the sun breaking through clear. It took hours to get warm, for the night mist penetrated to the bone. As I have said, we had those four oranges, but we decided to save them against the future. By popular vote I was made their custodian, and Cherry generously handed them over. We agreed to divide the first that morning, and the others on alternate days. That way, they would last eight days.

I cut the orange in half, then halved the halves, then halved the quarters, giving each man one eighth. With seven men watching, you can be sure I made an exact division. In fact, I studied the fruit a full minute before I cut. Some sucked and ate the peel, but Cherry and I saved ours for bait.

Men have been lost at sea before; others have spent more days on rafts than we did. A good deal of what we went through was what you might expect—hunger, thirst, heat, cold, and a slow rotting away. In some respects, the period from the second to the eighth day was the worst. A glassy calm fell upon the sea; the sun beat down fiercely all day; the rafts stood still, with the lines slack between; I even imagined I smelled flesh burning, and the sweet stink of hot rubber.

Face, neck, hands, wrists, legs, and ankles burned, blistered, turned raw, and burned again. In time De Angelis and Whittaker, having darker skins, developed a protecting tan, but the rest of us cooked day after day. My hands swelled and blistered; when the salt water got into the flesh, it burned and cracked and dried and burned again. Three months later the scars still show on the knuckles. Our mouths became covered with ugly running sores. Reynolds, having no covering for his legs, turned into a sodden red mass of hurt. Even the soles of his feet were burned raw.

These first five or six days were the worst I have ever known. The night I lay in a wrecked plane near Atlanta, with a dead man half crushed under my chest, had produced its own kind of suffering. But then the pain had been dulled by delirium, and after a while I knew help was near because I could hear people moving around in the dark. But on the Pacific I was something being turned on a spit. Without my hat, I would have been badly off. I would fill it with water, then jam it down over my ears. Before our rescue, the brim was half torn away from the crown.

Some of the others, to escape the terrible heat, paddled for hours in the water. But they paid a stiff price for the relief because their flesh burned again as it dried, and the salt brine stung. Without my handkerchiefs we would have had a much harder time. I passed them around and, folded bandit-fashion across the nose, they protected the lower part of the face. But there was no sparing the eyes. The sea sent back billions of sharp splinters of light; no matter where one looked it was painful. A stupor descended upon the rafts. Men simply sat or sprawled, heads rolling on the chest, mouths half open, gasping. Reynolds, from the cut on his nose, was a horrible sight. The sun would not let the wound heal. He washed the blood off with salt water, but it soon oozed again, spreading over his face, drying in a red crust. Bartek, too, was in agony from his cut fingers. He splashed them with iodine from the first-aid kit, but the salt water ate it away.

Daytimes we prayed for the coolness of the nights; nights we craved the sun. But I really came to hate the nights. Daytimes, I could see my fellow men, the play of the water, the gulls, all the signs of life. But the night brought us all close to fear. A cold, dense mist always rose around us. The damp soaked our clothes and we pressed together for warmth. Sometimes, when the mist was very heavy, the other rafts would be hidden. If the sea was calm and the line had fallen slack, I would sometimes come out of a nightmare, and pull in the towlines until they fetched up hard, and I knew the others were still there. Other times, I would hear moans or groans, or a cry and often a prayer. Or I would see a shadow move and twist as a man tried to ease his torture.

I know I can never hope to describe the awful loneliness of the night. Perhaps it affected me more than the others. I seldom slept more than an hour or so at a time, and even then, it seemed, with one eye open and one ear cocked. That was because I was always worried that the man who was supposed to be on watch might doze off and let a ship go by. I have gotten along most of my life with a good deal less sleep than most men are accustomed to have. This habit stood me in good stead on the Pacific. But the younger men had trouble staying awake. The stupor induced by the terrific heat of the day, together with the lulling motion of the raft as it listed and fell on the swell—a motion that at times was not unlike that of a hammock—seemed to put them quickly to sleep.

What also made the night hard for me was that I could never stretch out. Someday I shall meet the man who decided these rafts could hold two men and five men each. When I do, he is either going to revise his opinions or prove them on a long voyage, under conditions I shall be happy to suggest. Adamson weighed over two hundred pounds and I was not much lighter. On our five-man raft, he and Bartek and I shared an inside room measuring six feet nine inches by two feet four inches. Counting the narrow inflated roll, on which a man could stretch out for an hour or so with his feet dangling in the water, the dimensions were nine feet by five.

Because Adamson was in such pain, Bartek and I gave him one end to himself. He lay with his bumpus on the bottom, his head against the carbon-dioxide bottle, his feet across the roll. Bartek and I lay facing each other, or back to back, with our legs crooked over the roll. This was the way it was in Cherry's boat. But Alex and De Angelis in the two-man raft, although the smallest men, were much worse off. They had to sit facing each other, one with his legs over the other man's shoulders, while he took the legs of the other under his armpits, or they sat back to back, dangling their legs in the water. And sometimes De Angelis lay sprawled out, with Alex on his chest. Imagine two men in a small, shallow bathtub, and you will have a reasonably good idea of how much room they had.

Whenever you turned or twisted, you forced the others to turn or twist. It took days to learn how to make the most of the space, at an incalculable price in misery. A foot or hand or shoulder, moved in sleep or restlessness, was bound to rake the raw flesh of a companion. With the flesh, tempers turned raw and many things said in the night had best be forgotten.

The moon was turning into full. I was awake a good part of the time, hoping to catch the loom of a ship. In those first nights of utter calm the clouds would form the most unusual pictures, beautiful women, elephants, birds. It sounds fantastic. I remember seeing one shaped like a wild boar. I saw trees, completely formed.

The first two or three nights I thought I was seeing things. Finally I mentioned it to Adamson and he agreed with me that they were there. There was some reason for them because you could see them night in and night out, particularly during the first ten days. The moonlight helped to make these forms seem more vivid. I suppose there is a scientific explanation but I don't know what it is.

The forms were so vivid, so concise, so positive that they fascinated me. This helped some; it gave me something to think about during the long hours of the night.

The stars helped also to keep our minds occupied. We were on the equator and so all the familiar stars were in different positions, the Big Dipper, the Little Dipper, the North Star. We used to talk about them. Colonel Adamson had been in charge of the Planetarium in New York for a number of years and he was able to tell us a great deal about the different constellations and the movements of the stars. I kept promoting these discussions because of the good it did all of us.

What bothered us most of all was not knowing where we were. Every member of the party had his own ideas about this. I was under the impression—and later events confirmed it—that we were somewhere west or northwest of our island destination. Captain Cherry agreed with me in this.

The next day a terrible calm settled down which made the sea just like a glassy mirror. There were very little swells only and the sun was intensely hot. The glare was terrible on the eyes and most of the boys fell into a doze or sort of stupor. Most of them had injuries of one kind or another to add to their plight. I was afraid that Sergeant Reynolds had a broken nose. In getting out he had struck his head against the radio and the blood had dried on his face. He had no hat and the sun was beginning to burn him badly, and the combination made him an awesome-looking spectacle. Bartek had had all his fingers cut on the inside of the hand, two of them to the bone, and they had bled very badly. We had hauled out the iodine from the first-aid kit as soon as we settled down on the rafts and had done what we could to dress the fingers. The effect did not last long because the salt water would take it off. It would get into the little cuts and so kept him in agony for the first two or three nights. Finally, of course, it dried out and started to heal.

On the fourth morning the second orange was divided. Except for the orange on the second morning, we had then been seventy-two hours without food or liquid. Fish were all around; I could see hundreds swimming idly just below the raft. Cherry and I fished for hours with pieces of orange peel. I even borrowed Adamson's keyring, which was shiny, and tried to manipulate it as a spinner. The fish would nose the hook, fan their tails in curiosity, but they never struck.

For six days on that glassy, sizzling sea, the rafts did not seem to move. But by our watches we knew we were drifting; each morning the sun rose just a little bit later. This meant the rafts were inching west and south. We argued interminably over where we were, but it turned out only Cherry and I were right. We were positive of having overshot our island and, if our guess was true, we could count on no land nearer than certain Japanese-held islands four hundred to five hundred miles away. I studied the map two or three times a day, always returning it to my inside coat pocket, to protect it against the water. But the colors were already beginning to run.

Commencing the second night, Cherry sent up a flare every night. Having eighteen, we first decided to use three a night, the first after sundown, the second around midnight, the last before dawn. But of the first three sent aloft, one was a complete dud and the second flickered for only a few seconds. The third, swinging on its parachute, gave a scary, blinding red light, lasting perhaps a minute and a half. Next night, cutting down the expenditure to two good ones, we had another dud; this decided us to reduce the nightly allotment to a single good one.

Always, after the light had exhausted itself, my eyes strained into the darkness, hoping to catch a responding gleam—a gleam which would not settle into the steadiness of a star. It was plain that unless we soon had food or water or the terrible hot calm relented, some of us were bound to die. Adamson, being portly, felt the heat worse than the rest. Reynolds, thin anyway, was fading to skin and bones. Alex, though, was really in a bad way. His mouth was dry and frothing; he cried continually for water. He was only a boy—barely twenty-two—and thinking he was quitting, I pulled his raft in close and asked why the hell he couldn't take it? It was a brutal thing to do, yet I was determined to shock him back to his senses. I found out then what was wrong. He was only three weeks out of the hospital. In addition, he had contracted a lip disease, something like trench mouth, with a scientific name I do not remember. All this had left him with less strength than the rest from the start, and the salt water he swallowed when his raft capsized had helped to do him in.

Unfortunately for him that wasn't the only salt water Alex had had. De Angelis woke one night to find him half out of the raft, gulping salt water. Now I had admonished everybody the first afternoon out not to drink salt water, knowing that it would drive them wild with thirst. Alex admitted he had been doing this persistently. It explained the cries for water we didn't have. "I tried not to," Alex said, "but I had to. I just had to have water."

So it was only a question of time for poor Alex. He sank deeper into delirium, murmuring his "Hail Mary" and other Catholic prayers. In his wallet was a photograph of a young girl to whom he was engaged: he talked to it, prayed over it. Finally he could neither sleep nor lie down. De Angelis tried to keep the sun off him, but there was no shadow anywhere. So he burned and burned. At night in the moonlight I could see him sitting on the raft shaking as if with ague. He literally vibrated, he was so horribly cold. Yet, except to cry for water, he never really complained.

Bartek had a New Testament in his jumper pocket. Watching him read it, the thought came to me that we might all profit by his example. I am not a religious man, but I was taught the Lord's Prayer at my mother's knee and I had gone to Sunday school. If I had any religion in my later life, it was based on the Golden Rule. Yet I have always been conscious of God.

With the New Testament as an inspiration, we held morning and evening prayers. The rafts were pulled together, making a rough triangle. Then, each in turn, one of us would read a passage. None of us, I must confess, showed himself to be very familiar with them, but thumbing the book we found a number that one way or another bespoke our needs. The Twenty-third Psalm was, of course, a favorite. I have always been stirred by it, but out on the Pacific I found a beauty in it that I had never appreciated. Yet there was another that we never failed to read, because it so clearly set forth what was in our minds:

Therefore take no thought, saying, What shall we eat? or, What shall we drink? or, Wherewithal shall we be clothed?

. . . For your heavenly Father knoweth that ye have need of all these things. But seek ye first the kingdom of God, and his righteousness; and all these things shall be added unto you.

Take therefore no thought for the morrow: for the morrow shall take thought for the things of itself. Sufficient unto the day is the evil thereof. (Matthew 6:31–34.)

One or two turned scornful and bitter because the answer was slow in coming, but the rest went on praying with deep-felt hope. Yet we did not neglect anything that might help us to help ourselves. Whittaker tried to make a spear from one of the aluminum oars, tearing the flat corners away with the pliers. He drove it into the back of a shark which rubbed alongside, but the hide was tougher than the point. After several tries it was so blunted as to be useless. Whittaker threw it angrily into the bottom of the raft. He had gained nothing and wasted an oar.

Also, Cherry sat all day long with a loaded revolver in his lap, hoping to knock down a gull. But none came close enough for a shot. He broke the revolver open two or three times a day and rubbed the moving parts with oil from his nose and the back of his ears, but he could not halt the sea-water corrosion. When the parts froze solid he threw the gun into the Pacific. Adamson's gun rusted in the same way and I dropped it over the side.

To keep the sick men alive, we finished the oranges faster than we had intended. We had the third on the morning of the fifth day, the last on the sixth. The last two were shrunken, much of the juice appeared to have evaporated, and the last one was beginning to rot. So long as there was that sliver of orange to anticipate, no one complained of hunger. Now, memories of food and drink began to haunt us. We tried to catch the sharks that cruised near the rafts with our hands. I actually had several small ones by the back but the hide was too slippery for a firm grip.

The desire for food in several men became almost violent. They agonized over their hunger pains and talked constantly about food, and whether they could go on much longer without it.

Reynolds talked about how much soda pop he was going to drink the rest of his life. Cherry couldn't think about anything but chocolate ice cream. As I listened to the thirsty talk between the rafts, my own mind slowly filled with visions of chocolate malted milk. I could actually taste it, to the point where my tongue worked convulsively. The strange part is that I hadn't had a chocolate malted milk in nearly twenty-five years.

From the start I had advised against talk as I realized how necessary it was going to be for all of us to conserve our strength in every way possible; but looking back now I am rather amazed at the little talking that we did.

During the first few days, while we suffered from the shock of the fall and our minds were filled with speculation as to the chances of rescue, there was much more than later. This was particularly noticeable after several days had passed and the prospect of escape was becoming dimmer. It was then we began to sing hymns after prayer meetings. The singing seemed to release something in the minds of most of us and the talk for the first time became intensely personal. As I have already stated, there was no time that I lost faith in our ultimate rescue, but the others did not seem to share this state of mind fully with me. My companions clearly began to think of what lay beyond death and to think of it in terms of their own lives.

They began to tell of what they had experienced in life: their hopes, fears, ambitions, their achievements, their mistakes. I suppose it takes the imminence of death to release one completely from inhibitions. The talk was entirely honest and, I am sure, entirely frank. What was said will always be locked up in our minds. As far as I am concerned, no hint of those long, man-to-man conversations will ever be revealed. I am sure of one thing, that it did us a great deal of good.

As the days wore on and our strength left us, we talked less and less. A drowsiness, which in the later stages amounted almost to coma, had taken possession of us. We would lie for hours in the intense heat of the sun without a single word being spoken. What I seem to remember most about the last days was the almost complete silence. If one man spoke there would be no response. We were so completely divorced from living that we had nothing to talk about, even if we had had the strength for it.

I recall no mention of the war. It was continually in my own mind because of my conviction of survival. I was sure I would live to see the struggle through, and consequently did not get away from the speculations that I would have engaged in under normal conditions. I never put them into words, however. If my companions were thinking along the same line, they observed the same reticence that I did.

All conversation during the last stages had to do with the changes of position we found necessary in the rafts and the negative results of the Very lights we set off. Sometimes our hopes would kindle when one of us mistook a low star for the light of a ship. There would be eager discussion then, dwindling off into hopeless silences when it became certain that it had been nothing more than a delusion.

Twenty-one days of it, and during all that time, I am inclined to believe, we talked less than we would have done in the course of one normal day.

The eighth day was another hot, flat calm. It did not help our stomachs any to look down and see dolphin and mackerel, sleek and fat and twelve to eighteen inches long, and thousands of smaller fish swimming in the depths. That afternoon Cherry read the service, with the usual quotation from Matthew. About an hour later, when I was dozing with my hat pulled down over my eyes, a gull appeared from nowhere and landed on my hat.

I don't remember how it happened or how I knew he was there. But I knew it instantly, and I knew that if I missed this one, I'd never find another to sit on my hat. I reached up for him with my right hand—gradually. The whole Pacific seemed to be shaking from the agitation in my body, but I could tell he was still there from the hungry, famished, almost insane eyes in the other rafts. Slowly and surely my hand got up there; I didn't clutch, but just closed my fingers, sensing his nearness, then closing my fingers hard.

I wrung his neck, defeathered him, carved up the body, divided the meat into equal shares, holding back only the intestines for bait. Even the bones were chewed and swallowed. No one hesitated because the meat was raw and stringy and fishy. It tasted fine. After Cherry had finished his piece, I baited a hook and passed it over to him. The hook, weighted with Whittaker's ring, had hardly got wet before a small mackerel hit it, and was jerked into the raft. I dropped the other line, with the same miraculous result, except that mine was a small sea bass.

All this food in the space of a few minutes bolstered us beyond words. We ate one of the fish before dark and put the other aside for the next day. Even the craving for water seemed to abate, perhaps from chewing the cool, wet flesh while grinding the bones to a pulp. Alex and Adamson ate their shares, and I was optimistic enough to believe they were immediately better. I say in all truth that at no time did I ever doubt we would be saved, but as that eighth night rose around us I was sure we could last forever. The ocean was full of fish, and we could catch them.

As the sun went down, the sky clouded over, the air turned cool, a soft, uncertain wind made cat's-paws on the water—all portents of rain. I tried to stay awake to have everything in readiness if it came, but I finally dozed off with my head across Adamson's knees.

My next recollection is of being jolted awake, as if from a blow. The raft was slamming up and down on a heavy, irregular swell. It was pitch black—so black that I could scarcely make out the other rafts, except when they were thrown up on a swell. Gusts of wind came at us from every quarter. And I knew, if I ever knew anything, that rain was near.

From midnight we were on the watch for the rushing shadows of rain squalls. About three o'clock in the morning I heard the cry, "Rain." Drops splattered against my face and mouth, clean and sweet to taste. After the first few drops there was nothing more, but far off I could see the squall. The wind had a new sound, as if it were no longer empty. We paddled toward the squall and I prayed to God to put us in its path. We had a plan all worked out—bailing buckets ready and the empty canvas covers for the Very light cartridges. We took our shirts and socks off to spread over our heads and shoulders. The handkerchiefs were to be laid on the inflated roll until they became soaked. Adamson had even taken off his shorts to wring.

It was one hell of a night—all wind, waves, noise, lightning, and big black shadows. We paddled into it, shouting at the tops of our lungs. Out of that uproar came a cry for help. The little raft, with De Angelis and Alex, had broken loose. Bartek and I, with an oar to the side, set out after them, Cherry's raft following in our wake. I was afraid we'd lost them, but we sighted the raft against the white rush of a breaking wave, overtook it, and made it fast. A moment later the squall enveloped us.

Rain fell as from a waterfall. I spread the handkerchiefs on the roll of the raft, where they would catch the water, and fluffed my shirt over my head. Adamson, roused by the cool water on his body, draped his underpants over his chest to catch more water. I appointed myself wringer, and as fast as the others passed over the soaked pieces of cloth, I would twist them hard, forcing the water out, to rid the cloth of salt rime. I had done this several times with each piece, always tasting the last drippings for salt. I had finished rinsing out the bucket and cartridge covers, and was ready to collect the first water, when a sharp pull came on the bow line, twisting the raft around. Out of the corner of my eye I saw Cherry's raft being rolled over on its beam ends by a wave.

All three men were thrown out, and with Reynolds so weak I was sure he was going to drown. But in the next flash of lightning I counted three heads bobbing around the sides, we pulled in the line, bringing them in on our lee side, holding the raft steady while they helped each other in. Reynolds, gasping, mustered the strength to haul himself back. I shall never stop marveling at the hidden resources of men whose minds never give up. Cherry and Whittaker saved the oars, but they saved little else. The Very pistol and the last of the cartridges were lost. So were the bailing bucket and the little water they had collected.

All this—from the breaking away of the little raft to the righting of Cherry's—took no more than ten minutes, perhaps as little as five. But rather than wearing us down the exertions seemed to fill us with strength. I passed Cherry the bailing bucket, and while he bailed I watched anxiously for any letup in the rain. Adamson and Bartek sucked at the wet cloths, filling their mouths with the first water in eight days. To make up for his lost bucket, we gave Cherry the cartridge cover.

When they finally pulled away, I fell to wringing the sopping garments Bartek and Adamson had ready for me. Lightning flashed, the sea rumbled, the raft tossed wildly, but I was not really aware of them. My hands were terribly burned and blistered, and the flesh cracked and the blood spurted out, but I never felt it. As fast as I could wring out the cloths I handed them back to the others, who spread them out to soak again. I was gauging matters by just one thing—the water level in the bailing bucket.

Quite suddenly the wind died down and the rain stopped. The squall could not have lasted more than twenty minutes. But I had nearly a quart and a half of water in the bucket. Cherry, in his boat, had about a quart, but De Angelis and Alex, who had nothing to catch water in, had none. They had simply sucked their shirts.

In the calm that followed, the rafts were pulled in close. The round-table decision was that we'd better try to go on with as little water as possible—a half jigger per man per day. In the dark I poured what I guessed to be that much into one of the empty Very cartridge cases, and passed it seven times down the line of hands. It was the sweetest water I ever tasted. And the rain that had drenched our bodies, washing away the salt rime and cleansing the sores, had refreshed us quite as much.

On the ninth morning we shared the second fish and another half jigger of water. From this point on my memory may be hazy. Alex got no better, and on the tenth day, for his safety and Adamson's, we increased the water ration to two jiggers a day, one in the morning and one at sundown. On the following day we added another at noon.

The weather now took a change, and the sea turned rougher. The three of us in the middle boat had the worst of it, due to the yawing action from the pulls of the raft ahead and the raft behind. As each raft rose to a swell at a different interval, a shock would come on the lines and then would twist our raft first one way, then another. The little raft, being lighter, would coast down a swell and smack us, drenching us with salt water.

This was terribly hard on Adamson, and I insisted that the front raft exchange position with us for a few hours. This was done. It was much smoother. After Adamson had had a few hours' comfort, we returned to our original position in the middle of the line.

It was on the tenth evening, I think, that I asked Bartek to change rafts with Sergeant Alex, thinking that Alex might rest better. It took the combined strength of Bartek, De Angelis, and myself to move him. I stretched him on the lee side on the bottom of the boat and put my arm around him, as a mother cuddles a child, hoping in that way to transfer the heat of my body to him during the night. In an hour or so his shivering stopped and sleep came—a shallow sleep in which Alex mumbled intermittently in Polish—phrases about his mother and his girl "Snooks."

I kept Alex there all night, the next day and night, and the twelfth day. He was weaker, although more rational. When evening came, after the customary prayer, he asked to be put back in the little boat with De Angelis. I knew he couldn't last many hours longer, and so we pulled the other boat up and changed around again. We had to lift him like a baby. A strong wind came up and I slept fitfully that night, worrying about that little raft bouncing on the rough sea. Yet I must have dozed off, because my next recollection is of the sound of a long sigh.

I called to De Angelis: "Has he died?"

De Angelis said, after a pause, "I think so."

It was about 3:00 A.M. and very dark, and although it was hard on De Angelis to wait for dawn with a dead man across his body, I did not want to make a decision until there was light to see by. The other men stirred, woke up, and understood, almost without being told, what had happened. I remember someone saying, "Well, his sufferings are over." I think we were all a little frightened, with the wind blowing and clouds rushing across the sky, and Alex dead in that plunging raft. Somewhere I have read that sharks can sense the coming of death. That night there seemed twice as many as we had seen before.

At daybreak Bartek hauled Alex's little raft alongside, and Cherry paddled up in his. The body was already stiff, but I checked the heart, the pulse, checked in every way I knew. And I asked Cherry and Whittaker to do so, not wishing to accept the responsibility alone. We agreed Alex was dead. We removed his wallet and identification disc, which Captain Cherry has since returned to the family, and we saved the jacket. De Angelis murmured what he remembered of the Catholic burial service. Then we rolled the body over the side. It did not sink at once but rather floated off face down a little while.

This was the thirteenth morning.

II

It had been my habit, as soon at it was light enough to see, to count heads in the rafts. Seven (not including myself) was the number fixed in my mind. At times during the next few days, as I counted automatically, I would discover with a kind of shock that there were only six. Then I would remember. Alex was the seventh.

Alex's death left De Angelis alone in the two-man raft at the end of the line. Bartek asked De Angelis to change places with him. De Angelis was willing, but he preferred to be with his fellow officers in the head raft. So Sergeant Reynolds came back with me and Adamson, and Bartek shifted to the little raft. It did not occur to me to ask him why he wanted to change. He was getting pretty weak, and I assumed he would rest better alone.

Before daylight a morning or two later I woke up to find the little raft gone. The connecting rope was trailing in the water and, having tied the knot myself, I knew it could not have pulled loose.

At daybreak we saw his raft only half a mile away, bobbing up and down on a gentle swell. We waved and yelled. Finally Bartek heard us and paddled back, almost reluctantly. I asked what happened. He admitted having untied the line during the night. I have never been able to understand why and, although I asked him directly, he offered no explanation. He said he didn't know; he didn't know why.

My memory was a little off, but I think we finished the last of the rain water the evening before Alex died. Another calm spell settled over our piece of the Pacific. The rafts, securely moving, lay bunched together, and the sun started to burn our guts out all over again.

We went another forty-eight hours or so without water. After the last drop had gone, several men were almost raving wild in their thirstiness. There is really no limit to what men will try in their extremity. In the first terrible week we had saved our urine in the empty Very cartridge shells and let it stand for several days, hoping that the sun and air would work a beneficial chemical change. That was my idea. It was a bad one.

We had been without food since we ate the last fish on the ninth day. Cherry, who had been fishing patiently, lost the second and last line and hook on a big shark. But before this happened he had actually hooked a two-foot shark. With Whittaker's help, he managed to hoist it into the raft, where he stabbed it with a knife. Cherry cut the carcass into two pieces, keeping the smaller one for his raft and passing the other back to me, for Adamson, Reynolds, and myself, and for Bartek in the little raft.

I cut off equal pieces for the four. The meat was rubbery and tough; it took all my strength to force the rusty blade through it. Maybe we were more pernickety than some other castaways, but hungry as we were, no one had stomach for shark meat. It had a foul, rancid taste and the two or three of us who chewed and sucked the meat, mostly for the liquid in it, soon spit out the pieces, gagging as we did so. I kept my piece in the boat all day, hoping the sun would cure it and make it palatable, but I simply could not down it. When I offered them another piece, Adamson and Bartek shook their heads. The flesh was beginning to stink, so I threw it overboard, without regret. In a little while I heard a splash—Cherry's half had followed ours.

The sharks were around us all the time as I have already said. Whether it was because they scented food on the rafts or whether they resented these unfamiliar objects, or even because they were trying to dislodge the leeches on their backs, they kept attacking us. They would come up under the boat and hit the bottom a vicious jolt; so hard, in fact, that it would be raised several inches from the water. They did this with their mouths, which are round. Fortunately, the boat was taut and they could not get their teeth into it. We comforted ourselves with the thought that we were safe from that peril until later we discovered a series of tiny jagged breaks on the bottom of all the boats. They looked as though they had been caused by the bottom teeth of our untiring enemies. Another disturbing habit they had was to come up day and night and slap the sides of the boats with their tails, showering us with water.

While trying to stab the shark in the raft, Cherry had driven his knife through the rubberized canvas floor, making a quarter-inch tear, through which water seeped. Because the day was calm, Cherry decided to try to make a patch with the repair kit. In the kit were a tube of glue, a piece of sandpaper, and a small roll of patching material. The problem was to dry the raft bottom so the patch would hold. Cherry and the other two got out of their raft and turned it bottom side up, so that it floated on the inflated roll, leaving an air space underneath. Then they hauled themselves back on the bottom, resting there while the canvas dried.

The patch was a failure—perhaps because the patching

material was ruined by salt water. It pulled loose soon after they righted the raft. They never tried another. The rent didn't let in enough water to be dangerous, but enough to make them miserable. Unless they bailed frequently, there was always two or three inches of water in the bottom.

That was bad, not just because it was uncomfortable, but also because the salt sores that covered them never had a chance to heal. We all had them, and in many ways they caused the most pain. First there was an evil-looking rash that spread over the thighs and bumpus. Then the sores would come—hard, angry red things, full of pus, that looked like boils and hurt worse. When they broke, they left running sores which never seemed to dry.

Our bodies, our minds, the few things we had with us were slowly rotting away. All the watches except Whittaker's stopped running, as salt-water corrosion froze the works. The compass needle ceased to point and finally rusted hard in the direction in which it had set. The silver coins in my pockets took on a discolored look. The secret orders that Mr. Stimson had given me faded and became unintelligible. The colors and the print came off our only map, which finally stuck together at the folds and could not be opened. But by then I had memorized the position of every island or bit of land of any possible use to us.

In the breast pocket of my coat I have carried, for many years, a little leather case containing a crucifix and three St. Christopher medals. The crucifix was given to me in 1917 when I left with the A.E.F. by a ten-year-old girl, the daughter of a friend. Whenever I flew on the Western Front, I always had that case in my flying suit. As the case wore out I had it replaced—half-a-dozen times, I'd say. It was with me the night I flew into a hill near Atlanta. And it was with me again on the Pacific. Like all the other metal things, the crucifix and the medals started to corrode and disintegrate. I am not a Catholic and, aside from the sentiment connected with such things, I was certainly under no illusions as to what they could do for me. Yet after all the years, and the good fortune associated with them, I found myself believing, as men will when everything else is going to pieces, that my fate was somehow involved with them.

The watch I had was a gift from the city of Detroit after World War I. It was a fine, expensive timepiece; I valued it for that and other reasons. Yet not to be able to tell the time turned out to be no particular loss. Time, merely as something to keep track of, ceased to be any real concern of ours. One of the men who had a small notebook kept a diary through the first week but as far as I could see he never wrote afterward.

Adamson used to pencil terse notes on the side of the raft, with the date. But by the second week he was satisfied merely to scratch the day. His last note I remember clearly:

"Fourteenth day. Rick and I still alive."

Either the fourteenth night, or the night before, an unexpected and depressing event occurred. After Alex died, I began to despair of Adamson. The nagging pain in his back, aggravated by salt-water sores, gave him no peace. To my knowledge he never slept deeply. He just slipped off into a permanent semi-consciousness, occasionally broken by feeble gusts of fury and intolerable pain. His feet, legs, arms, wrists, and face had been burned to a red pulp and any movement in the raft, however slight, was certain to communicate itself to his back.

Hans Adamson is an old dear friend. It was a terrible responsibility to sit there and watch the strength go out of him. His clothes were rotting on his back. The colonel's eagles on his tunic were corroded. His uniform shirt and pants were water-stained and coming to pieces. A gray stubble covered his face, and his eyes were bloodshot and swollen.

On this particular night I felt the raft give a violent lurch. My first thought was that a shark was attacking. Adamson's body was no longer against mine. His end of the raft was empty. I saw something struggling in the water close by and my hand gripped Adamson's shoulder. He was too heavy for me to hold up alone, but my yells for help brought Cherry and Whittaker up in their raft. We were a long time at it, but we managed to haul him back into the raft.

In the morning Hans had a long, lucid interval. We talked about many things, familiar and pleasant things done together, the mission we were on. But from that day on he seldom spoke or asked for anything.

It does us no dishonor to say that we were all becoming a little unhinged. We were unreasonable, at times, in our demands upon one another. Wrathful and profane words were exchanged over nothing at all. Every night the rafts were drawn together for prayer meeting. We continued to read from Bartek's New Testament, now yellowed and stained by salt water. But one or two, who had been most fervent, became backsliders. Because their prayers were not answered within twenty-four or forty-eight hours, they condemned the Lord for His failure to save them. They wanted deliverance immediately.

I tried to impart my own philosophy to these men,

hoping to stimulate their desire to carry on. It was based upon the simple observation that the longer I have had to suffer under trying circumstances, the more certain I was to appreciate the deliverance. That is part of the wisdom that comes to older men.

If that didn't work, I would turn to the only other weapon left, and that was to brutalize and jar those whose chins sagged too far down on their chests. One man said to me across twenty feet of water: "Rickenbacker, you are the meanest, most cantankerous so-and-so that ever lived." Some of the things I said could have been a heavy weight on my conscience. But I felt better after we reached land. Several of the boys confessed that they once swore an oath to live for the sheer pleasure of burying me at sea.

There were occasions when I myself was pretty hard pressed: when my private store of aches and pains reduced me to something less than a good companion. My legs and hip were rather severely torn in the Atlanta crash. Right up to the time of the Pacific trip I was under regular diathermic and physiotherapeutic treatment. If anyone had told me I could live for twenty-one days with two other men in a space approximately nine feet by five, I would have said he was crazy.

As I got thinner and thinner, my teeth began to give trouble. The gums seemed to shrink in proportion to the rest of me, and the new front bridgework which my dentist finished a few days before I left turned loose and uncomfortable. My mouth dried out, and under the bridge the saliva formed an evil-tasting, cottony substance that felt like mush. However, by washing the bridge four and five times a day in the ocean, and forcing salt water against the gums with my tongue, I found some relief. Knowing the fix I'd be in if the bridge ever slipped out of my hand, I was extremely cautious about this ceremony—overcautious, in fact. One time it did slip from my hand, but I had it back before it had sunk six inches. For me that was the most frightening moment in the twenty-one days.

Naturally, as time went on, the days grew longer. We could see moving objects, we could see each other, we could see the waves breaking, and the swells of the ocean. Sometimes we would see seagulls, and always they raised false hopes that we were near land. I should have known better; I have crossed most of the oceans of the world and found gulls everywhere and at all distances from land.

The nights grew more deadly. Some of the boys would talk in their sleep, others would cry out in nightmares, and at times I could hear some of them praying. Each period, from darkness to daylight, seemed like eternity. Always I kept trying to think and rack my brain for a way out of our dilemma. I had never lost my belief that we would be found. How, where, or when, was what I was trying to think through.

I had one hope and wish since we were drifting southwest, that a violent storm might come up and catch us in its clutches and carry us at a much greater rate of speed into some island haven.

So hard did I think of the many possibilities that during the last few nights, and particularly from midnight until dawn when the mist was at its worst, I would doze off and dream of having landed on an island where I found an old friend with a lovely home who was happy and glad to welcome us, and who put me up in a nice soft bed and gave me a most delicious breakfast, with an abundance of fruit juices which I craved. And after breakfast, all I had to do was to wait until Mr. Stimson, Secretary of War, arrived at his office. My friend in these dreams had a telephone, and I could reach Secretary Stimson directly, telling him where we were.

Then as the gray dawn came over the horizon, I would awaken to find to my horror and amazement that I was still on the broad Pacific, with its thick mist and that everlasting rocking to and fro that goes with the ocean swells.

Even after we were picked up, for many, many nights in the hospital I would awaken with that same hallucination and dream, with the everlasting rocking and swinging of the raft under me.

Both Cherry and I were convinced we were well to the north and west of the convoy and air-ferry routes. We tried from time to time to paddle in a southeasterly direction, but the efforts taxed us and we gave up. It seemed much more important to conserve our strength.

Naturally, during all these days of drifting, we did not go in the same direction. Sometimes the squalls would drive us in the opposite direction for hours at a time. Always, however, the tendency was to the southwest. This meant that we would see the squalls coming up from behind and at first we were afraid they would miss us. We would paddle like the devil in their direction, hoping to get into their path. They traveled so much faster than we could that we often missed them. We all got to be experts in knowing which one was going to come our way and which was not.

On the fourteenth night or so we got a wonderful break. A series of squalls, one behind the other, passed over the rafts. It was a wild night. I doubt if I have ever worked so hard, or to such good effect. When I finished wringing the last shirt and sock dry at dawn, there was a gallon of water in my bailing bucket. Cherry had nearly as much in the Mae West. In the morning and again at noon we had a jigger around. This, with what we had sucked from the clothes before we squeezed the water out, refreshed and heartened us.

But because our last resources were plainly running out, we held council the next afternoon and decided to chance a course that I had steadily held to be risky. Ever since leaving the airplane I had insisted that the rafts stay together. But now I had come to believe that our only hope was for one raft, manned by the strongest three, to try to beat across the current to the southeast. In that direction they stood a better chance to fall in with a transport plane or a ship; and if they were lucky enough to be picked up alive, they would direct the search for us. Cherry agreed to go, and Whittaker and De Angelis, who were in better shape than any of the others, also volunteered. I gave them most of the water and the last oar in the little raft.

They set out in the early afternoon. Or I should say they tried to set out. They untied the line and paddled off. The sea was flat, but there was a slight head wind. Hours later they were still in sight, not more than a mile away, perhaps less. Watching, I could see two men paddling while the third rested. Long after the sun had set, I saw their shadows rising on the swell. Then I lost them in the night mist.

When day came and I hauled myself over Reynolds' back for a look around I saw they were only a short distance away, sleeping. Presently, they paddled back, exhausted. Cherry said it was a physical impossibility to force the raft against the current and that little breeze. This was a heavy disappointment to all of us, but in an odd way the incident marked a turning point in our fortunes. Thereafter we were never without water. The skies clouded over, and there were few hours during the day or night when rain squalls were not chasing across the horizon.

We also invented a storage system for water. I hated to leave it in the bailing bucket on the bottom of the raft because there was always the risk of knocking it over. And the loss by evaporation during the heat of the day could be very heavy. The idea of using the Mae West life jacket, which I wore, occurred to me. This had two double compartments, filled with carbon dioxide, each closed by a bicycle valve.

I let out the gas and, taking a mouthful at a time from the bailing bucket, forced the water down a narrow tube past the valve into the compartment. This took a long time—perhaps fifteen to twenty minutes to transfer a quart. All the while the boys had their eyes fixed on my Adam's apple, watching for a convulsive jerk. The honor system has seldom been put to a more severe test, and I can't blame the others for being suspicious. One night I heard one man muttering to a companion that while it only took a count of three for Rickenbacker to fill his mouth from the bucket, it took a count of sixteen for him to transfer the mouthful to the jacket.

The three empty Very cartridges that we had saved served as drinking cups. They were about six inches long and perhaps an inch and a quarter wide. There was one in each raft. Proving how far men will go in adapting themselves to hard conditions, we also urinated in them since we dared not stand up in the raft. (Throughout the twenty-one days, even when we were without water, our kidneys functioned almost normally. On the other hand, I do not recall that anyone had a single bowel movement.)

With water we also gained a little food, by a great stroke of luck. One night in the third week there was a tremendous splashing all around the boat. It was pitch dark, but the water blazed with zigzagging phosphorescent streaks. We could hear heavy bodies hitting the water terrific smacks.

A pack of sharks had hit a school of mackerel with the rafts in the middle of the slaughter. The terrified mackerel shot out of the water like star shells. One landed in my raft and I fell on him before he could flop out. Simultaneously another landed in Cherry's boat and was bagged. They provided food for two days. It was our first in nearly a week.

Cherry was the only one who could claim to have been hurt by a shark, and this was by mistake. One time we were all aroused by a bloodcurdling shriek. There was a God-awful thrashing around in the forward raft and finally I heard Cherry yelling, "A damn shark came up and hit me and broke my nose."

We pulled the boats together and from Cherry's misery it was plain that he had been hit a hard wallop. Blood was streaming down his face and shirt. Whittaker made him lie down while he heaped wet handkerchiefs over his nose. This stopped the bleeding and, after the pain eased, Cherry decided that his nose hadn't been broken after all. He had only the foggiest idea how it happened. He was stretched across the raft, with the upper half of his body across the inflated bulge, and while asleep he must have rolled out, just far enough for a shark to reach him with a flick of the tail.

The seventeenth day brought the first tantalizing hint

that we had finally drifted within the reach of assistance. We had been through several days and nights of squally weather which blew us in all directions. The rafts had taken a pounding, and the interminable slap-slap of the waves, the everlasting pitching and swaying, had left us sleepless, exhausted, and miserable. I would wring rain water from clothes until my fingers turned stiff and useless. Then I would rest and wring some more. The reserve in the Mae West grew steadily; it had a fine heft when I lifted it. And we were drinking three jiggers a day per man.

This particular afternoon was heavily overcast; the sea was quite rough, with whitecaps, and I was worrying about the strain on the connecting lines. I saw Cherry in the raft ahead sit up and cock his head. Then he shouted back, "I hear a plane. Listen!"

In a few minutes we all saw an airplane off to the left. It came out of a squall, flying low and fast, about five miles away. Bartek was back in my raft that day. He stood up while I held him, and waved his arms and shouted until he slid out of my arms and fell exhausted across the raft.

The seven of us yelled our lungs out. The plane came no nearer. It was a single-engine pontoon job. I doubt that we had it in sight more than three or four minutes. It was too far off for us to make out its markings. A squall moved in between and we did not see it again. The yelling stopped, and for a long time no one talked. My throat hurt from shouting so much.

Yet just to see that airplane was a terrific stimulus. It was the first outside sign of human life visible to us in two and a half weeks. Here at last was proof that land was close by, or at least a ship capable of catapulting such an airplane. Only the sick men slept that night. Cherry, Whittaker, De Angelis, and I talked steadily across the rafts.

On the eighteenth day, again in the afternoon, we saw two more airplanes of the same type, flying close together, perhaps six miles away. We waved our shirts but did not shout, knowing it was useless. On the nineteenth day, in the morning, there were four more airplanes, first a pair to the north, then another to the south, perhaps 4,000 feet high. First the strong, resonant note of the engines came from below the horizon; then we saw the planes themselves; then we watched them disappear. The sound lingered after they had gone.

That afternoon no airplanes appeared and somehow the fear took hold of us that perhaps we had gone past the land, perhaps we had drifted through a string of islands and were moving into the open Pacific. Being picked up, quite obviously, was going to be a chance in a million. We had assumed that an airplane with a vigilant crew could not miss the bright yellow rafts. Now we knew otherwise. In a rough sea the rafts must be just flecks against the whitecaps.

Yet this should have been our best time. We had water in reserve and we also had food. In the early morning, in the gray half light before dawn, hundreds and hundreds of finger-length fish, resembling sardines, collected around the rafts. With practice and diligence we learned how to scoop them up. The trick was to bring your hand from behind and pin them with a quick move against the raft. But for every one landed, a hundred were lost. Through the last three days we must have caught between twenty and thirty. They were divided, share and share alike, and the fishes were still wriggling when we bit into them. I crunched them and downed them whole.

We came to the evening of the twentieth day—about six o'clock. Cherry and De Angelis were arguing. I paid no attention until a phrase, louder than the others, came across the little stretch of water. It was the first inkling of what was afoot. Captain Cherry wanted De Angelis to give up his place in the little raft. "Why do you want it, Cherry?" I asked. He answered, "I'm going to try to make land. Staying together is no good. They'll never see us this way."

I told Cherry then he was wrong, and I still think he was wrong, despite the fact he was the first to be picked up. We argued back and forth between the rafts for at least an hour. My point was that he had no way of telling which was the best direction to take. The various airplanes had appeared in the north, south, east, and west. And if they couldn't see three rafts bunched together, what chance did they have of seeing one? But Cherry was insistent. He argued that our only chance was to scatter. Yet he left the decision to me, saying: "I won't go unless you agree it is all right for me to."

I realized that no good would come out of prolonging the argument. De Angelis paddled past us in the little raft, transferred to the lead raft, and Cherry took his place. I wished Captain Cherry well and said so long. He had some water in his Mae West, so I was not worried on that account. He drifted off alone, carried by the swell and a slight breeze.

Whittaker and De Angelis watched the receding raft with increasing nervousness. I heard them saying that maybe Cherry was right and there was nothing to be gained by staying together. They, too, decided to go

off. I remonstrated with them as I had with Cherry. I
was angry now. "What about Reynolds?" I said. "You
haven't asked him." They couldn't ask him, Reynolds
was too sick, too weak, to understand.

I gave in again. The talk had worn me down.

Cherry was almost out of sight when Whittaker cast
off the line. Both rafts were out of sight before night fell.
Now there were three of us, Adamson, Bartek, and myself. Adamson and Bartek were more dead than alive.
They hadn't been drawn into the arguments of the afternoon. I doubt that they even heard what was said.
They were scrunched up at opposite ends of the raft.

I was terribly worried that night. If we had indeed
drifted past land, our chances of holding out much
longer were damn poor. I had perhaps two quarts and
a pint of water in the Mae West. Half of this, in one
compartment, was good, sweet water. The rest was du-
bious, being from the first wringing of the soaked rags.
To be sure of getting rid of all the salt in the rags we
had at first thrown away the first pint or so, after using
it to rinse out the bailing bucket and the Very cartridge
cases. However, a sip convinced me this water was
drinkable and thereafter I frugally transferred the first
water of a rain to the inside compartment of the Mae
West. This became the emergency supply. The product
of subsequent wringings went into what I called the
"sweet-water" chamber. This provided the regular ration.

On the twenty-first morning I woke from a particularly pleasant version of my usual dream. I issued the
morning jigger of water, but Adamson and Bartek were
almost too weak to raise their heads to drink. As I measured the water into the shell, my hand trembled so much

I spilled some. Part of Bartek's ration ran down his chin, and I had to give him more to make up for it. After two hours of scooping I caught several more of the little fishes. But I was nervous and impatient and my hand moved with exasperating clumsiness.

The sky had cleared during the night and after the sun got up it turned terribly hot. I watched for seaweed and debris—anything suggestive of land. But the ocean was bare. Even the gulls were absent. Some time during the morning Bartek emerged briefly from his coma and asked: "Have the planes come back?"

I said, "No, there haven't been any since day before yesterday."

He seemed to have difficulty understanding this. Then he mumbled, "They won't come back. I know. They won't come back." He said that over and over again.

Yet it was Bartek who first heard the planes when they returned late in the afternoon. I am quite sure that I was awake, but my senses must have been dulled, because Bartek pulled at my shirt and whispered, "Listen, Captain—planes! They're back. They're very near."

There were two airplanes approaching from the southeast. Adamson and Bartek were too weak to stand themselves, or to hold me up. Sitting down, I waved as hard as I could with my old hat. The planes, only a few hundred yards off the water, passed within a couple of miles and disappeared into the setting sun. My first elation was swallowed up in despair. Night was only a few hours away. This was our last chance.

Half an hour later we heard them again, much closer. They came directly out of the sun, straight for us. The first dived right over the raft. We yelled like maniacs. The plane was so low that I could see the pilot's expression. He was smiling and waving. Not until then did I look at the insignia. It was the United States Navy, and gratitude and happiness filled me. I waved and waved, out of a half-crazy notion that the pilot must be made to understand we were not three dead men on a raft.

The first airplane made a full circle around the raft, then set off after the other. They disappeared into the direction from which they first had come. Like the others, they were single-engine pontoon jobs.

Bartek kept asking, "Are they coming back? Are they coming back?" I said yes, they know where we are, and they are certainly coming back. My idea was that they had returned to some island base to report and a PBY flying boat would be sent to pick us up. In fact, I worked out half-a-dozen reasons to account for their leaving us. But, as it turned out, I overlooked the obvious one—they were short of gas.

As the minutes dragged, my confidence weakened. The sun was going down fast, and a dangerous-looking squall was making up in the south. About three quarters of an hour later the same two airplanes reappeared, skirting the squall. While still a mile or so off they veered off into a low cloud and vanished. Obviously they had lost us again. But a few minutes later they burst out of the heart of the squall, headed directly for the raft. They must have seen us instantly, because they glided down and circled. Then one plane went off, while the other stayed overhead.

He circled, circled, circled. I waved and waved and waved. Never have I known myself to possess such strength, showing what mind can do over matter.

The eastern horizon was already quite dark. I wondered what program the pilot had in mind, whether he was waiting for someone else, or planned to land and pick us up himself. The sun finally set, but he just went on circling, and the fear took hold that now he would have to return to his base and we would be in for another night on the raft, and if this squall caught us, God knows where we would be blown by morning. I couldn't understand why he didn't land.

Only a little light was left in the western sky when a white flare flamed below the plane. A minute later the pilot fired another—a red one. The reason for the circling now became clear. The pilot was waiting for a boat. Far off on the southern horizon two lights blinked a code signal.

The plane straightened out and made a cautious landing on the darkened sea. Fortunately, it was smooth, except for a long swell. After taxiing within a few yards, the pilot shut off the engine. I paddled up and caught hold of the pontoon. The radioman climbed down to help me. The pilot joined him, and I remember thinking how clean and handsome they were, how proud I was to have them as countrymen.

They introduced themselves—Lieutenant Eadie (W. F. Eadie of Evanston, Illinois) and Radioman Boutte (L. H. Boutte of Abbeville, Louisiana). Eadie said a PT boat was on its way to take us in. But he went on to say that he didn't want to show another light, since there might be Japs in the vicinity. So rather than wait, he proposed that we taxi into the base, which he said was forty miles away.

I told the lieutenant that first we had to dispose of a piece of unfinished business. The afternoon before, after the others had gone off, I had made this deal with Bartek and Adamson: the moment we knew we were safe, all the water in the Mae West was to be divided. They were to have all the sweet water and I the "tainted." This would give me twice as much water, but they were all for it.

I opened the valve in the Mae West and poured the sweet water into the bailing bucket for Adamson and Bartek. There was enough to give each a pint. While they were drinking, I unscrewed the other valve, lifted the tube to my lips, and drank to the last drop. I must have had nearly a quart. It was salty all right, but if there had been a gallon I would have taken it.

Lieutenant Eadie meanwhile gave us the good news about the others. Captain Cherry had been sighted the afternoon before about twenty-five miles away by a Navy plane on routine evening patrol, piloted by Lieutenant Frederick E. Woodward of Davenport, Iowa. With him was the same radioman who was with Eadie, and he was first to sight the raft.

Luckily for Cherry, a PT boat was near by. Cherry, not knowing where we had drifted during the night, was able to give only vague directions as to our likely position. Every available plane was put in the air, and in the midst of the search a radio call from a near-by island informed the base that natives had seen three castaways on the beach of an uninhabited island several miles away. This news was supplied by an English missionary who had a small radio transmitter, and presumably it accounted for Whittaker, De Angelis, and Reynolds. A doctor had already been dispatched to them in an airplane.

We were really the lucky ones. Our raft, during the night, drifted through the chain of islands into the open sea. The next landfall was hundreds of miles away.

There is, of course, no way of telling how far we drifted during the twenty-one days. My guess is between four hundred and five hundred miles. Unknowingly, we had drifted across the International Date Line, losing a day. By our calendar we were picked up Wednesday, November 11—or Thursday, November 12, by the pilot's. We were then a few hours into our twenty-second day.

After we had finished the water, Eadie and Boutte hoisted Adamson eight feet into the cockpit. The plane had room for only one passenger and I took it for granted that Eadie would leave Bartek and me behind. So I said to Lieutenant Eadie, "Would you mind waiting until the PT does come up? I don't want them to miss us in the dark."

Eadie said calmly, "Why, Captain Eddie, you fellows are going too."

I looked at the cockpit. "Where?" He smiled and said, "On the wing."

Eadie had the strength of Hercules. With Boutte's help he hauled Bartek to the wing, lifted him over the cockpit, and sat him on the right wing with his legs hanging over the leading edge. In that position he was tied securely to the wing and cockpit. I was boosted to the left wing and tied in the same way. I was deeply impressed by these two young Navy fliers. They knew their business, they asked no foolish questions. All that we could say was "This is heaven," and "Thank God," and "God bless the Navy."

I don't know how long we taxied—perhaps half an hour. It was pitch dark and with the propeller wash battering my eyelids I couldn't see much anyway. Presently the shadow of a PT boat loomed up ahead. Eadie cut the engine and drifted within hailing distance. After a three-cornered argument involving him, the skipper of the PT boat, and myself, it was arranged that Bartek and I be transferred and that Adamson continue in the plane rather than be put to the discomfort of another change.

It was no hardship for me to change. I knew there'd be water and food—but water, above all—on the boat. They lowered Bartek and me back into the raft, and I paddled across to the boat. Planting my feet upon an American deck was the next-best thing to being home. The crew gave us a cheer. It bucked us up no end, but we hardly deserved it. There's no great honor attached to saving your own skin.

Bed rolls and blankets were laid out. Bartek fell asleep instantly, but all the excitement made me wakeful. Moreover, the salty water I had drunk stimulated a bowel action that took me to the toilet. My legs were rusty after days and nights of just sitting. Nevertheless, by holding on to things I managed to get to the washroom.

Water was the only thing on my mind. One of the men led me into a cabin where I downed four China mugs of water in quick succession. The skipper, who was barely half my age, became alarmed. "Aren't you overdoing it?" he asked. I said yes, maybe too much water would be bad. So I had a couple of mugs of pineapple juice and a mug of hot beef broth, one after the other.

By this time we were at the base, and a beaching boat had come alongside. A Colonel Fuller, the ranking doctor, appeared with several pharmacist's mates. They had two stretchers, on which they lowered Bartek and me to the other boat. A few minutes later the keel

crunched on the beach. We were carried across the
beach and down a road, under the most beautiful palm
trees I have ever seen. The moon was shining through
the clouds, the air was warm—it was a lovely evening.

They took us into a little one-story hospital, with
eight or ten cots in a single room. Colonel Fuller said
proudly it had just been built and we were the first
patients. My clothes literally came apart as they un-
dressed me. As soon as they put me to bed, I demanded
water. The colonel turned to the pharmacist's mate and
directed him to give me two ounces every two hours. I
said I wanted it in a bucket, not a medicine dropper. "If
you drink too much," the colonel said, "the aftereffects
could be quite serious." I told him what I had had on the
PT boat. "All the more reason," he said severely. "Two
ounces every two hours."

That was all I got and that night I was literally afire.
I thirsted as I never had the worst day on the raft. The
salt in the water I had drunk was doubtless responsible.

I slept badly. The burns on my wrists, neck, and face,
the loathsome sores that covered my legs, thighs, and
bumpus were plastered with healing compounds, but
they hurt now as they never hurt on the raft. My old
dream repeated itself, but with a nightmarish twist at
the end. I was again in that fine house, eating and drinking with gluttonous pleasure. Then the dream dissolved
and I woke almost in terror, imagining the raft was rocking and swinging under me, and mistaking the moonlight through the windows for the ocean mist.

In the morning I was aroused by a fearful hammering
and pounding. I was told that a new and bigger hospital
was being built a short distance away. Cherry was
brought in that day and on the following day Whittaker

and De Angelis arrived. After being picked up, they had all been taken aboard a Navy tender. Poor Reynolds, however, had to be left behind. In his weakened condition the doctors were afraid to move him. I found I had lost forty pounds on the raft. Adamson and Cherry, both heavier than I to start with, had each lost fifty-five pounds.

Whittaker and De Angelis had a hair-raising tale to tell. The morning after they left us they saw palm trees a long way off to the north. Whittaker said he rowed for hours. Every approach to the island was guarded by reefs, over which the surf broke heavily, but they took a chance and rode the breakers to the beach. Too weak to walk, Whittaker and De Angelis crawled on their hands and knees, dragging Reynolds between them.

After propping Reynolds against a palm tree, they searched the underbrush for food and water. A short distance away they found a partly finished hut and the half-finished hull of a canoe, carved from the trunk of a coconut tree. The canoe had collected considerable rain water. They skimmed off the dead bugs and drank to their bellies' content. The rubbish was infested with rats. They got close enough to one to club it to death, and devoured it raw. Afterward some natives arrived in a canoe and took them to an island several miles away. Here they were cared for by the English missionary until the Navy doctor arrived.

That same afternoon a flying boat brought two doctors in from Samoa—a Captain Jacobs of the Marine Corps and a Lieutenant Commander Durkin of the Navy. They gave us a careful going over and decided that all of us, except Bartek, should fly back with them to Samoa. Bartek was still too sick to be moved. As for

Reynolds, the last word was that it would be best for him to remain on the tender. Adamson had failed to bounce back as rapidly as the rest and the doctors deliberated some time over the wisdom of moving him. They finally decided to chance it, since the base hospital at Samoa was much better equipped to take care of him. It was a good thing they did. Had they left Hans there, I am sure he would have died before another week was out.

In three flying boats we took off early Monday morning. I was mighty glad to be on my way, but I was also sorry to leave my friends on the island. My affection went beyond the fact that they had done so many wonderful things for us. I liked their spirit, the conscientious way they went about their patrols, and I liked the way they put up that hospital. College men for the most part, pharmacist's mates by Navy grade, few of them knew anything about carpentry. But they put up that hospital in three days. They were up before dawn and they worked until dark. There's no forty-hour week on Island Z.

ALONE IN SHARK WATERS

By John Kruse

There is a modern touch in John Kruse's personal record. Born after World War I in England, he emerged from Harrow School to be an infantry captain in World War II in the Middle East and Italy. Thereafter, with peace breaking out, he was a laborer, truck driver, street photographer, and movie cameraman. So he arrived at filming "The Outcast of the Islands" in Ceylon. This led to spear-fishing and underwater adventure.

Mr. Kruse decided that making movies was not what he had imagined, so he is giving it up. He is rising, we may timidly suggest, through the dangerous waters of the movie ocean into the daylight of literature. This is one of his best stories to date.

Down in the hold, the noise was earsplitting. Every timber, the length and breadth of the *Ben Sidi Tajir*, seemed to be shrieking in agony. The single hurricane lamp swung sickeningly overhead, swilling its anemic light around in the blackness. Mike Gardener shut his eyes and braced himself against a crate; he felt the ship lift and drop away crabwise in a quick, double movement that sucked his stomach about inside him like water in a goat skin.

The native passengers around him were now fully awake. They were sitting up among the cargo, chatter-

Reprinted from *Collier's Magazine*, 1953.

ing shrilly, the whites of their eyes showing clearly in
the lamplight. There were about twenty of them, trav-
eling freight, like himself, from Ceylon to the Maldive
Islands.

The *Ben Sidi Tajir* was a Maldivian schooner, and
her run was between Colombo and the islands. She was
a cross between a felucca and a Spanish galleon, and
her crew was a ragged bunch of moplas, descended
from the old Malabar Coast pirates. There was nothing
those moplas didn't know about the sea. They had
smelled the wind coming five hours before it hit the
ship. The ship was a full day out of port. There was
nothing they could do but keep running and hope to
miss it. When the wind was an hour away, they knew
by the sky that they didn't have a chance. It was two
in the morning, and Mike was asleep on deck. They had
shaken him awake and told him to get below. Then they
had dropped the big triangular sail, battened down the
hatches and heaved to.

The only passenger accommodation was the hold, and
Mike had gone down there wondering what the panic
was. He didn't wonder for long. It was a hurricane.

It hit the mainmast with a shock that went right down
into the ship and set up a howl in the rigging that made
Mike's hackles creep. The ship was half empty, and with
all her galleonlike superstructure in the stern, she began to roll like a tar barrel.

Mike braced himself with his feet and listened to the
grinding timbers and cursed. There were safer ways of
getting to the islands than in this relic, but not as cheap;
that was the rub. When you speared fish for a living, you
couldn't afford to ride fancy.

He was on his way to the Maldives to try the spearing there. He was planning to fish his way through the reefs, selling his catches as he went—a sort of working vacation. His spear gun lay on the rice sacks beside him, with his fins and mask strapped to the trigger guard. His only other baggage was a pack containing a change of clothing, a dozen harpoon heads and the sixty-foot reel he used for spearing in deep water.

The storm seemed to be getting worse. He could hear the Diesel auxiliary laboring hard in the struggle to keep the ship's head into the wind, felt the screw race in the air each time she toppled down into a trough. Near him a mopla woman lay on the sacks clutching her belly and whimpering. She was pregnant, and Mike couldn't tell if she was in labor or just seasick. She didn't seem to belong to anybody. He spoke to her in Singhalese, but she made no sign that she had heard him.

Suddenly the ship gave one of its quick, double movements. There was a slow, grinding crash, and the vessel seemed to convulse. The lantern leaped from its hook, smashed against a crate and went out. Through the infernal din Mike heard the natives screaming and, in the blackness, felt the ship heave over on its side.

His instantaneous thought was that they had hit a reef. Then he knew they couldn't have. They were a full day's sail west of Ceylon; the water here was five hundred fathoms deep. The ship was breaking up. He grabbed up his most valuable possession, the spear gun, and struggled toward the mopla woman. He fell across her and she screamed. He shouted at her that it was the American and, gripping her under the armpit, lifted her to her feet and half carried, half dragged her toward where he knew the gangway out of the hold to be.

The natives blundered together in the darkness,

screaming and groping for the doorway. A match spurted near him. There was an instant of wild eyes and gleaming bodies. He spotted the gangway. The match went out as the crowd surged forward. The next moment, he and the woman were caught up in a crazy, struggling mass. Someone grabbed onto his back, clawed a way up over him. He kept hold of the woman and his gun, and shoved.

Suddenly something gave, and they were moving forward through water already knee-deep. It was deluging down from above, and there were figures up there against a faint square of sky, trying to fight their way up through the water, but it was forcing them back. Then the boat rolled and the deluge stopped. Mike got the woman's hand and clamped it onto his belt, then heaved himself up onto the companionway. Someone got hold of his gun and tried to pull him down by it. The gun was so long that it was fouling everything, and he nearly decided to let it go. Then he changed his mind. It was his livelihood, and he had brought it all the way from Genoa.

He wrenched the gun free and struggled up the ladder. There was someone above him; he lifted him by force clean out on deck, fell on top of him, rolled over, and reached back down the hatch for the woman. He got hold of her by the hair just as a wave smashed down onto them. It flattened him against the deck; if he hadn't had hold of the woman, it would have knocked her off the ladder. Someone screamed. The water dragged at him and drained away. Mike gasped and opened his eyes.

The deck slanted right down into the sea; there were no lights anywhere. The native beside him had disappeared. He had an impression of black mountains heaving against a sulphurous sky, of smashed rigging. Another wave crashed down on him like a ton weight, but he had the woman under the arms now and her weight anchored him.

As the wave hissed away, Mike pulled her out and got her down beside him on the slanting deck. More natives stumbled up out of the hatch. He was trying to remember where the lifeboats were. But the onslaught had been so quick, the crew wouldn't have had a chance to launch them. Something was sticking into his belly. It was the gun, with the fins and mask attached to it. He picked it up and looked around for something that would float. There was a life belt against the deckhouse; he caught the gleam of it in the darkness.

He took the woman's arms and hooked them over the hatch. He waited for the ship to roll back and tried to run along the sloping deck. His plimsolls slipped. He hit the planking with a smack and began to slide.

Mike's mind cleared; beyond fear, coolly and carefully, he watched for the rail, preparing to check against it with his feet. Its silhouette stood out clearly a foot or two above the foam. Then something crashed down on top of him, and he was under water again, tons of it, black and heavy and solid. It burned up into his sinuses, filling his brain with stars. Then the weight seemed to lift, and he lifted with it, up and up and up. Then surprisingly, there was air. He gulped at it, opened his eyes, and saw the dark shape of the ship. It was below him. Scared that he would be smashed against it, he began to swim.

He swam with the wind, angling past the wreck. He was lifted and flung like a cork toward the tilted deck.

A native was clinging to the rail. Mike was dashed to within a foot of him, and sucked back. He saw the shine of water on the man's back, saw him hanging in the sudden vacuum; then the sea heaved up and tore the native loose. He couldn't see what happened to him. The next moment, Mike was clear of the stern, surrounded by blackness, unable to see or to gauge the waves, trying to time his breaths to coincide with his rises to the surface. There was so much water in the air, it was difficult to tell when he was under and when he wasn't.

Hopelessness welled up in him. He was being swept away from the wreck into the raging blackness of the Indian Ocean. The nearest land was Ceylon, maybe a hundred miles to the east. He knew that no boat had got clear of the ship and that his chances of being picked up were nil. But he made no attempt to fight his way back to the vessel. If he had he would have been drowned inside of a minute, and instinctively he knew it. He kept right on with the storm, out into the vastness and the darkness. And he was afraid.

He struggled in the whirl and plunge of the waters, sobbing for air, trying to think. But he couldn't think of anything. He felt that something was dragging him under and realized that it was the spear gun. The mask and fins strapped to it were cupping the water. It was natural for him to have the gun; he didn't wonder about it any more than a carpenter would wonder about having his hammer. Its five pounds of duralumin and steel were a part of him; now they were gripped in his right hand in a clutch that nothing short of death could have broken.

The familiarity of the gun steadied him. It never occurred to him to drop it. He hugged it in to his chest and kept swimming, and a process began in the back of his mind that suddenly became defiance. He was in the sea and he had the gun. It was the same sea—the sea that was his life, the sea that he dived and hunted in every day all day—whipped up now into a frenzy, but still the same sea. There were jokes in Colombo about his being half fish. Maybe he was. Well, this was his sea.

The idea grew, and the storm seemed to change; maybe it was really letting up—he didn't know, but he knew suddenly that he could beat it, the way a fighter can sometimes tell with his opponent the first moment he comes in against him. He could ride it out, and there would be a plane. They would be bound to send out a plane.

A big wave curled over on top of him from behind and buried him in darkness. He didn't fight it; he just lay in the water holding his breath. He felt himself falling. He was out of the back of it. He breathed until he felt the lift of the next one, gasped a lungful of air, and, as it broke over him, ripped off his pants and shoes. In the next wave he got rid of his shirt. He was naked now except for his belt and knife. He thought of trying to put his fins on, but he knew he could never make it.

He needed all the buoyancy he could get. With every gasp of air, he began to swallow some. He felt the bubbles form in his stomach and fought back the desire to belch them out again.

He wrestled the spear gun around to the small of his back and clipped the butt hook onto his belt, so that he had the use of both arms.

He could lie along the surface then. It was like body-surfing, only the waves weren't breaking, they were running. Instead of carrying him with them, they swept

by underneath, lifting and dropping him, with a feet-
to-head movement, so far and so fast he was jarred
nearly senseless. The speed of the sea against the fins
and mask drove the harpoon down between his legs and
turned him over. He went under and nearly didn't come
up.

He didn't want to jettison the gun, so he pulled
around into the wind and faced the sea. The spray was
wicked, but the movement was better. The gun behind
him acted as a rudder.

Mike stayed that way, with the sea tearing past him,
breaking through the waves, his mind stopped down to
a pin point of concentration. Keep alive, he thought.
Never mind where the wind is taking you. Just keep
alive. Planes will scour the whole area. Ride it. Just ride
it out. You've been in a spot before. How about Iwo
Jima? What did you do then? Ride it out!

Wave after wave came—rush, rush, rush. The sounds
dabbed and cleared in his ears monotonously, and it
was the roaring and fading of sea shells, and then it was
voices—loud, then soft. Then it was anesthesia, with
great whirling lights and the punch-punch of watery
fists in his eyes growing duller and, as time dragged by,
imperceptible; he could feel nothing, and yet he knew
it was still going on. There was movement and a sense
of flying and sinking, but no feeling at all, nothing, and
he got scared. He thought he was unconscious, that he
was drowning. If only he could see something—anything—he would be able to tell!

He stared up at the sky blindly and twisted around,
searching the darkness. Then behind him he saw a single, pale rent in the clouds. Dawn! Then he *was* conscious—the excitement, the relief of it. Mike twisted and

began to swim toward the light but the spear gun fouled his legs instantly, and he went under.

As he sank down under the waves, something touched him. Despite his numbness, he felt it distinctly against his thigh—scaly and muscular and cold. The shock sobered him. He kicked convulsively to the surface.

The roughness and solidity had felt like a shark. He braced his muscles to resist the impact he thought must come. His softness and nakedness became huge in his mind, as they do under machine-gun fire. He sucked in his belly, beat with his legs in an effort to get up above the sea. He imagined the great shape of the shark below him negotiating the heaving water, waiting for a trough. A trough came. Mike dropped down into it, feeling his belly vulnerable and unprotected. He clenched his teeth, eyes, fists, toes, and waited. Another wave came, another trough; again the tension, again nothing. Mike knew that he would soon exhaust himself. He must relax; if it came, it came.

But it didn't come. He relaxed gradually, prayed for light and snatched another look at the east. The clouds were lifting off the horizon, revealing a long ingot of yellow light.

Hurry, hurry, he thought. But it didn't. It spread very slowly until the sea emerged from grayness and revealed itself fully, rolling and vast and lonely; he wished he had never seen it.

No creature rose to attack him, and gradually he got a hold on himself. He could handle the waves better now that he could see them; he could time his breathing. It was no worse than swimming in a monsoon sea, and he had had plenty of that.

He kept watching for a boat or a raft, but in all that

endless expanse, there was only him. What of the other passengers, the crew? he wondered. Surely he wasn't the only one?

Then suddenly the wind dropped. The effect was like deafness. The wind must have been diminishing for some time, and now suddenly there wasn't a breath, only the sea whishing and washing, but no spray and no thunder against his eardrums. Relief came to him and hope, and then something more arrogant—conquest. He had outlived the wind. The loneliness was back, worse than before. The sea stretched all around, endless and inescapable.

At last, the sun itself broke the ocean's rim, blazing a trail of weaving fire across the sea. The trail elongated and merged with the sky. The waves marched on Mike now in pink-gold echelons.

He felt all beaten up. Snap out of it, he thought, remembering the shark. Soon the fish would start feeding, and killer fish got very nasty in the early morning.

He got the gun unclipped and, lying with his face in the water, unstrapped the fins and mask. He got the fins on, sinking slowly down as he fitted them onto his feet. He came up quickly, very quickly, and got the snorkel mask up out of the water and peered at it blearily. The glass was intact; so was the breathing tube. The valve which kept the water out of the tube during a dive hinged freely. Thank God, he thought. He emptied the mask out, spat on the glass to stop it from clouding when he breathed, rinsed the mask out again, pulled it on and took a quick look down into the water. He did not know why he was so jumpy; there was nothing down there— only a few small shapes in the grayness. There wasn't enough light yet to see deep.

The harpoon was lashed against the barrel of the spear

gun with the steel line. Lying on his face again but breathing now through the snorkel tube—interruptedly, because the high sea kept dabbing the valve shut—Mike unwound the line and got the harpoon into the projector. He wrestled with the propulsion unit for nearly a minute before he managed to compress the heavy, double spring. As he floated to the surface and lay there; gasping weakly, he knew that that was the last time he would have the strength to do that. One shot—that was all he had.

The undersea dawned slowly beneath him. The rising sun rayed down through the plankton particles in bewildering, shifting patterns. He saw numerous fish, all fairly well down and shadowy still. It looked unbelievably deep. Something seemed to open up in his diaphragm and let the draught in. There would be fish out here he didn't know about—predatory giants as different from their reef relations as lions from alley cats.

The farther the sun got down into the water, the more fish he could see. Five, six, seven fathoms—there were fish and more fish, the deepest gleaming in the blue-blackness like sunken coins. Even as he watched, the pulse of their actions seemed to quicken. A pack of big bluefish cut into a shoal of mackerel four fathoms below him. The mackerel raced off in a tight, terrified wedge. It had started.

The whole of the visible undersea seemed to speed up like a film. The fish became no more than streaks of color in the ice-blue upper fathoms, tracing firework patterns of fear and hunger. Jacks and bonitos were everywhere, sometimes combining to tear with snapping jaws into a big shoal, then turning on one another to fight for the spoils.

The water became filled with little puffs of blood. The

smell of it seemed to excite the fish to even greater ferocity and fear. This battle period lasted, normally, half an hour in the morning and the same again at nightfall. Mike wished to hell they would stop. Barracuda and sharks went crazy at feeding time; they seemed to lose all their normal fear of noise and hostile action and behaved much more in accordance with their reputation.

Suddenly three six-foot torpedolike shapes shot up out of the depths toward him. He had barely time to pull himself together before they had veered off and beaten away into the blueness. They were gun metal and silver, and shaped like gigantic mackerel—tuna. Hell, he was slow! He realized then what a sitting target he was. Lucky that was all they had been; his reflexes were all to pieces from the storm.

Almost at once another big shape appeared below him, followed by several more. They moved through the water with a sickening rush, the big one in front working its jaws like a buzz saw. They were blue shark, with pectorals like bomb fins, and paper-knife noses. Mike didn't have time to stir a muscle. They swept by underneath him, the big one spitting out fragments of fish into the water, which were snapped up by the ones behind. They were gone in an instant, and he was just letting go his breath when suddenly they were back.

It was as evil a procession as one could ever wish not to see: three pilot fish were above and slightly in front, their stripes fairly screaming danger; behind them came a ten-foot chunk of barrel-like blue muscle and, bringing up the rear, four half-grown versions of the same creature.

The sharks surged by, slamming their jaws, and disappearing into the dimness. Mike lay in the water and waited; but this time they didn't come back.

He sucked in a deep breath. It had been a matron shark airing the kids. If a plane didn't hurry up and come soon, he thought . . .

Presently, the tempo of the underwater slowed down. Breakfast was over. Mike relaxed, flattened on the surface, beating automatically with his fins, rising and falling steadily, saving his strength. The sun climbed slowly up the sky. He was really tired now, tired and thirsty. He estimated that he had been in the water for seven hours. During a full day's spearing he sometimes kept going for eight without touching down. But that was in a calm sea and in sight of land. Land, he thought longingly, with the elephants plowing the coconut groves along by the sea.

It must have been about eleven o'clock when he heard the plane. He hoisted himself as far up in the water as he could and ripped off his mask. He saw it at once. It was a biplane. It was puttering over the sea about a mile to the north, with its nose high, obviously on the lookout for something. Mike waved his mask frantically, shouted and splashed about in the water, but it kept going steadily, and eventually disappeared over the horizon.

It'll be back, he thought wildly. It's looking for the wreck. It's got to come back! He kept the mask off, forgetting the danger, forgetting everything but that up there was a fellow human being and that he must make him see him. His heart began to thump, and a great deadness spread outward from his diaphragm into his limbs.

The waves lifted and dropped him. From the crest of each he craned toward the horizon, openmouthed, hoping to hear the engine. An especially big wave heaved up in front of him. He glanced at it, gauging it automatically, then stared at it, shocked. Incased in it, as though in green ice, was a shark. It was drifting sideways in the wave, its dorsal fin lazily breaking the crest.

In a moment it would be on top of him. He threshed about with his fins to scare it, at the same time fumbling with the mask. He got it on—half filled with water—blew it out and dived.

The creature had gone. He twisted around under the water. It was behind him. It was a heavily mottled shark, seven or eight feet long. It had seen him, all right, and seemed idly curious. With a careless flick of its big tail, it nosed to within six feet of him.

Mike had one idea in mind; that was to get rid of it. Spreading his arms and legs, he hooted into the mask.

The shark's languor left it instantly. With a bewilderingly swift movement, it turned and shot away at right angles; stopped, turned and hung there, staring at Mike with its little, catlike eyes.

He cursed. These pelagic sharks weren't like the reef ones. That would have been enough even for a blackfin. He raised one ear out of the water and listened for the plane. It was coming! Its clatter reached him clearly over the waves. He took another look at the shark. Did he dare ignore it? The shark made a movement.

God! Mike thought. Not now. It can't come at me now!

But that was just what it did. He had to face it. He headed straight for it; desperation lent him strength.

Uncertainly the shark checked its advance with its pectorals. Mike kept right on, and when he was a dozen feet away from the shark he blew a burst of bubbles at it through his snorkel tube. The big mottled body jackknifed and turned and fled, thudding the water with its tail.

Mike hit the surface and snatched off the mask all in one movement. The roar of the plane spanked his ears like a thunderclap. It was right overhead. He tried to shout, but he hadn't any air. He gasped to fill his lungs, took in some water, and choked.

The blind belly of the plane passed over him. It was an old Gladiator, with fixed undercarriage. He managed to get the gun up and wagged the duralumin in the sunlight, but the plane just pulled away steadily across the waves. He made a noise at last, something between a gasp and a scream. It just had to see him! Weird sounds dragged from his throat as he watched the machine diminish, and heard the engine grow fainter, fainter, then merge with the rush of the sea.

He was alone. He subsided, exhausted, into the waves, lying there weak and uncaring, letting the water drain into his parted mouth, letting its green weight close over him.

Oh, God, he thought. Oh, God, oh, God, oh, God.

The sun had swung over behind him and was sinking slowly toward the sea. He had been swimming since morning, weakly but steadily. After the plane, he had lain in the water a while; then some inward strength had got hold of him, turned him toward the eastern horizon, and forced his limbs to move.

Everything that was reasonable in him resisted. If another plane or a ship were to come, it would come; swimming wouldn't help. And if it didn't come the sharks would. Land, allowing the maximum for drift, was about seventy miles away, and he had never swum more than twenty in his life.

But the stubborn spirit in him did not listen. It only

knew that there was land over there below the eastern rim, solid and sweet-smelling and green, and that here there was only death. It drew him through the water—desperately.

His thighs were cramping a little, and he had chafe from the fins across the insteps of both feet. When they began to bleed, the sharks would pick up his trail, and yet he kept on, at intervals rolling his head up—sideways, to save energy—to look along the sea and at the sky. They were clear and empty and endless, and the light was glorious. He felt small in so much emptiness.

From his mouth and his throat right down to his stomach, he was puckered dry with brine. There wasn't a bead of moisture left in him. He wouldn't last the day. Sea creatures like Halloween masks came and went, appearing suddenly an inch from his face, then darting away. All day it had been the same, and he had let them come, grateful for their company.

Now suddenly he shortened the gun in his hand, jabbed at one with the protruding spear and transfixed it. He trapped its fin movements with his fingers, glancing round instinctively. Experience had taught him that often when you speared a fish, sharks, drawn by the sound of finny panic in the water, jumped you so fast they might have been fired at you.

He waited. Nothing happened. Without any conscious reasoning, Mike turned on his back and wrenched the fish off the barb, pushed back the mask and squeezed the lymphatic juices from its wound into his mouth. They were rank and oily and mingled with blood, but they were free from salt, and he wondered vaguely how he had known they would be.

When he had squeezed the fish dry, he threw it as far

from him as possible and spiked another. He caught six; then, using his knife, cut the last one, a sea bream, into strips and ate it raw.

He felt strange and defiant, and when he sprawled back under the water, he felt no nausea but a sort of amazement. He would get stronger; he could keep alive for days like this. Then reason reasserted itself. Not without sleep, it said. His eyelids felt heavy at the thought of it. His legs stopped beating. The water was soft and warm. The movement of the waves had subsided to a soothing rhythm. His head sank.

Suddenly his eyes flicked open, and he was staring along the underglow of his own stomach. A yard from his legs was the bluish head of a shark.

He slapped the water with both fins and got himself around somehow. The solid body flicked sideways and circled lazily around him. It was more than twice his length. Then somehow there was another, rock-steady in the water and growing toward him. Mike knew he couldn't fight them. He hadn't the strength. They circled around him, puzzled by his reluctance to escape.

Mike watched them, heavy-eyed; watched a third one come—smaller, this one, with a newtlike head and dappled like a newt—a tiger shark.

There was always the gun. It was his ace, he thought, admitting to himself now what had been in the back of his mind all along. He would put it under his chin and squeeze the trigger with his bare heels.

Now, he thought. Before it's too late. The deliberate circles were narrowing steadily. He lay in the water wondering vaguely why he didn't act. There seemed to be five of them now, then six.

The undersea was darkening fast. Feeding time, he

thought. They would go crazy, and it would be too late to do anything. But still he lay in the water. Deep down in him there was something that refused to die. Coward! he said angrily.

Then he was panning the gun carefully, aiming at the tiger, centering on one eye. And he knew why; it was half-grown and softer-skinned than the others, and he had to cripple it. It came in close. At seven feet he let the shark have it.

There was the sound of slithering steel and a blur and a jolt. The gun leaped out of his hand, and he was gasping air through the snorkel while the shark spun around in a tight clockwise circle. It didn't pull out of it or stop, but just tore on round and round like a Catherine wheel, and Mike knew he'd got it right in the eye.

The other sharks froze in the water; surprised, they hung there for a full moment; then they got it. All five of them hit the tiger together, rending and snapping crazily. A great cloud of blood spread in the water.

Mike dragged himself away from the scene. It was better without the gun. He swam until he couldn't go another stroke. Then he lay out in the water, panting so hard that the mask sucked in against his face with every breath.

He stared back behind him, but there was only a redness. Nothing came after him. He had played his ace.

There was no moon. The water heaved in the sultry darkness, glimmering with phosphorescence. Stars drifted above and below him. He seemed to be beating slowly through space. Darkness engulfed him; then schizopod shrimps would rise like lonely suns, thicken into constellations and drift away, and brilliant dusts would form on the undertide, then condense and flood the sea with protozoic flame. He watched his hands, leprous and white, grope through the fiery sea and traced with half-dreaming eyes the comet paths of fish. Then there was only darkness, blacker than before.

He would lift his head with an effort, into the cooler air, check with the dimmer stars for east, and hear the immeasurable sigh of the ocean. Sometimes he heard across the waves, like a gun, the sound of manta hitting the sea, and knew that somewhere nearby great thirty-foot bodies were rushing together, leaping high into the air, pressed wing tip to wing tip in their mating dance.

The Pleiades swung, and the waters gleamed and died, and once something vast and terrible rose like a city in the waves. Mike heard the water draining from its sides and saw its darkness blotting out the sea. It made a sound—something between a hiss and a moan—and presently it slid back into the depths. He heard the water sucking down after it long after it had gone.

Another sun rose, a burning eye set level with the sea. And still Mike's legs were moving, just moving. Now, he thought, now the sharks will come again, and he thought of them as only liberators who would free him from the instinct that tortured him on.

Again the undersea dawn began, and nothing came—nothing but jellies, colored like sunset on ice, filling the sea with their tilted, opening-and-closing parasols; and the dorados, they came. With a glint of gold and greeny-blue, they skidded into him and turned him over. They were under him and over him and around him and away, kicking up the water in bursts of saline fire. And there was blood in the sea where the tuna caught the dorados. And still nothing came.

Mike caught a fish in his hands and ate it. He couldn't

see any sense in it, but he couldn't stop himself, either. His legs continued to move, almost automatically, and at high noon he saw his mother, her little-girl face collapsed with age, and she was saying in her child-voice: "All failure is a kind of death," and he thought how right she was. He had forgotten her failure with the old man. It seemed to him then that they were still together and perfectly happy. He was a little crazy.

And then a shark came. It came up behind him in the molten-metal sea, cutting through the water like the keel of a sailing ship.

Come on, you dog, Mike said to it, and: You're late! Just like the ten o'clock scholar. (He was back at school.)

He waited for it, but it wouldn't come in, just sniffed at his fins and took a wide turn around him. He wanted it to come in, but it wouldn't take him. Yesterday he had wanted to live, but now, he didn't care. If he could have slept, he would have been all right, but now he just wanted the shark to hurry up and get it over with.

So he turned his back, and when he looked round again the shark was gone. It stayed gone, and the sun burned down on the sea, which became like watered silk, very glossy and silent, and the sound he made blowing through the snorkel seemed to grow very loud, like the roaring of the locomotives in Bay St. Louis station. He relaxed into a kind of dream, and he was back in the old city, in the old apartment, dirty from working at the garage. The old man was there, and Mike had just said he couldn't stick it any more with Mum gone and everything shot to pieces the way it was—that he was heading for the Far East, Ceylon maybe. His old man looked up at him over the tops of his glasses, with his mouth turned down and his eyes preoccupied with other people and other places, and, seeing him like that, Mike suddenly realized that he really was an old man.

Then the sun drowned in a sea of blood, and he was alone in the dusk with night moving up the sky. This was his last night, he thought. Tonight he would die. There was nothing left in him to regret with or to pray with, nothing but this instinct driving him on with limbs he could no longer feel.

At last the sharks came. They came with the departing light, like slim blades in the sea. There was nothing to stop them, but they came on carefully, avoiding his fire-trail in the darkening water. He closed his eyes. It was getting late.

The sunset's imprisoned image burned dimly in his brain, like a candle guttering low, and sounds grew enormous in the water. For an instant, poised on the edge of delirium, he heard the whisper of his own fins and, behind them, the shudder of tails, like someone thrumming the deadened bass string of a harp with their fingernails. The tempo increased. Now, he thought. At last! The water shook against him, beat on his eardrums, diminished and was still.

His lids flickered. Below, in the iridescence, fish-trails sparkled through the water like a million shooting stars. They streaked ahead of him and were gone; then more, in gleaming panic, raced by—then more and more.

There was thunder in the sea, but he didn't hear it. He fell into a dreamy state. It seemed to him that the waters were boiling around him with phosphorescent light; that he was lifted and flung, buffeted by tails, flung again; that in the luminosity he saw the ocean packed solid with gleaming backs, heard their panting and heaving. Then he was down under the water, and the migrating false killer whales were above him, lighted by the phosphorescence, belly upon belly, rank upon rank.

Then somehow there was air and the sea eddied and gleamed, and the turmoil rumbled away across the sea, and he was alone.

A light forced its way under his lids, and he turned away from it. There were cold bodies around him, and when he moved they squirmed. It was still a dream, and it was wrong somehow that there should be a man in it, holding a lamp, and, in the dimness, others staring at him.

They wore ragged sarongs, and they looked for all the world like Singhalese fishermen. For some reason their eyes were wide and frightened. Their hands were dragging at a net; Mike realized suddenly that he was in the net—caught!

He learned later that he had wound up a mile off Galle, South Ceylon. He never knew how; probably the current had been working with him all the way. But somehow he had made it. The fishermen admitted afterward that they had thought he was some strange kind of monster and had nearly lit into him with their gaffs. The incident certainly gave rise to some queer tales which Mike didn't altogether like. The Ceylon *Courier* gave him a full-page spread. "Fish-man," the article called him again and again, and when he got out of the hospital and went down into Colombo, people looked at him strangely and weren't quite sure what to do with their eyes when they talked to him. He never spoke about it much himself, because of the feeling he had had in the net.

He knew it was a net and that they were men around him—and he was afraid. The lamp seemed to draw his eyes till the flame filled his mind, and in the darkness all around, there was terror. He gasped for air, but none would come. He struggled, and the other fish around him struggled, and he twisted and kicked, knowing only that he must get back to the sea, that he must slither back somehow into the dark cavern of the water and dart away through the softness and the silence to where he belonged. It was a sensation of the purest fear—uninhibited by logic or pride or anything human, undiluted and nightmarish—such as only a wild creature might feel when it falls a victim to man.

Then one of the natives bent over him and took off his fouled-up mask, and there was air in a cool rush and he blacked out.

ARCHERFISH

BY COMMANDER EDWARD L. BEACH, U.S.N.

*After Pearl Harbor, when the decision was made by the
Allied High Command to concentrate first on the Atlantic
and European theatre, the naval war in the Pacific against
Japan was left almost entirely to the United States submarine
service. To them was assigned the task of sinking Japanese
troop transports, tankers, and coastwise commerce. For obvious reasons, this operation was kept top-secret; no word
was allowed to leak out to the American public. That public,
their eyes turned toward Europe and the coming invasion of
France, uneasily wondering whether Pearl Harbor had not,
after all, ended American naval dominance in the Pacific,
were unaware of one of the most brilliant operations of the
entire war. Here was indeed a silent navy. Washington would
not, and Tokyo dared not, make public the spectacular destruction the American submarines were wreaking on the
Imperial Japanese Navy.*

*Now it can be told, and by great good fortune, a submarine
officer who can tell it with force and gusto has survived ten
years of that gruelling service. Submarine! by Commander
Edward L. Beach, U.S.N., is a series of vivid narratives of the
exploits of the Pacific underwater craft. Beach was on U.S.S.
Trigger, which was lost with all hands off Japan in 1945. He
had been transferred the year before, and was thus spared to
narrate her life and death.*

The most extraordinary feat of all, however, the most

From *Submarine!* by Commander Edward L. Beach. Copyright 1948,
1952 by Edward L. Beach. Reprinted by permission of Henry Holt &
Company, Inc.

dramatic, and the feat which, as Commander Beach says, probably took the heart out of the Japanese navy, was the sinking by torpedo of the largest aircraft carrier afloat. How U.S.S. Archerfish *tracked down and sank the* Shinano *in November of 1944 will probably remain a mark to aim at for all submarine personnel for some time. It is highly probable that this disaster did more damage to the morale of Japanese naval power than even Hiroshima. Commander Beach has concentrated, in a score of pages, the daring, the peril, the excitement, the glory, and the triumphant efficiency of the modern submarine.*

SOME OF THE stories of World War II can never be fully told. Some will live only in the hearts of men who took part in them, who will carry their secrets silently to their graves. Some stories will not be told at all, because the only men who could tell them lie at the bottom of the sea. And some are part of our naval heritage, and will go down in history with stories of *Old Ironsides,* Thomas Truxton and his *Constellation,* John Paul Jones and *Bon Homme Richard, Enterprise,* and many others.

Such a story is the story of *Archerfish,* the ship which broke the heart of the Japanese Navy.

The keel was laid for USS *Archerfish* in Portsmouth, New Hampshire, on January 22, 1943. Exactly one year later she sank her first ship. And on November 28, 1944 —but let's start at the beginning.

The story really begins in 1939 in Yokosuka, Japan. The probability of becoming involved in the European war was growing greater and greater; the probability of them finding their nation pitted against the United States was almost a certainty. How, then, to assure

Japan of a telling superiority? How to fight that great American sea power in the Pacific? And how to do away with the London Treaty, which limited Japan to an ignominious three fifths of the war vessels allowed the United States?

There was only one answer. The treaty already had been violated—tear it up. Start building in earnest for the war they know is coming.

Secret instructions were sent to the largest shipyard in Japan. Millions of board feet of wood came from the forest reserves, and thousands of carpenters were employed to build a gigantic yard. Houses for 50,000 people were requisitioned and these, too, were fenced in around the fenced Navy Yard. Finally, one day in 1940, an order was issued from the Commandant's office: "From this date henceforth no one leaves the Navy Yard." And so was born the battleship *Shinano*.

By the summer of 1942 she was not quite half finished. This super-battleship with two sisters *Yamato* and *Musashi*, was bigger than any war vessel ever before constructed in the history of the world. Bigger than *Bismarck*, the German behemoth of 50,000 tons. Almost three times as big as *Oklahoma*, lying bottom up in the mud and ooze of Pearl Harbor. Armor plate twenty inches thick. Engines of 200,000 horsepower. Guns throwing projectiles eighteen inches in diameter.

Then at the Battle of Midway, in June, 1942, the flower of the Japanese naval air force met destruction. *Akagi, Kaga, Soryu,* and *Hiryu*—all first-line carriers— were sunk. The attack on Midway was turned back, a complete failure. The Naval Ministry met again in secret session, and decided that completion of new aircraft carriers was paramount. So *Shinano* was redesigned.

Some of the tremendous armor plate was removed from her side. Her huge barbettes, turrets, and eighteen-inch guns were never installed, and the weight thus saved was put into an armored flight deck made of hardened steel four inches thick. Under this flight deck were built two hangar decks, and below them another armored deck, eight inches thick. She was capable of storing 100 to 150 planes, and could land them and take them off simultaneously from an airfield nearly one thousand feet in length and 130 feet in width.

But all this took time, and as 1944 drew to a close, the need of the Japanese Navy for its new super carrier became increasingly acute. Finally, in November, 1944, *Shinano* was nearly completed. The commissioning ceremonies were held on November 18; a picture of the Emperor in an ornate gilded frame was ceremoniously delivered to the vessel, and she was turned over to her commanding officer.

Then the bad news arrived. Japanese strategic intelligence reports indicated that air raids on the Tokyo area would become increasingly severe, with a good possibility that the brave new ship would be seriously exposed at her fitting-out dock. There was even a possibility that United States Forces would discover the existence of the huge vessel and make a special effort to destroy her before she could get to sea. This could not be permitted. The Tokyo area was too vulnerable. The ship must be moved to the Inland Sea.

Now the Inland Sea is the body of water formed between the islands of Honshu, Shikoku, and Kyushu. It has three entrances: two, the Bungo and Kii Suidos, into the Pacific, and one, Shimonoseki Strait, into the landlocked Sea of Japan. It is an ideal operating base for an inferior navy which must depend upon being able to hide when it cannot fight.

But *Shinano* is not ready to go to sea. True, she is structurally complete, her engines can operate, and she floats, but she is not quite ready. Her watertight integrity has not been proved. Air tests have been made of only a few of her hundreds of compartments. Many holes through various bulkheads have not yet been plugged. Watertight doors have not been tested, and it is not known whether they can be closed; furthermore, even if they can be closed, no one knows if they are actually watertight. Electrical wiring and piping passing through watertight bulkheads have not had their packing glands set up and tested. Cable and pipe conduits from the main deck into the bowels of the ship have not been sealed. The pumping and drainage system is not complete; piping is not all connected. The fire main cannot be used because the necessary pumps have not been delivered.

Most important of all, the crew has been on board for only one month. They number 1,900 souls, but few have been to sea together. Many have never been to sea at all, and *none have had any training whatsoever on board Shinano*. They do not know their ship. *They are not a crew. They are 1,900 people.*

But it is decided, nonetheless, that *Shinano* must sail to safer waters immediately. To do so she must pass out of Tokyo Bay, steer south and west around the southeastern tip of Honshu, and enter the Kii Suido, a trip of only a few hundred miles. But about half the trip will be in waters accessible to United States submarines. That risk she must take. Give her an escort of four destroyers, and send her at high speed so that the submarines cannot catch her. Make the move in absolute secrecy, so that there will be no possibility of an unfortunate leak of information.

The die was cast, and on the afternoon of November 28, 1944, *Shinano* set sail with her four escorting destroyers. Sailors and workmen crowded about her docks, and the gilded frame glittered in the late afternoon sunlight on the flying bridge. From within the frame, the image of the Son of Heaven beamed happily on this mightiest of warships.

Thus was set the stage for the greatest catastrophe yet to befall the hapless Japanese Navy. Work for four years building the biggest ship of its kind that has ever been constructed by man; put 1,900 men on board; install a picture of the Emperor on the bridge, and send her out through a few miles of water exposed to possible operations of American submarines.

There was nothing particularly portentous about the laying of the keel of *Archerfish*. She displaced 1,500 tons, or one-fiftieth of the tonnage of the huge vessel fated to be her adversary. She was only one third the length of *Shinano*, and her crew of eighty-two men and officers was about one fortieth of the 3,200 estimated full designed complement of the Japanese ship.

Leaving New London, *Archerfish* zigzags southward through the center of the broad Atlantic, in waters infested by her enemy sisters. Do not think that a submarine is not afraid of other submarines. We are probably more afraid of them and more respectful of them than any other type of vessel would be. A submarine cruising on the surface is a delicious morsel. It almost always travels alone, and its only defense is its own vigilance. Zigzag all day and even at night, if the visibility is fairly good. Keep a sharp lookout and radar watch. Tell yourselves over and over again, "Boys, don't relax. We are playing for keeps now."

The weather becomes perceptibly warmer. Finally, land is sighted, and *Archerfish* slips through the Mona Passage into the Caribbean Sea. Here the waters are even more infested with German submarines than are the wide reaches of the central Atlantic. *Archerfish* puts on full speed and dashes across the Caribbean to Cristobal, at the Atlantic end of the Panama Canal. She arrives early in the morning and proceeds immediately through the great locks, and through Gatun Lake to the submarine base at Balboa on the Pacific end of the Canal.

No danger here from German subs. No time, either, for any rest for the tired crew, for they have lost the edge from their training and must be brought back "on the step" again. One week is all that is available. *Archerfish* is issued nine practice torpedoes, and fires them again and again. Target convoys are provided. Day and night exercises are conducted. Rarely does the crew turn in before midnight, and all hands are always up at 0500. *Archerfish* does not even stop for lunch, but instead distributes sandwiches to all members of the crew, making up for it with a good breakfast and a good dinner.

One week of this; then, her crew once again in fine fettle, *Archerfish* sails across the broad Pacific, on the final and longest leg of her journey to Pearl Harbor. She and her crew have had a steady go of it. They have been training strenuously and incessantly for the past two months with practically no rest, but they cannot be allowed to relax.

They know that the competition in the far western

Pacific is mighty tough, so they drill steadily, on every maneuver of which the ship is capable, except the actual firing of torpedoes. *Archerfish* cannot fire torpedoes, because she is transporting a load of "war shots." One of the most convenient ways of getting torpedoes to Pearl Harbor was to send them by submarine.

Finally land is sighted. A PC boat signals through the early dawn to *Archerfish*, "We are your escort," and swings about to lead the submarine to Pearl Harbor. This is the last stop. Below decks all hands are feverishly cleaning up the ship and themselves. They intend to make a good entrance into Pearl; they are proud of their ship, and will not willingly allow her to suffer by comparison with any other in looks or efficiency.

Finally *Archerfish* gently noses into a dock at the submarine base, Pearl Harbor, where a small group of officers and enlisted men await her. Admiral Lockwood, the Commander Submarines, Pacific Fleet (also known as "Uncle Charlie"), is on hand to greet this newest addition to his forces. With him is an array of talent: the squadron commander, the division commander, the officer in charge of the repair department, the submarine supply officer, a submarine medical officer, an electronics officer, and a commissary officer.

The enlisted men are evidently a working party. As *Archerfish* approaches the dock, they scamper to catch the weighted heaving lines thrown by members of her crew. Pulling in swiftly on the "heevies," they haul heavy hawsers from the deck of the submarine to the dock. Others stand by with a narrow gangway and, when the submarine finally comes to rest alongside the dock, bridge the gap between dock and ship with it.

The moment the gangway has been placed, Admiral

Lockwood, followed by his train of experts, walks aboard to greet the skipper, who by this time has jumped down from his station on the bridge. Asking if there are any outstanding emergency repairs or other troubles, Uncle Charlie chats for a few moments. Like a man who has just had a new automobile delivered to him, he is interested in all the new wrinkles and gadgets on board. Then, bidding the skipper good-by until lunch, to which he has been invited at Uncle Charlie's mess, the Admiral leaves the ship.

This is the opportunity the rest of his staff have been waiting for. Each one of them searches out his opposite number on board and makes arrangements for necessary repairs. In addition, there are several last-minute alterations which must be accomplished before the ship can depart. The workmen—all Navy men—who are to perform these operations are to a large extent already en route to the deck with their tools and equipment. By this method of making alterations virtually on the fighting front, so to speak, our submarines always went into battle with the very latest and finest equipment.

Meanwhile, the enlisted men who had come on the dock with the Admiral, and who had handled lines for the ship, have not been idle. Three or four bulging mail sacks, a crate of oranges, a box of nice red apples, and a five-gallon can of ice cream were brought down with them on a handcart. These they now passed over the gangway to the eagerly awaiting crew of *Archerfish*.

On December 23, 1943, while *Shinano* was still building, *Archerfish* departed Pearl Harbor on her first war patrol. Too bad she could not have stayed for Christmas, but orders must be obeyed, and operations seldom take notice of such things. Besides, her crew had been brought up to the fever pitch of enthusiasm. Christmas or no, she was eager to be on her way.

On January 8, 1944, *Archerfish* entered her assigned area, near Formosa. If any of her crew expected even this final lap of her 13,000-mile voyage to war to be a rest cure, they must have been disappointed, for every day of this two-week period was utilized for drill. Practice makes perfect.

To some extent a submarine is a weapon of opportunity. You cannot attack ships which do not arrive. If the seas are too rough, you have the devil's own time keeping an efficient periscope watch, for if you run too close to the surface in order to increase your effective periscope height and see over the wave tops, you stand grave danger of "broaching"; that is, surfacing involuntarily as a result of wave action.

On her first patrol *Archerfish* and her disgusted crew fought heavy weather for two solid weeks, but finally she reported radar contact with four large and five smaller ships heading in the general direction of Formosa. The leading ship was attacked and sunk and *Archerfish's* patrol report stated, "We had celebrated the first anniversary of our keel laying in right smart fashion."

Months passed, and she was a veteran. The vast Pacific was her playground and her no man's land. Then, as Joe Enright, her skipper, recorded in the fifth war patrol report of *Archerfish*, on November 28, 1944, she was patrolling submerged to the south and west of the western entrance to Sagami Nada, or outer Tokyo Bay. No ships had been sighted. No contacts of any kind (except fishing boats) had been made thus far in the patrol, which had begun twenty-nine days before.

At 1718 she surfaced, the visibility having decreased to such an extent that surface patrolling was feasible and desirable. With no premonition of the events which were to give him an enviable place in our naval history, the Commanding Officer ordered the regular routine of nighttime functions. A radar watch had of course been established the instant the ship broke water. Two engines were put on battery charge and one engine on propulsion at leisurely speed. Air compressors were started, and garbage was assembled, ready to be thrown over the side in burlap sacks. The crew settled down to the routine of alert watchfulness which is a concomitant part of night surface submarine operations in enemy waters.

At 2048 Fate finally uncovered her hand and brought together the characters she had been coaching for so long. Four years for *Shinano* and almost two years for *Archerfish*—time means little to the gods. How she must have sat back in her big, soft, easy chair, and chuckled. Having brought the two major characters of her play together, now she would leave it up to them, and see what would happen.

"Radar contact!" These words never fail to bring a shiver of anticipation to the submariner. From the size of the pip, the range, and the speed which the first few hasty moments of plotting show this target to be making, there is no doubt whatever in the minds of any of the crew of *Archerfish* that she is really on to something big. The word passes almost instantaneously throughout the ship, "Something big and fast!"

With the ease and sureness of long practice, tracking stations are manned. On the first word of radar contact, the Officer of the Deck had turned the bow of *Archer-*

fish directly toward the contact, and had stopped. This gave the plotting party an immediate indication of the direction of target movement. As soon as this had been determined, *Archerfish* roared off in hot pursuit, not directly at the target, but on such a course that she might have an opportunity of getting ahead of him. The main engine still on battery charge was replaced by the auxiliary engine, and all four great nine-cylinder Diesel engines were placed on propulsion. Within minutes after the initial contact, *Archerfish* was pounding along at full speed, 18 knots, throwing a cloud of spray and spume from her sharp knifelike bow as she hurried across the sea.

This is where the long, monotonous labor of patrol starts to bear fruit. Plotting and tracking the target is no simple matter. Every minute a range and bearing; every minute the singsong "Standby, standby, *mark!*" Every minute plotting parties plot the ship's course and its position at the instant of the "mark"; then, from that point, they draw range and bearing, and thus locate the position of the enemy ship at the same instant. Your own ship twists and turns in the dual effort to gain firing position and to keep range to the target so that he will not sight her, or get radar contact on her, but keep close enough so that her radar will have no difficulty in keeping contact on his much larger bulk. After a few minutes of chase, the target's course is determined to be roughly 210. The target's speed is 20 knots; he is zigzagging, and by the size and strength of his radar pip is mighty big and mighty important. Radar also indicates four smaller vessels; one ahead, one on either beam, and one astern.

Joe Enright is climbing all over his ship like a monkey. First up to the bridge to be sure all is under control, then down to Plot to get an idea of what it is doing. Next, a quick look at the radar scope for a personal evaluation of what the operators have on there; then a quick look at the TDC; then back to the bridge. Then the whole thing over again.

The well-drilled crew are responding beautifully and solving the problem like clockwork, but all the information collected by his attack party must be transmitted to the Captain. It must be weighed in his mind; he must collect all the tiny details, any one of which might suddenly assume tremendous proportions. In no type of vessel is the Commanding Officer so personally responsible for the actual handling of his ship as in a submarine.

What is the state of moon and sea? It is better to attack with the moon silhouetting the targets instead of the submarine. But torpedoes run better if fired down the hollow of the waves rather than across them. The two considerations must be evaluated; the best decision reached. Not content with the mere reports of progress from junior officers and crewmen working below, the Captain has to be personally sure that they are not making mistakes. In his climbing up and down from control room to conning tower to bridge, it is necessary that he protect his night vision, as it would not do to have him partially blinded on the bridge when the crucial moment comes. Therefore, all below-deck control compartments are blacked out. No lights are allowed except the dim red glow of plotting party lights and the orange and green lights of the radar. All is silent in the control party, except the hushed reports which are continually going back and forth.

Archerfish is logging only 18 knots. This will not be

sufficient. The call goes down from the bridge: "Maneuvering, make all the speed you can! All ahead flank!"

Watching their dials carefully, the electrician's mates in the maneuvering room slowly increase their speed another 20 r.p.m. The pitometer log registers now a little more than 18½ knots.

Again word from the bridge, "Control, give her a five-minute blow! Blow safety! Blow negative!" The scream and grind of the low-pressure air-blowing pump fill the interior of the ship. This low-pressure pump is used in the latter stages of surfacing when a large volume of air is required to complete emptying the ballast tanks of water. In this case, the intention is to blow out what residual amounts of water might remain or have leaked back in, in order to speed up the ship. Negative tank and safety tank are always kept full of water in order to carry out their designed purposes. Negative tank is so built that when it is full, the submarine properly compensated, and the ballast tanks flooded, the sub has negative buoyancy and will sink. Thus she dives faster. Safety tank, on the other hand, is used to give the ship quick, positive buoyancy, if she should need it. Altogether, these two tanks carry approximately thirty-six tons of sea water. Emptying them, while it decreases the safety factor with which the ship ordinarily operates, also decreases the amount of weight she has to drag around with her and hence increases her speed.

But in spite of these measures, *Archerfish's* speed quivers around 19 knots or possibly a shade more. Still not enough. A third time from the bridge comes the order: "Maneuvering, give her all you've got! To hell with the volts and amps! Watch your motor temperatures, but *give me more speed!*" Shaking their heads—this is foreign to their training and upbringing—the electrician's mates carefully manipulate their rheostats once more. By means of the engine remote-control governor linkage, the r.p.m. of the four huge main diesel engines have already been increased to the maximum, and they are racing just as fast as they possibly can. Doubtfully the generators are loaded a bit more, and the amperes flowing to the four straining motors increase a trifle. The propellers increase their speed by another five or six r.p.m. *Archerfish* has done all she can, and the pitometer log dial now indicates 19½ knots.

At about this point, approximately one hour after the initial contact, the patrol report states, "Saw the target for the first time, an aircraft carrier! From here on it was a mad race to reach a firing position."

It is every submarine skipper's dream to find himself in hot pursuit of such a target. *The jackpot—an aircraft carrier!* The biggest game of all! *Archerfish,* the huntress. Can she bring this monster down in his own environment?

The skipper is all over the ship again, and visits the control stations at frequent intervals. He calls for Lieutenant Rom Cousins, the engineer officer, sends him back into the engineering spaces with instructions to squeeze out every possible extra turn on the laboring screws. He sends Dave Bunting to be sure that all last-minute adjustments are made on his torpedoes. There might even be time to pull and check all fish. When you stick your neck in the mouth of the dragon in hopes of getting a shot at him, you want that shot to be good.

The Communication Officer comes in for his share of attention. Joe Enright jots down a message on a piece of paper and hands it to him. Gordon Crosby disappears into the radio room, codes the message, and then stands watch on the radioman as he transmits: *"NPM V W3TU —K . . . NPM V W3TU—K . . . Radio Pearl from Archerfish, I have an urgent message. . . . Radio Pearl from Archerfish, I have an urgent message."*

Straining their ears, the radiomen listen to the welter of dots and dashes filling the ether. Radio Pearl is busy; a lot of ships are calling it, and it is receiving a steady stream of messages. *Archerfish* must wait her turn. The answer from NPM says, *Archerfish from Radio Pearl, Wait.*

But this won't do. *"NPM V W3TU 000 K. . . . Radio Pearl from Archerfish, this message is really urgent!"* There must be some means whereby a ship with an excessively important message can demand and receive immediate attention. Only in this way can any semblance of communication and traffic discipline be maintained.

Radio Pearl comes back immediately with a procedure sign to *Archerfish.* "Go ahead, we are ready."

FROM ARCHERFISH TO COMSUBPAC AND ALL SUBMARINES IN EMPIRE AREAS AM PURSUING LARGE AIRCRAFT CARRIER FOUR DESTROYERS POSITION LAT 3230 N LONG 13745 E, BASE COURSE 240, SPEED 20.

NPM answers simply and very specifically, "R," which means, "Received, I assume responsibility, will forward this message to proper authority."

By this time it is early morning at Pearl Harbor, but Admiral Lockwood has left orders with the duty officer to call him no matter where he may be, upon receipt of such a message. He hurries down to the office with his

Operations Officer. It isn't often that one of his submarines latches on to a prize of this kind. Together, with the large wall chart of the Japanese Empire before them, they lay plans to insure the destruction of *Archerfish's* target. In less than an hour messages pour forth from Radio Pearl. The position, course, and speed of *Shinano* are given. All submarines which might be in a position to intercept her are ordered to proceed to various strategic points and there to lie in wait. Then a further message to *Archerfish:* KEEP AFTER HIM JOE YOUR PICTURE IS ON THE PIANO. The levity in this dispatch is not misplaced. Uncle Charlie knows his boys, and his boys know him.

On and on, on and on, straining every nerve, *Archerfish* pursues her quarry. The carrier is tracked at 20 knots. *Archerfish* can do no more than 19 or possibly a shade better. But the carrier is zigzagging. If *Archerfish* can detect his base course and parallel that, disregarding the zigs, she may be able to overtake him in spite of the disparity in speeds. But this is tricky, too, because on a zig toward *Archerfish*, the target group might approach close enough for one of the flank escorts to sight the laboring submarine. Conversely, a zig away might lead them out of radar range, where a course change would result in *Archerfish's* pursuing in the wrong direction. So *Archerfish* cannot blindly charge ahead, but must conform to maneuvers of the target; she cannot lose him, nor can she let him get too close. With these considerations, resisting every move which might tend to increase the distance she must run, *Archerfish* doggedly sets about making an end around. Theoretically, it is possible to get around a target going faster than you are. It *is* possible, but mighty damn hard to do!

One hour before midnight the target group zigs toward, not enough to give *Archerfish* an opportunity to dive and attack on this leg, but sufficiently so that one of the flanking escorts approaches perilously near the submarine—6000 yards. Determined to take every conceivable, practicable chance to avoid being forced to submerge prematurely, the skipper orders all bridge personnel below, except for Lieutenant (j.g.) John Andrews, the Officer of the Deck. If *Archerfish* receives gunfire on the bridge, there will be only himself and Andrews up there to worry about.

But the escort ignores the submarine, and Joe Enright calls his lookouts back to the bridge.

At midnight the carrier force makes another big zig, to the west. *Archerfish* had expected that he was probably headed for somewhere in the Pacific, and therefore had chosen the left or southern flank of the convoy to trail from. A change of base course in the most probable direction, to the south, she hoped would drop the whole outfit into her hands. But such was not to be. The zig to the west puts the submarine even farther out in right field, but doggedly she digs in and continues the chase.

For two and a half hours the pursuit goes on. Racing to crawl up the left flank of the task group, *Archerfish* finds that her top speed is just barely allowing her to pull ahead. But there is obviously no chance of attaining a firing position before dawn. Regretfully, the skipper composes another message.

URGENT—FOR COMSUBPAC AND SUBS IN AREA X TARGET COURSE 275 SPEED 20 X AM TRAILING LEFT FLANK X DO NOT EXPECT TO REACH FIRING POSITION BY DAWN X CONTINUING CHASE.

The answer is prompt. ARCHERFISH FROM COMSUBPAC

X KEEP AFTER HIM JOE X ALL SUBMARINES IN THE FORCE
ARE PULLING FOR YOU AND ARE BACKING YOU UP.

They are keeping a sleepless vigil at the operations
office of ComSubPac, fortified by much coffee and Coca-
Cola. But their encouraging message is never received
by *Archerfish*.

For at 0300 the sands run out for *Shinano*. Base course
is changed again, this time to nearly due south, and incredulously *Archerfish* finds herself almost dead ahead
of the target. Fate picks up her dice and stows them
away.

"*Right full rudder!*" The submarine changes course
rapidly, heeling to port as she does so. At last *Archerfish*
heads for the enemy.

Ah-oooh—gah! Ah—oooh-gah! The diving alarm seems
more piercing than usual. "*Dive! Dive!*" "*Flood negative! Flood safety! Battle stations submerged!*" A few
men dash through the ship to their battle stations, but
most are already there.

"Hatch secured, sir!"

"*Shut the induction!*"

"Green board, sir!"

"*Bleed air in the boat!*" "*Eight degrees down bubble!*"
"*Easy on the bow planes!*" "*Blow negative!*" "*All ahead
one third!*" "*Fifty-five feet!*" Expertly each man does his
job, and *Archerfish* smoothly slips beneath the waves.
Radar gets a final range as the antenna goes under
water: 11,700 yards, closing fast.

"*Up periscope!*" The long, shiny tube hums out of the
periscope well. Squatting on his haunches before it,
hands poised to catch the handles the moment they
emerge, Enright resembles an ageless devotee of some
obscure occult religion. Perspiration stands out unno-

ticed on his forehead, his face is immobile, his eyes staring. You would say he is in a trance, and in a trance he
is, for his eyes do not see the crowded darkened conning
tower around him. His eyes and mind already are on the
surface of the ocean, watching the enemy task group as
it comes closer—and closer. . . .

Finally the periscope handles appear. Capturing and
unfolding them with both hands, the skipper applies his
right eye to the eyepiece and swiftly rises with the periscope to a standing position. He has become so accustomed to this procedure that he is entirely unconscious
that he has performed quite a neat little stunt—for from
the moment the periscope eyepiece appeared out of
the periscope well he has been looking through it, has
risen to a standing position with it, and has stopped rising smoothly as the eyepiece reaches its upper limit.
He slowly rotates the periscope from side to side, searching through the faint pre-dawn light.

"Down periscope! Target not yet in sight. What range
do you have on the TDC?"

Since it still lacks more than an hour till dawn, the
conning tower and control room are still darkened in
order to make it possible to see through the periscope.
The radar has been secured, and only the faint red glow
of the TDC dial lights, the torpedo ready lights, and the
sound gear dial lights are permitted. Dave Bunting con-
sults the TDC range dial. "Range, eight oh double oh,
Captain. Bearing two nine five."

"Up periscope! Put me on two nine five!" The Captain
snaps the command to his exec, "Bobo" Bobczynski, now
functioning as Assistant Approach Officer. As the periscope comes up, the latter places his hands beside the
Captain's on the handles and swings the 'scope until the

etched hairline stands at 295. The skipper looks long and hard, and infinitesimally rotates the periscope from one side to the other.

Throughout the ship the men are waiting for the answer to their unspoken questions: "Have we dived in the right place?" "Have we really outguessed him?" *"Does the Captain see the target?"*

Finally, in a low voice which hardly expresses conviction, and which certainly is far from showing the relief he feels, the Captain speaks. "I see him."

The word flies through the ship. Men look at one another and smile, some a little shakily, but most, a tight-lipped grin of relief and pride. *"We have him in the periscope!"*

The Captain's voice now comes a little stronger. "Bearing—mark! Down 'scope! No range yet!"

"Two nine five," Bobo sings out the bearing. Bunting checks his TDC. Down below in the control room, Plot gets the bearing, plots it. There has been a temporary hiatus, while the ship pulls itself together for the final effort, but it is over now.

"Up periscope! Bearing—mark!"

"Two nine six!"

"Range—mark! Down periscope!"

"Six five double oh!"

"Angle on the bow. Starboard five degrees!"

Things are really clicking now. At 20 knots the target will travel the distance between himself and *Archerfish* in nine minutes and a few seconds. It is time to maneuver to gain a favorable firing position as he goes by.

"What's the distance to the track?" The Captain can't be bothered with doing the calculation himself.

Bobo does it for him by trigonometry, multiplying the sine of the angle on the bow by the range. He has what amounts to a slide rule to make the computations, and the answer is almost instantaneous. "Five five oh yards!"

Much too close! The submarine is also headed toward the target's projected track. At minimum submerged speed of 2 knots, in nine minutes she will have traveled 600 yards, and will be almost directly beneath the target as he goes by. These thoughts and computations flash across Joe Enright's mind in a split second, even as he gives the order to mitigate the situation. "Left full rudder! Left to course zero nine zero!" By turning her bow more toward the target, *Archerfish* will be enabled to fire torpedoes a little sooner, thus catching *Shinano* at a reasonable range; also, she will not close the track so quickly.

All this time *Shinano* is pounding on to his doom. As soon as *Archerfish* steadies on the new course, her periscope rises above the waves once more, remains a moment, then disappears. Range, bearing, and angle on the bow are fed into the TDC and plot. Her skipper's mind is functioning like lightning. There are three things which *Shinano* may do: Continue on his present course, which will put *Archerfish* in the least favorable firing position, necessitating a sharp track shot ahead of time. Or, zig to his right, causing the submarine to shoot him with stern tubes. Most favorable would be a zig of about 30 degrees to his left, which would leave him wide open for a square broadside shot from the bow tubes.

"How much time?" rasps the skipper, motioning with his thumbs for the periscope to go up.

"He'll be here in two minutes!"

The periscope rises out of the well. "Zig away, to his own left! Angle on the bow starboard thirty!" The TDC dials whirl as the new information is fed into it.

"Bearing—mark!"

"Three four eight!"

"Range—mark!"

"Two oh double oh!"

Swiftly the Captain spins the periscope, making a quick scan of the situation all around. Suddenly he stops, returns to a bearing broad on the port beam.

"Down 'scope! Escort passing overhead!"

The periscope streaks down. For the first time they are conscious of a new noise, a drumming noise—propeller beats—coming closer. With a roar like that of an express train, the high-speed destroyer screws sweep overhead.

"This is a shooting observation! Are the torpedoes ready?" Unconsciously, the Captain's voice has become clipped and sharp. This is the moment they have worked for all night. He must not fail!

"Shooting observation. All tubes are ready, sir, depth set fifteen feet. Range one five double oh, angle on bow starboard eight five. We are all ready to shoot, sir!"

The cool, self-possessed voice of Sigmund Bobczynski surprises both himself and the Captain. There is no wavering, no lack of confidence here. A quick look of affectionate understanding passes between these two who have traveled so far and worked so long together.

"Up periscope! Looks perfect! Bearing—mark!"

"Zero zero one!"

"Set!"—from the TDC officer.

And then that final word, the word they have been leading up to, the word they have all studiously avoided pronouncing until now. "*Fire!*"

At eight-second intervals, six torpedoes race toward their huge target. Mesmerized, the skipper of *Archerfish* stands at his periscope watching for the success or failure of his approach. Forty-seven endless seconds after firing, the culmination of *Archerfish's* efforts is achieved.

"Whang!" then eight seconds later, "Whang!" Two hits right before his eyes! But there isn't time to play the spectator. That destroyer who just passed overhead will be coming back, and the trailing escort will surely join the party in short order.

A quick look astern of the carrier. Sure enough, here he comes, and less than five hundred yards away. *"Take her down!"*

Negative tank is flooded and the planes put at full dive. Over the rush of water into and air out of negative tank, four more solid, beautiful hits are heard.

The next thing on the docket after a torpedo attack is usually a depth charge attack, and this case proves no exception. But after their glorious experience, it will take a lot of depth charges to dampen the spirits of these submariners. The patrol report actually indicates surprise that the depth charging was not more severe, and merely states, "Started receiving a total of fourteen depth charges," and a little later, "Last depth charge. The hissing, sputtering, and sinking noises continued."

And what of *Shinano* all this time? *Archerfish* made but one mistake in her report. Her target did not sink immediately, as she believed, and, as a matter of strict truth, it would not have sunk at all had its crew possessed even a fraction of the training and indoctrination of its adversary. After all, *Shinano* was theoretically designed to survive twenty or more torpedoes. If she had been properly handled by her crew, and if she had been properly built, she could have made port in spite of *Archerfish's* six torpedoes.

But water poured from damaged compartments into

undamaged ones via watertight doors which had no gaskets; through cable and pipe conduits not properly sealed off and stuffing tubes not packed. The Japanese engineers attempted to start the pumps—and found they had not yet been installed, the piping not even completed. They searched for the hand pumps, but the ship had not yet received her full allowance of gear, and only a few were on board. In desperation, a bucket brigade was started, but the attempt was hopeless. The six huge holes in *Shinano's* side and the innumerable internal leaks defied all efforts to cope with them.

And then her organization and discipline failed. The men drifted away from the bucket brigade by ones and twos. The engineers gave up trying to get part of the drainage system running. The officers rushed about giving furious orders—but no one obeyed them. Instead, fatalistically, most of the crew gathered on the flight deck in hopes of being rescued by one of the four destroyers milling around their stricken charge. Faint, pathetic hope.

Four hours after she had received her mortal wound, *Shinano* had lost all power, and was nothing but a beaten, hopeless, disorganized hulk, listing to starboard more heavily every moment, a plaything of the wind and the sea. There was only one thing left to do.

The Emperor, in his gilded frame, was removed from the bridge and, after being thoroughly wrapped, transferred by line to a destroyer alongside. Then the work of abandoning ship began.

Shortly before 1100 on the morning of November 29 *Shinano* capsized to starboard, rolling her broad flight deck under and exposing her enormous glistening fat belly, with its four bronze propellers at the stern. For several minutes she hung there, lurching unevenly in the moderately rough sea.

Here and there the figures of several men who had not leaped into the sea with the others stood upon the steel plates, silhouetted against sea and sky. Evidently they had climbed around the side and the turn of the bilge as the ship rolled over. Whatever their reasons for not abandoning the ship, they were now doomed, for none of the four destroyers still holding the wake dared approach closely enough to take them off. And the suction of the sinking vessel was certain to take them down with it.

Slowly the massive rudders and propellers started to dip under the seas splashing up toward them. A trembling and a groaning communicated itself to the whole giant fabric, and it began to sway noticeably, swinging the afterparts and the foreparts under alternately. Each time an end dipped, the sea gained a little, and the trembling and groaning increased.

Finally, during one swoop, the stern failed to reappear. Startlingly and suddenly, the bow rose partly out of water, displaying a single eye formed by one gigantic hawsepipe, as if *Shinano* desired a final look at the world she was about to leave. Swiftly then she slid under, stern first, and the last thing seen was the broad bulbous bow, like the forehead of some huge prehistoric Moby Dick, accompanied by the blowing, bubbling, and whistling of air escaping under water.

For several minutes there was considerable turbulence and bubbling to mark her grave, but *Shinano* was gone from the ken of men.

She had known the open sea for less than twenty hours.

THE CHEERFUL TORTOISE

By James Norman Hall

In point of popularity there have been few literary collaborations to compare with Charles Nordhoff and James Norman Hall. The entire reading world became familiar with Captain Bligh as a character in fiction. But one of the penalties of such a successful team is that what the members produce individually has a tendency to be overshadowed by the joint achievement. Only in rare cases, as with the brothers Goncourt, do the literary Siamese twins remain unsevered. This was particularly the case with James Norman Hall. No matter what he wrote on his own, he is as completely identified with the famous Bounty saga as was Conan Doyle with Sherlock Holmes.

As though to get away from Bligh and his mutineers for a while, Hall invented a jolly nautical character named Surgeon Dogbody of the Royal Navy. Dr. Dogbody had a wooden leg. The stories he told to account for the loss of the missing member were legion. I have chosen the first of the series, most of which is told in the parlor of the tavern, The Cheerful Tortoise, *on the waterfront.*

It might be argued that such creations as Dr. Dogbody have small relation to the facts of life at sea. He is more in the tradition of Paul Bunyan, Mr. Pickwick, and Commodore Trunnion. Those who were at sea in the days before world wars know that sailors used to love the grandiose, the grotesque, and the superb exaggerations of a genuine teller of

*tales. So, for that matter, do landsmen. Men in tall ships can
tell tall tales, and all men enjoy that suspension of disbelief
which is half the charm of living.*

On a dreary autumn evening when the clouds hung low
in the heavens and the masts and yards of the tall men-
of-war in the harbour were obscured by a chill drizzle of
rain, there was no more inviting spot in Portsmouth than
the taproom of Will Tunn's Cheerful Tortoise. But times
were dull, now that Napoleon had been safely exiled to
Saint Helena; half the fleet was paid off, ships laid up,
and the Royal Dockyards, which had hummed with activity two years before, were reduced to the peacetime establishment.

The Cheerful Tortoise had suffered with the rest of
the community from the return of peace, although the
creature which gave the inn its name smiled down upon
passers-by with its old-time air of wistful geniality. The
inn sign, as Mr. Tunn himself was willing to admit, was
a veritable work of art. Carved from a huge slab of oak
by an old seaman, many years before, it was impervious
to wind and weather; only the strongest gale would
cause it to swing slightly on its heavy gilded chain. Many
a thirsty seaman, just ashore, would stop short to gaze
in admiration at Will Tunn's tortoise, touch his hat to it
with a grin, and seek no farther for refreshment. The
carapace was a bright sea-green, the calipee pale blue,
and the flippers yellow, while the head, with its eager
smiling face, was richly ornamented and picked out in
gold leaf. But the tortoise was greater than the sum of
its parts, thanks to a happy stroke of seaman's genius.
Its attitude of absorbed interest as it craned its neck to
one side, as though to gaze past the lintel of the doorway

into the taproom, combined with its smile, in which sadness at thought of its own deprivations seemed to be mingled with unselfish delight at thought of the good cheer and good company within, had made it a famous tavern animal amongst innumerable swans, blue boars, cocks, dogs, and ducks, red lions, green dragons, white harts, and horses that adorned the highroad between Portsmouth and London.

Mr. Tunn's house stood on a corner a short distance from the waterfront. Although not one of the great posting-inns of the time, it was a place of call for some of the principal London coaches, and was especially frequented by men who followed the sea. It was a brick building of three stories which had been raised in the substantial manner of the period, to last for centuries. A door studded with brass nails gave directly upon the taproom with its dark paneled wainscoting, its floor of red bricks, well worn and scrubbed, its casks on trestles with a line of bright spigots behind the high old-fashioned bar, and its comfortable recesses with oaken tables, the chairs and settees upholstered in breeches-polished leather. One such recess alongside a mighty fireplace at the far end of the room was reserved for the "props" of the house, as the landlord called them, old friends and steady patrons who well deserved the name.

Beyond the taproom and connected with it by a wide passageway was the kitchen, an apartment equally spacious, whose dusky rafters were festooned with sides of bacon, hams, sausages, strings of onions, and parcels of dried herbs. Pots and pans polished to a degree of brightness something past perfection hung on pegs about the fireplace, where an entire bullock might almost have turned on the spit. At one side of the kitchen stood a long deal table, scrubbed white, where guests of the humbler sort were furnished with food and drink. On the floor above, reached by a staircase from the taproom, was the handsome apartment in which Tunn's famous dinners were served, and where four tall windows looked to the westward toward the Royal Dockyards and the shipping in the harbour. Along a carpeted passageway were the sitting rooms and bedchambers for travelers. On the third floor, where mullioned windows projected from the steep slope of the roof, were the quarters for postboys, coachmen, and hostlers, and for the landlord and his staff.

Mr. Tunn was a stoutly built, muscular man of sixty, with a clear ruddy complexion, a solid paunch, and a fringe of iron-grey hair framing a bald head. His had been a blameless, useful life, and he deserved well of the world if any man did; but on a certain evening in November his thoughts were as cheerless as the autumn day. He stood in the kitchen, superintending with little of his wonted relish the preparations for supper. Bilges, the kitchen boy, was seated on a stool opening a cask of oysters fresh from Newport. Another boy stood at the spit where a stubborn goose and a splendid saddle of mutton were turning under the landlord's direction. So pleasant a prospect would have caused Tunn's mouth to water at another time.

His worries were unselfish ones, for he was not a man to permit his own troubles to weigh heavily upon him. Mr. Tunn was a widower who revered the memory of his wife. A cousin of hers, a Mrs. Quigg, had done well with a lodginghouse during the long years of war, and although times grew hard after the defeat of the French, she had clung to her lease, waiting and hoping for lodgers who seldom came. Mrs. Quigg was a sturdy independent woman who would accept no help from her kin, and it worried Mr. Tunn to see a connection of his beloved Sarah reduced to such straitened circumstances. Thinking of this, he sighed, wiped his hands on his apron, and walked along the passage to the taproom, just in time to see one of his drawers toss off a pint-pot of ale. Tunn stopped short.

"Tom!"

The drawer, a spindle-shanked cadaverous fellow with a colourless face and a surprisingly round belly, turned his head with a grin, half guilty, half impudent.

"Tuppence in the till, ye rogue!" said the landlord, indignantly. "Tom Tapleke! Curse me if ever a man was better named! It's so ye help your master, is it? And custom fallen away to naught in these days! Tuppence in the till, I say!"

Tapleke, who knew to a shade his master's moods, sighed with the doleful air of a deeply wronged man, produced the coins with reluctant ostentation, and dropped them in the till. Tunn was about to say more when the drawer nodded toward the window. Dimly discernible through the frosted panes, a hackney coach was drawing up outside. The landlord turned in that direction as a smallish active man flung open the door and stumped in on a wooden leg. He wore a cocked hat of a style somewhat past the fashion, a handsomely embroidered waistcoat, and a coat which, though plain, was well cut and of the best materials. The buckle of the single shoe below the white silk stocking was of silver.

"Mr. Tunn?" he asked briskly.

"Will Tunn, sir, at your service."

"Doctor Dogbody, at yours, sir. I was directed to you . . . but damme, I'm parched! You've good rum here?"

"The best old Port Royal, sir."

"Then I'll thank you to take a glass with me while I tell my errand."

The visitor seated himself at a table and removed his hat, displaying a head of thick white hair, brushed neatly back and gathered in a queue. Doctor Dogbody's eyes, of the clearest blue, twinkled with shrewdness and good humour, in a face as ruddy as a winter sunset. It would have been difficult to guess his age with any exactness, although he appeared to be on the latter side of seventy. But the vigour of his movements, his erect carriage, and his small, well-shaped, muscular hands were those of a much younger man. Taking up the small glass of spirits the drawer had set before him, he nodded to the landlord and drained the contents at a gulp.

"Hah! That's better!" he exclaimed. "Ahoy, you at the tap! What's your name?"

"Tom, sir."

"Another of the same presently, Tom. And draw a pint of ale for yourself."

"Thankee, sir," said the delighted Tapleke, with a malicious grin for the landlord's benefit. The doctor turned to his host.

"Of all the drawers, Mr. Tunn," he said, "in all the inns between London and Portsmouth, five in six are named Tom. On the Dover road the ratio is seven Dicks to four Toms, whilst on the Exeter road there's naught but Joes as far as the King's Arms, Salisbury, whence, curiously enough, the Toms begin again and continue without break to the Elephant, in Exeter itself."

"You're a great traveler, sir?" Mr. Tunn asked, politely.

"By sea, yes. By land, no. But when I do travel, ashore, there's little I miss by the way, sir."

The doctor lifted his refilled glass, holding it toward the light as he examined the contents, critically.

"A prime old spirit, landlord. It has made a new man of me, I declare! Now, sir, to my errand. But before I proceed, just send out a tankard of your best to the coachman. The fellow's waiting for me and looks as dry as ashes.

"For some fifty years, Mr. Tunn, I've been a surgeon in His Majesty's Navy. For the moment I'm ashore, but London doesn't suit me. Damme, no! Portsmouth's the place for an old seaman, where he can cross tracks with shipmates now and again. At the Angel, in Town, the landlord's told me that Will Tunn, of the Cheerful Tortoise, was the man for me. It's lodgings I'm after, with a well-found inn, like yours, sir, close at hand. Now then, do you know of a snug berth near by? My compliments once more!"

Tunn raised his glass with a pleased smile and pretended to reflect for a moment before he spoke. "I know the very place, sir. A quiet house, and kept by a decent woman, a Mrs. Quigg."

"I'm no ordinary lodger, Tunn. It's not every woman would put up with me. I might make a bit of a noise abovestairs, getting about on my larboard leg. Then, it's not easy to cook for me, and there'll be times I want to dine in. Not that I demand any fiddle-faddle fare. I'm an old seaman; I've been nourished, and well nourished, on pease, oatmeal, good salt beef, cheese, and such simple food, but I'll have it dressed as I want it, in the best old Navy fashion. Would this Mrs. . . . what's her name again? Quiggs?—would she be the woman for my money?"

"The very one, Doctor Dogbody! Her husband was a warrant officer, and as choice a man about his victuals as ever I see. You could ransack Portsmouth from the waterside up without finding a woman with her knack for making a man comfortable."

"There's another thing. I'll have no bed. I must have my hammock battens made fast to the wall."

"No trouble about that, sir, Mrs. Quigg's lodged none but seamen since her house was opened."

"Then, Tunn, if you'll show me there, we'll board the coach." The surgeon fumbled in his waistcoat pocket and tossed a sovereign on the table. "Credit me with the balance of that," he said. "You've not seen the last of me, here."

"I trust not, sir, indeed," said the landlord in a pleased voice; then, taking his hat from a peg on the wall, he glanced from Tom Tapleke to the line of spigots with a look conveying a warning and a menace, and followed the surgeon out through the door.

The hour had gone six before Mr. Tunn again appeared in the taproom, entering from the kitchen with the air of a man who had dined well and is deeply content with the world. Two old patrons of the house came in at this moment, and with a nod to the landlord went to their customary corner at the left of the fireplace. The first, Ned Balthus, was a burly man of middle stature, dressed in a worn and weather-stained coat, with anchor-buttons of silver, and wearing a wig of the kind called "Grizzle Major." There was not a better old fellow in Portsmouth, nor one with a kinder heart, but his face was marked with the scar of a deep cutlass slash that gave him a most forbidding frown. He had been a Navy gunner for nearly half a century, and now, at the age of retirement, some small employment had been found for him at the Portsmouth Arsenal. His companion, Mr. Ostiff, engraver of charts to the Admiralty, was a tall spare man in middle life, whose small mouth, sharp nose, and long upper lip gave him an air of solemnity belied by a pair of nearsighted grey eyes with a twinkle of mischief in them. As the drawer was attending to their wants, the landlord joined his two old friends.

"Gad, Tunn," Mr. Ostiff remarked drily. "You look as though you'd come into a fortune."

"And so I have, Mr. Ostiff," said Tunn, taking a seat at the end of the table, with a comfortable sigh. "I do believe it! A landlord's fortune is the guests who choose his house. I've had the luck to add one to-day, a rare gentleman, if I'm a judge. If ye'll allow me to say so, he'd make a companion to those of ye who favour this corner."

"We'd best decide that for ourselves," said Ostiff, still more drily.

"I'd be far from wishing to foist him amongst ye, Mr. Ostiff," Tunn replied; "and he'd be the last to permit it. But he's to lodge close by, at Mrs. Quigg's, and he's done me the honour to say the Tortoise will suit him well for his evenings."

"What name?"

"Doctor Dogbody."

Mr. Balthus set down his pot with a bang.

"Dogbody!" he exclaimed. "Not F. Dogbody?"

"There could be only the one, surely," said Ostiff. "You mean to say it's the man's true name?"

"Tunn, is it F. Dogbody?" Balthus repeated, eagerly.

"I'll not be certain as to that," said the landlord.

"One leg?"

"Aye. His left one's off above the knee."

The gunner brought his hand down on his thigh with a resounding smack. "Damn my eyes! He's here? In Portsmouth?"

"He was in this room not two hours gone. Ye know him, then, do ye, Mr. Balthus?"

"Know him!" said Mr. Balthus. "God's rabbit! Where's the old Navy man that don't know Doctor Dogbody? I'm astonished at the pair of ye who've not heard of him till this day. But there's this to be said: he's none of your half-pay surgeons. I'll warrant he's not spent six weeks ashore in a quarter of a century. A better-loved man never trod a ship's deck."

"How did he lose his leg?" asked Tunn.

Balthus sat back in his seat with a look of pleased recollection on his face. "Well may ye ask, Tunn! I've heard him tell the tale a dozen times if I've heard it once, and never twice the same."

"The man must be the very king of liars," said Ostiff, testily.

The gunner smiled. "Say ye so! I'll say naught. My belief is that *all* his tales are true! And mark ye this, Mr. Ostiff! If ever a man lost his leg in some strange way and survived the loss miracle-fashion, as ye might say, that man is Surgeon F. Dogbody. There's nothing humdrum about him. If he no more than spits to leeward he does it with an air of his own."

The door opened at this moment and another old patron of the Tortoise entered. Captain Thankful Runyon was a merchant from Boston, in America, who owned two Nantucket whaling vessels commanded by his sons. He was also half-owner of a vessel which plied chiefly between Boston and Portsmouth with sperm oil, for which the British Admiralty was an excellent customer. Captain Runyon, whose business it was to dispose of the oil, spent most of each year at Portsmouth, and, despite his being a Yankee, was well liked at the Tortoise. He was in his early sixties, rawboned, wiry, with a sun-burned leathery face and neck. Although he had spent much of his life at sea, he was a man of excellent education, most of which he had acquired himself.

"Here's one will bear me out, I'll warrant," said Balthus, as Captain Runyon took his place amongst them. "Mr. Runyon, ye must have heard of one of our old Navy surgeons, F. Dogbody?"

"Never, Balthus, never," Runyon replied, in his curt manner. "Hot pot for me, Tom," he added to the drawer, who stood at his side. He turned again to the gunner. "Peabodys, yes; ye can raise three or four in a ten-minute walk anywhere in New England. I know a Fairbody or two, and one Angelbody in the West India trade. But a Dogbody or a Catbody it's not been my fortune to meet. Friend of yours, Balthus?"

"I'd wish him to think me one," the gunner replied, gravely, and the reproach implied by his manner was obvious.

"No offense, Balthus," Captain Runyon replied. "We've names on our side as odd as any of yours. My partner, in Boston, is Ralph Soilbibb, and well he lives up to the allegation. And the best friend I had in the world, in my younger days, was George Pigwart. Lost at sea, off Cape Horn, poor fellow! But what did ye wish to say of Surgeon Dogbody?"

"He's here, gentlemen!" Tunn put in, in a low voice. The street door swung open, admitting the surgeon himself, and a gust of damp air that made the lamps flicker for a moment. Balthus half rose from his seat, thought better of it, and dropped back once more. "Wait!" he cautioned the landlord. "Say naught!"

After a sweeping glance about the room, Doctor Dogbody was about to take a seat at a vacant table on the other side of the fireplace when Balthus roared out: "Clean sponges, damn your eyes, and be quick about it!" The surgeon stopped short, spun round on his peg, and brought down his bushy eyebrows as he peered through the dimly lighted room. Then he stumped across to the table, his blue eyes twinkling.

"Not Ned Balthus?" he exclaimed. "Not that cornyfaced gunner of the old *Minerva?* Gentlemen, does the man call himself Balthus?"

"Aye, that he does!" said the gunner, heartily. The surgeon took him by the shoulders and held him at arm's length. "By God, Ned! I've mourned ye as dead these five years! D'ye mind Captain Farshingle, of the *Trent?* 'Twas him that told me. You were back on the West India station, he said, and went off with the yellow fever."

"He might well have heard it, Doctor," Balthus replied. " 'Twas a near thing. I was in the *Acteon* that year, and a good half of the ship's company left their bones in the cursed place. But let me make ye known to these gentlemen."

There was a gleam of honest triumph in the gunner's eyes as he noted the reception accorded the surgeon. That the others approved of him was plain, and it was Ostiff himself, hard to please in company, who invited him to take his place amongst them. The surgeon, sensing the sincerity of these overtures, needed no further urging.

"So ye've come ashore at last, Doctor?" Balthus asked, when the drawer had attended to the wants of the company.

"Ashore? Damn my eyes! Who says it?" the surgeon replied, with a snort.

"I understood as much from the landlord here."

"Begging your pardon, sir, if I took your meaning wrong," Mr. Tunn put in, hastily. "I was telling these gentlemen ye'd honoured the Tortoise with a call this afternoon, and I'd the notion ye'd retired from the service."

"Temporarily, sir, but not for good. No, no! There's a score of years' use in me yet. But I won't say I'm not pleased with a bit of a holiday, now that old Boney is safely caged."

"And well ye might be, Doctor," said Balthus. "Ye've not been ashore long, then?"

"Six weeks come next Thursday. I was paid off out of the *Bedford*. She's to be broken up."

Mr. Ostiff shook his head. "Many's the good ship will go that way now," he said. "I wish we may not live to regret them."

"As to that sir, I'm of the same mind as yourself," said the surgeon. "It tears my heart to see them go. But since go they must, the Admiralty might better have scuttled 'em all, off soundings. The oldest and the least of them deserve a better fate than the breaking yard."

"Your Admiralty Board had fewer for that end at the close of the American War," said Runyon, with a sly grin.

"Pay no heed to this Pompkinshire Yankee, Doctor," said Ostiff. "By God's grace, the Americans managed to raise up one seaman amongst them—Paul Jones, and even he was born on this side. But Runyon will boast of him, in season and out. To hear him you'd think Paul Jones had destroyed the entire British Navy."

"I'll do them the honour to say they'd more than one of his mettle," the surgeon remarked.

"Handsomely admitted, sir!" said Runyon, warmly. "I've never had such an acknowledgment from Ostiff. You've met them at sea, I take it?"

"Aye; to both my pleasure and my sorrow."

Captain Runyon turned to Ostiff, with a triumphant smile.

"There, sir! The best of testimony for the defense!"

"For the defense?" said Ostiff. "Gad, sir, I like the way you put it! I'll leave it to Balthus, here, if you've ever taken a defensive position."

"He'll not acknowledge, Doctor Dogbody," said Runyon, "that an American ship of war ever came off best, in a battle against odds. There was the old *Protector*, for example. You may have heard of her?"

"The *Protector?* Captain John Foster Williams?"

"The same, sir. You knew her, then?"

"From truck to keelson," the surgeon replied, quietly. "Oddly enough, it was the *Protector* that cost me my leg."

"You don't tell me!" said Runyon, an expression of keen interest upon his face. "Would you be willing, sir, to favour us with the circumstances?"

"Quite, if these other gentlemen are of the same mind as yourself."

"We'd esteem it a privilege, Doctor Dogbody," said Ostiff, with a slight bow. Balthus stole a cautious glance at the surgeon, who was gazing before him with a grave, musing, abstracted expression.

"You'll mind, Ned," the surgeon began, with a glance at the gunner, "the first time we were on the West India station together, and *I* came so near to a taking-off with the cursed yellow jack?"

"Aye, well, sir," said Balthus, with an emphatic nod. "And how grieved we was at thought of leaving ye behind."

"I need say nothing of the two months that followed. I took what comfort the place afforded in the way of convalescence, and when recovered was appointed surgeon for the homeward voyage to a Company ship, the *Admiral Duff*, returning to England with a cargo of sugar and tobacco which we'd taken on at Saint Kitts. The *Duff* was a well-found ship. We had a crew of two hundred and fifty, and, for the weight of armament, thirty-six twelve-pounders on the gun deck. Her captain was Richard Strange—Mad Dick he was called behind his back, and well he deserved the name! But mind you, he was mad in the way of genius. His men worshiped him; it was a happy ship, and we'd not been a week at sea when I was perfectly recovered, and as content as an old Navy surgeon could be in a merchantman.

"Well, sir, Dick Strange thought no more of the valuable cargo he was taking to London than did his men. It was so much ballast, and his owners could whistle for it. He was a born fighter and I saw how matters stood before we'd lost the land. We were for prizes, so I spent my time with my loblolly boys preparing sponges, dressings, tourniquets, and the like, certain that we'd have use for a plenty before Dick Strange would consent to sail home.

"We took two Yankee brigs the first week and a third

the week after, and sent all to Saint Kitts; then, b'gad, you'd have said the seas had been swept clean. Not a sail did we spy, though we were in the direct track of shipping up and down the Atlantic coast. We had dirty easterly weather and could scarce see a mile; even so we'd expected better luck than that.

"We got well north, and crept to within ten leagues of the American coast. On a morning in June, after a thick fog had cleared away—this was in 1780—a sail was sighted to the eastward not two leagues off. We made sure he was a Yankee by the cut of his royals and were ready to eat him up. Damme, I had my share of the prize money already spent! But we had to reach him first, and there was not wind enough to lift a feather.

"In ten minutes we'd four boats out, towing. The men put their backs into it, but you'll know what headway they made with a thousand-ton ship. Nevertheless, we moved. Captain Strange was halfway up the mizzen ratlins, egging them on, one minute with his eye to his spyglass, the next, roaring out encouragement to the seamen. Then he made out that the Yankee was towing as well, and in our direction, so we felt easier. It was clear they wanted to engage.

"So it went for near an hour, but the breeze came at last. The Yankee had it first, and as soon as we spied their boats at the falls, in came ours. Being to windward, they edged down toward us, and it was a near thing but they'd have caught us without so much as steerageway, the breeze was that light. But the *Duff* felt it at last. Long before this we had the hammocks up and stuffed into the nettings, decks wet and sanded, matches lighted, and the bulkheads hooked up. They flew the English ensign, but Strange was not deceived by that.

As we passed him, Strange called out, 'What ship is that?' The only reply was from their sailing master bawling out orders to his men. They steered to cross our stern and hauled up under our quarter. At that moment up went their true colours and their captain replied: 'Continental ship, *Protector!* Come on! We're ready for you!'

"B'gad, gentlemen, they were! But no more ready than ourselves. We'd caught a tartar, as we learned, directly we were abreast of him once more. He let go every gun on his starboard side, and every shot hulled us, I'll take my oath! The *Duff* was a higher ship, and our gunners were hard put to bring their guns to bear where they would do the most damage. But the noble fellows performed prodigies, and, for all the advantage of the Yankees, our fire was near as murderous as their own.

"The action began within easy pistol shot, and it was yardarm to yardarm from then on. We were fairly matched as to armament, but they had seventy marines amongst them whilst we had none, and seamen are no match for marines in the use of small arms. They killed our topmen as fast as we could replace them, and they'd not forgotten, the rascals, that there were fair targets, aft. But Dick Strange's quizzing-glass never dropped from his eye, save for an instant when the ribbon to it was cut by a musket ball. He caught the eyepiece before it could fall, twirled it carelessly by the bit of frayed ribbon, and replaced it just as our lads let go a broadside that might have taught them better manners.

"Aye, it was warm work, but the end of it was that they made a sieve of us from wind to water. Down came our foremast, then the main, and, b'gad, the mizzen followed! There was nothing left a yard high to hoist our colours on. The Yankee thought we'd struck and ceased firing. Little he knew Dick Strange. D'ye know what he did, sir?"

Doctor Dogbody paused and took up his glass. Finding it empty, he turned to the drawer, who was standing near by, forgetful of his duties while he listened. "Here, Tom, you rascal! I might positively die of thirst with you looking on!" Tapleke, galvanized into action by the abrupt summons, was away to the bar and back in an instant. The surgeon then resumed.

"Well, sir, Strange was fairly beside himself, though you'd not have guessed it by his manner. To have been thought to have struck was an insult so rank he could scarce bear it. He glanced coolly around the quarter-deck—the place was a shambles of the dead and dying —and his eye fell upon a lad standing near by. 'Fetch me a boat flag,' said Strange, 'and be quick about it!' The lad was back with one in twenty seconds. Strange fastened it to his cane, for he fancied his little stick even on shipboard. With this he sprung onto the bulwark and roared out to Williams: 'I've not struck, sir! Tell your bloody bang-straws to try and hit my stick!'

"Gentlemen, I give you my word: he stood there, holding that small flag aloft for a full ten minutes. But in the end, hit it they did. The shot from a carronade clipped off the stick within three inches of Strange's hand. Meanwhile, our three remaining guns continued to fire when they could be brought to bear, but without a rag of sail left you can imagine our situation.

"I and my assistants were at work on the orlop, but with the best will in the world we could not keep pace with the stream of shattered bleeding fellows that were carried or came crawling down to us. Aye, it was raw-meat day, one of the worst in my experience; the tubs were heaped high with arms and legs. Busy as we were at the bloody work, we'd no time to know what was taking place above us, and you can imagine my astonishment when one of the lieutenants came with orders to move all my wounded to the gun deck. We were sinking. It was the first intimation I'd had of the seriousness of our situation.

"Serious, do I say? Damme, it was hopeless, as I saw a moment after, but Dick Strange would not call it so. And there was that in his spirit to have made a ravening lion out of the veriest sheep in his ship's company, had there been any such, which there were not. By God, they fought like devils, even the lads of fourteen. The Yankee was right alongside, and we'd not carried above a dozen of our wounded up from the orlop when, even above the uproar overhead, we heard Strange bellow out: 'Boarders! Boarders! Every man on deck!'

"There was no more thought of the wounded then, nor would they have wished us to think of them. My cutlass and pistols were in my cabin, and I seized the nearest weapon that came to hand, a tomahawk, and rallied with the others at the starboard bulwarks. There were not above a score of us left, but with Strange to lead us we felt equal to a gross of Yankees. He'd a pistol in one hand and a cutlass in the other, and his quizzing-glass with the frayed ribbon was still at his eye. I was pleased that he should have a word for me at such a moment, with the Yankee closing in, not twenty yards off. 'Dogbody,' said he, coolly, with a nod toward the *Protector*, 'we'll have a noggin of rum directly, in my cabin yonder.' And I've not the least doubt that he was perfectly convinced we should.

"There had been no time to get out our nettings, and

the Yankees swarmed into us the moment they grappled. They were five to one, and the *Duff* had settled to such an extent that our bulwarks were now lower than their own. Two stout fellows were upon me at once, to their cost, if I may be permitted to say so. The third I did not see until too late, else I might have lost both legs in the place of one. I had my right foot raised and resting on a casing by the bulwark, when I felt a most peculiar numbing sensation in my left leg, and immediately fell back on my buttocks. As I did so I beheld my severed leg lying beside me, and a gigantic Indian,—he looked all of eight feet high, although I later found he was but six feet six,—who by this time had rushed by me, drawing back his cutlass for a swing at the man beyond. Him he fairly cut in two, at one ferocious blow.

"I spare you the details. It is enough to say that we were taken, but the Americans had little good of their prize. There was no surrender. We sunk under their very feet, not five minutes after they had boarded. Strange went down with his ship, by a miracle unwounded, but he was not one to suffer the humiliation of capture. Lacking his delicacy of feeling in this respect, I seized the first floating object I could get my hands upon in the swirl of waters that closed over the *Duff*. Fortunately, I had had the presence of mind, after my leg was off, to tie up the femoral artery with a bit of marline, and had then plunged the stump into a bucket of tar, else I should have died before I could be taken up. As it was, I'd lost a deal of blood by the time I was laid amongst the wounded, both ours and theirs, aboard the *Protector*.

"Their surgeons were working at top speed, but with so many to be served, they were obliged to choose those most likely to live. Two of their dressers were about to take up a fellow, one of their own men, lying beside me, but the surgeon said, 'Let Little lie. Attend to the others first. He will die.' Indeed, he might well have thought so, for the poor fellow had been horribly wounded in the face by a charge of grape. I rose on my elbow and turned to look at him. The man was perfectly sensible, and I saw that within his eye which gave me a most vivid impression of indomitable courage. It was curious: as our glances met, something passed between us—complete sympathy, mutual respect, and I was convinced not only that the man would not die, but that I could learn to love him like a brother.

"My professional interest in his case was immediately aroused. I have a brusque way with me in my capacity as surgeon, and in an instant I had one of their dressers fetching for me. He brought me a basin of water, sponges, and lint, and, managing to raise myself to a sitting position, I proceeded to dress Little's wounds. Strangely enough, I then felt no sensation of pain in my severed leg, and suffered but little inconvenience from it.

"Little had been wounded by three balls: one between the neck bone and windpipe, one through the jaw, lodging in the roof of his mouth and taking off a piece of his tongue, and the third through the lip, which had destroyed nearly all of his upper teeth. I worked over him for an hour, removed the lodged ball, cleansed the wounds, sewed up his lip, and staunched the flow of blood. The event of it was that he perfectly recovered."

Doctor Dogbody rose abruptly. "I ask your leave for one moment, gentlemen," he said; then, turning to Tapleke: "Tom, your necessary-house."

"This way, sir," said the drawer, leading him toward a passageway to the left, and the surgeon followed him out with great dignity.

Mr. Ostiff looked after him with a faint smile, in which puzzlement and admiration were mingled.

"Balthus," said he, "I can scarcely believe our friend to be the liar you've pictured him."

"A liar!" said Runyon. "The tale has the very stamp of truth upon it! Some of the details are inexact, but I've often heard, at home, of the fight between the *Protector* and the *Duff*, and I'll take my oath that the latter was conquered as the surgeon has related the circumstances. What's this, Balthus?"

"I said naught of his being a liar," Balthus replied, warmly. "What I did say was that I've heard him tell the tale of his lost leg a dozen times, and never twice . . ." He broke off, for the surgeon was again approaching. Captain Runyon waited with impatience for him to be seated.

"Sir," he said, "the man whose wounds you dressed could have been no other than Captain Luther Little."

"So it was, sir," said Dogbody, "though he was not a captain at this time. He was a young man on the *Protector* and served in her as midshipman and prize-master. An older brother, George Little, was a lieutenant in the same vessel. They belong to a family, Little in name only, from the town of Marshfield, in the Massachusetts colony."

"I've no doubt that you became excellent friends, after such a meeting?" said Runyon.

"The very best, sir. Mr. Luther Little was considerably my junior, but the small service I was able to render him whilst wounded, combined, as I have said, with something compatible in our natures, served to draw us together upon terms of sincere liking and deep understanding. His elder brother, George, became no less my

friend. For the next eight months I was a guest in the
Little home. I was, to be sure, a prisoner-of-war, but not
the least restraint was put upon my liberty, nor upon
my sentiments as a loyal Englishman. And I came to
understand the sentiments of our late colonists better,
perhaps, than many an Englishman who has never had
occasion to live amongst them. They are an admirable
nation, and I have little doubt will be a great one in the
course of time. It could scarcely be otherwise when one
considers the stock from which they sprung."

The surgeon paused to give Captain Runyon a keen
glance. "You are acquainted with the Littles, sir?" he
asked.

"I have not that honour," Runyon replied, "although
I have more than once passed through the town of
Marshfield. The place was as famous at one time for a
gigantic Indian follower of the Little boys as for the
family itself."

"Of the name of Powana?" the surgeon asked.

"Bless my soul! The very same! . . . Jehoshaphat!
Could it have been . . ."

"Yes, sir. It could have been, and was, Powana who
deprived me of my leg, and a cleaner blow was never
given with a cutlass. I could not have made a better
amputation at leisure, with my saws and razors, than
was done by the Indian before I could have said 'Oh!'
His name, Powana, signifies 'whale' in the Natick tongue,
and a whale he was in stature. He carried me about like
an infant at Marshfield, whilst my stump was healing,
and when it had healed he made me a very serviceable
wooden leg to replace that he had taken."

"Is it the one you are wearing, Doctor?" Will Tunn
asked.

"No, Mr. Tunn, it is not. Curiously enough, Powana's leg was to serve me but a short time, as I shall explain in a moment. . . . Nine months, almost to a day, from the time of our first meeting, Little and I were again at sea, though not, to be sure, as companions-in-arms. He was now in virtual command of the letter-of-marque brig *Jupiter,* carrying twenty-one guns and one hundred and fifty men. I say in virtual command, for the owner and nominal captain was a merchant of the town of Salem, in Massachusetts, a man of the name of Gorme. My status was still that of a prisoner-of-war. Little had gone bail for me to the American authorities, and whilst he would have liked nothing better than to release me, that he was in honour bound not to do until I could be exchanged for some American prisoner of my own rank. He meant to arrange for this at sea, at the first opportunity.

"We cruised for a full three weeks, in a southerly direction, without any particulars worthy of mention, but I am bound to say that this result was due to the excessive timidity of Captain Gorme. We often sighted English vessels, whereupon Gorme would examine them through his spyglass with the fluttery apprehension of an old woman, and would not allow Little to approach nearer than two leagues. His mouth watered for prizes, but he would not bring himself to take the least risk in obtaining them.

"One morning whilst crossing the Gulf Stream not far off the American coast, we sighted an object a mile or so distant to leeward which Gorme, for once, was willing to approach for a nearer view. There was a light breeze from the northeast, and a curious popple, due perhaps to the action of the Gulf Stream itself. We soon made out the object to be a floating log of considerable size, and clinging to it were three men whom we first took to be Indians. They were dressed in skins resembling that of the raccoon, though there were but three rings on the tail instead of five. Their hair was long, straight and black, like that of the Iroquois, but strangely enough their eyes were of the deepest blue, and their skins almost as light as those of Englishmen. They were nearly dead when picked up, and in spite of my ministrations and those of my Yankee colleague on the *Jupiter*, they lived but a few days. Powana, who was, of course, on board, was unable to exchange a word with them, either in the Natick tongue or in any of the other Indian dialects with which he was familiar. But, astounding as it may seem, a Welsh quartermaster discovered that they spoke a language closely akin to his own. To the great loss of science, they died before he was able to learn whence they came.

"But what I wished to say was that we took on board the log as well as the Indians, if such they were, who had clung to it, for Captain Gorme hoped that it might be useful for spars. We found it to be of a nature as strange as the mysterious castaways. No one on board could identify the wood. The heartwood was almost as hard as iron, and yet it could be worked. When sawn, its peculiar fragrance attracted clouds of butterflies from the main; they appeared in countless thousands, so that, for some days, the ship could scarcely be navigated. I discovered, later, that this heartwood sank like lead in the water, and, strangest of all perhaps, it was impervious to the teredo worm, the ruination of our ships in warm seas.

"The log, though useless for spars, was a valuable find,

and Captain Gorme was beside himself with vexation that he had not been able to learn, from the Indians, whence it came. From a morsel of the heartwood, Mr. Colbarch, the ship's carpenter, fashioned me a leg to replace the temporary one made by Powana, and a more comfortable, serviceable peg, once I was accustomed to it, I have never had the pleasure of wearing. It is the one I have on at the moment.

"We proceeded on our voyage, and, as the days passed, my friend Little and the entire ship's company became more and more impatient with their faint-hearted captain. At last the captain himself, finding himself incapable of making a resolute decision, placed Little in command. Thereafter, Gorme kept to his cabin. As the event proved, he had not long to keep it.

"The following morning, at dawn, we sighted a schooner which showed no colours, though Little was convinced, as well as myself, that she was English. 'Dog-body,' said he, 'if she proves to be such, and has American prisoners on board, you shall be exchanged immediately.' He then ran up a signal of a parley and we bore down on the vessel. As we approached, we made her out to be a smart little privateer of eighteen guns. I went to my cabin to prepare for quitting the *Jupiter*, and whilst there, I heard the parley which followed.

" 'What ship is that?' Little roared through his speaking trumpet.

" '*Lion*, of London,' came the reply, so clearly that, though I could not see the schooner, I knew that she was right alongside. 'Who are you?'

" '*Jupiter*, of Salem,' Little replied. 'Have you prisoners to exchange?'

" 'That's as may be,' replied the British captain. 'What d'ye offer?'

" 'A one-legged surgeon,' said Little, 'and better with one than any you've got with two.'

" 'A sawbones? What name?'

" 'Dogbody.'

" 'Dogbody!' came the reply. 'Ye don't mean F. Dogbody, late of the *Duff?*'

" 'Aye, the same,' said Little.

" 'You mean ye've got him there, on board?'

" 'Aye,' said Little, 'all but his larboard leg.'

" 'By God, sir,' said the British captain, 'for Dogbody I'll give ye two Yankee lieutenants, a boatswain, a gunner and a gunner's mate, three quartermasters, and a half-dozen reefers for a makeweight. Will ye trade?'

" 'Send 'em across. He's yours,' said Little, and within the quarter-hour the boatload of Yankee prisoners came on board, the *Lion's* captain with them. I knew him well. We'd served together three years earlier in the *Lowestoffe*, frigate, under Captain William Locker. His name was Irons, and he had been a lieutenant in the *Lowestoffe*.

" 'Dogbody,' said he, clasping my hand warmly, 'I hate to buy ye home at so cheap a rate, but these'—with a nod toward his prisoners—'are all I have on hand at the moment. I sent threescore off, a fortnight since, in one of my prizes. Well, sir,' he added, turning to Little, 'for once I've got the best of a Yankee in a trade, but a bargain's a bargain, as your countrymen say.'

"He had a provoking way with him, did Irons. He was tough as an old lanyard knot, and, fine seaman that he was, I regret to say that he had no delicacy of feeling. Indeed, he had a deep respect for the seagoing American, but he took pleasure in showing the contrary.

"Little nodded, with a grim smile. 'I'm content,' said he. He then clasped my hand. 'Good-bye, Dogbody, and God bless you!'

"'Little,' said I, 'I would not have believed that a prisoner of war could ever leave the hands of his captors with any degree of reluctance, but so it is in my case. I respect you as a man, sir, and, if you will permit me to say so, esteem you as a friend.'

"'Then why leave him, Dogbody?' said Irons. 'Shall we take his little ship with us?'

"Little's eyes blazed. 'By God, sir! Will ye fight?' he asked.

"Irons, who was a short thickset man, bristled up like a bulldog. 'Have ye ever met an Englishman that wouldn't?' said he.

"'Then get ye gone to your vessel,' said Little, 'for ye've not long to command her.'

"Captain Gorme, who had come out of his cabin meanwhile, stood by, pressing his hands together with an expression of perfect anguish on his face, but Little paid no heed to him. The *Jupiter* buzzed like a nest of hornets before we were down the side. 'Irons,' said I, as we were being rowed across to the *Lion*, 'you've a wild-cat by the tail this time.' 'Never ye mind, Dogbody,' said he. 'I'll have him by the throat, directly.' He was silent for a moment, then he added: 'I must make him strike within the half hour, for I'm damned short of ball.'

"And, b'gad, gentlemen, we did! 'Twas a miracle, no less, for we deserved to have been taken. Irons had told the plain truth: he'd powder a plenty, but only sufficient ball for six charges for each of his guns. But the man was a veritable firebrand and would have used his own head for ammunition had it been necessary. We were overmatched, both as to men and guns, but the *Lion* had a picked crew and was a worthy foe for a ship twice her size. I've never seen a vessel better handled; every shot from our guns went home. The *Jupiter's* mainmast went over the side in the first five minutes of the action, and the mizzen followed shortly; and whilst the *Lion* received her share of punishment, she'd lost nothing in her sails. Little performed prodigies with his disabled ship. He was tearing to board, but we kept clear. Damme, I was more than glad, for I could see Powana towering above the *Jupiter's* bulwark, and I knew he'd as soon cut off my other leg as look at me. What cost them the victory was, past question, the cowardice of Gorme. He was for running away, and gave orders counter to those of Little, which confused the Yankee seamen. But having shot and to spare, they poured them into us at an appalling rate. More than half our company was either dead or wounded.

"I'd removed my wooden peg directly upon boarding the *Lion,* for the stump of the limb was still tender. I could not bear the heavy peg for long at a time, and so would make shift, for an hour or two, with a crutch. Fortunate it was that I did so on this occasion, for it was the indirect means of victory.

"The *Lion's* gunners had fired their last broadside, and a murderous one it was, but we'd not a ball left. One shot had all but shattered their foremast, and Irons was dancing round our quarter-deck shouting, 'Fall, blast ye! Fall!' At this moment the gunner came aft; he was dripping with sweat and breathing heavily. 'Sir,' said he to Irons, 'we've fired our last shot.' 'What's that to me?' Irons bellowed at him. 'Get back to your guns! Use marlinspikes! Get back to your guns, damn your blood! Use deadeyes, chain plates! Get back to your guns, I say!"

"And, b'gad, gentlemen, he did! All the rusty raffle in the ship went into the guns and on to the *Jupiter,* and with it my new peg which might well be classed as hardware. One of the gunners, seeing it resting by the bulwark, seized upon it and rammed it down the muzzle of his piece amongst iron spoons, bolts, nuts, and fragments of brick prized up from the galley floor. I was told afterward, upon unimpeachable authority, for I was, of course, then at my own bloody work below, that it was my leg that cost the Yankees the day. It caromed off the *Jupiter's* tottering foremast and then struck my friend Little a glancing blow on the head, which, thank God, only knocked him unconscious. The other oddments of the charge worked great havoc as well, amongst the ship's company, and Gorme, who was then forced to take command, immediately struck his colours."

Doctor Dogbody broke off, refreshed himself at his glass, and touched his lips with a richly coloured silk bandana.

"And what then, sir?" Will Tunn inquired, when it seemed apparent that the surgeon had no intention of proceeding.

"What then, Will Tunn? Why, nothing then. What more could there be save that, when we had made temporary repairs on the two ships, we carried our prize to the West Indies? It was a sad blow for Little, but he took it like the man he was, and whilst he must have despised Gorme with all the strength of his being, no word of censure crossed his lips. I was not surprised, later, when Gorme jumped his parole. Little refused to give his. Despite my protestations, he insisted on being put aboard the *Regulus*, a dismantled seventy-four, moored in the harbour of Saint Kitts, and used to confine prisoners-of-war. 'Never fear, Dogbody,' said he, 'I shall not remain long aboard of her, and I refuse that you should be compromised by my escape.' Two days later, when I went aboard the *Regulus* to visit him and to bring him some delicacies from shore, he was gone, and Powana with him. I have never heard of either of them from that day to this."

"It is my pleasure, sir," said Runyon, "to tell you that he is still living, and an honoured citizen of the town of Marshfield. Powana, as well, survives."

"I am profoundly glad to hear it, sir," the surgeon replied.

"You have said, Doctor Dogbody," Ostiff put in, "that the strange wood of which your peg was made was impervious to the teredo worm. How could you be certain of that?"

"It was a piece of good fortune for me, sir, that the peg was not lost when fired into the *Jupiter*. After wounding Little, it struck the bulwark, and the smaller end penetrated four inches into the oak. Captain Irons recovered it for me when he went on board to receive the ship. Some months later, whilst we were lying at Port Royal, in Jamaica, I lost the leg overboard, having unstrapped it, as my custom then was of an evening, to rest my stump. I offered a hogshead of the finest rum the island produced to the man who could fetch it up. During the next fortnight, scores of negroes attempted to secure it, and one poor fellow was taken by the sharks. I immediately withdrew the reward and ordered that no further search should be made. Imagine my surprise, six months later, upon returning from Barbadoes, to find that one persevering fellow had dived it up! He was a veritable sea otter, else he could never have reached bottom at such a depth. Needless to say, I rewarded him handsomely. The peg was as good as upon the day I'd lost it; not the mark of a worm appeared upon it. It was like meeting an old friend to strap it on once more, and my stump being perfectly hardened by that time, I never again exposed myself to the risk of losing it. . . . Bless me, Tunn! What's this?"

A great commotion was heard in the kitchen, and a few seconds later a huge black rat came running into the taproom, followed by Hodge, the dwarflike waiter, Bilges, the kitchen boy, and several others, all in a mad chase after the rodent. Doctor Dogbody, who had already donned his hat and coat in preparation for going home, skipped across the taproom with the agility of a boy, and, with a dexterous side blow with his wooden leg, caught the rat fairly in the middle and sent it hurtling through the air against the tavern wall, where it fell lifeless. Then, with a slight bow, "Gentlemen," he said, "I bid you good evening," and a moment later the door closed behind him.

THE RELUCTANT HERO

By William McFee

December, 1951 was ending in Europe with a series of phenomenal gales. Sunday, the thirtieth, winds of hurricane force were reported, and the Irish airport at Shannon was closed. "Seas Lash Europe," the New York headlines ran, in moderate type. Sixty-three were dead and seventeen persons were missing in Great Britain and Ireland. *Queen Mary*, the great Cunarder, was seventy-two hours late, after buffeting what were described as sixty-foot waves. Who measured them we are not informed. We will come across that figure, sixty, more than once in this story.

Captain Harry Grattidge, commander of *Queen Mary*, was content to say that it had been "terrific," while an official called the scenes in the dining saloons as "a nightmare." A German freighter, *Irene Ollendorf*, went down off Borkum in the North Sea. A Dutch and a Norwegian tanker were wrecked in the Bay of Biscay. Another Norwegian tanker lost her master and her third mate when her bridge was swept away in a huge wave. A six-thousand-ton British tanker, *Mactra*, was disabled off the Cornish coast, and was being towed in by "the most powerful tug in the world," *Turmoil*.

On the last day of the year *The New York Times* carried the headline, "*European Storm Toll Grows. Captain*

182

Alone on Listing Ship. New Jersey Man Is Trying to Save Battered Craft off Irish Coast." The paper went on to describe the scene:

> "A lone figure was reported last night to be clinging to the bridge of the battered *Flying Enterprise* as the U.S. cargo ship was tossed about in the stormy waters of the North Atlantic some 300 miles S.W. of Ireland. He was Kurt Henrik Carlsen, 37-year-old skipper of the 6,711 ton vessel, a veteran shipmaster. He lives with his wife and two children in Woodbridge, New Jersey."

Biographical data of the lonely figure clinging to his ship is no more than adequate. Born at Hilleroed, Denmark, in 1914, Kurt Henrik Carlsen went to sea at fourteen in Danish vessels, and we may assume, from his recent record, that he was a good example of the industrious apprentice and lost no opportunity to improve his education and his professional skills. We know he is a ready radio operator, which many shipmasters are not, and the little-publicized achievement on board a sister ship of the *Enterprise* in 1948, when he was thirty-four, marks him as a fellow of unusual character and manual dexterity. One of his engineers, in a quarrel with a crewman, was stabbed in a dozen places, and was bleeding to death. Captain Carlsen carried out "an extremely delicate operation," in the middle of the Indian Ocean, and saved his officer's life. Some seagoing engineers would be willing to maintain that any shipmaster who saves an engineer's life is already marked out for greatness.

Nine years before the storm we are now dealing with in 1951 (1942, that is), Captain Carlsen entered the service of Hans Isbrandtsen, a Danish shipowner operating a round-the-world freight and passenger service, a gentleman of great enterprise and vigorous independence in what he regarded as international free trade. Apart from the surgical exploit in the Indian Ocean in 1948, Captain Carlsen rejoiced in the obscurity he considers proper to the dignity of a shipmaster.

About the time the captain entered Isbrandtsen's service, something occurred which profoundly affected not only him and his owner but the state of Denmark, something so rotten that the author of *Hamlet* had never dreamed of it. This was the Nazi onslaught. Ships of Danish, Dutch, and Norwegian registry which were at sea took refuge in Allied harbors. Hans Isbrandtsen, who had had offices for years on Lower Broadway, eventually established his reconstructed business under American registry. In due course the personnel became American citizens.

It is generally conceded that hurricanes do not usually invade the Narrow Seas around the British Isles, but in December of 1951 there was no other word to describe what was going on when Captain Carlsen took *Flying Enterprise* out of the Elbe on the twenty-first. Part of his cargo consisted of pig iron. Just why an American ship was bringing pig iron to America nobody seems to have inquired. There it was, however, properly stowed. The subsequent inquiry made a great deal of this pig iron, arguing that it might have been improperly stowed, thus causing the frightful list which forced the captain to send everybody away except himself. The cargo, he insisted, was properly stowed. If he had to load the ship again, he would stow it as it was on that occasion. A shipmaster of his quality was undoubtedly able to load his ship correctly for a voyage across "Winter

North Atlantic," which officially implies the worst possible conditions.

Ships were foundering in the North Sea, and the weather recalls Kipling's "Ballad of the Bolivar:"

> "We put out from Sunderland, loaded down with rails,
>   We put back to Sunderland 'cause our cargo shifted,
>   We put out from Sunderland, met the winter gales,
>   Seven days and seven nights to the Start we drifted."

For Sunderland and rails read Hamburg and pig iron, and you have the situation Captain Carlsen coped with from December twenty-second to thirtieth. His cargo did not shift, however, until he had worked his ship some four hundred miles west of Brest and a hundred miles southwest of Ireland. It was when he was facing the full onslaught of the Western Ocean that his steering gear carried away. Out of control, *Flying Enterprise* swung broadside to titanic seas which threw her on her beam ends, and she began to open up.

She began to split. We have Captain Carlsen's word for it that she developed two vertical three-foot fractures and a horizontal crack across the front of number three hatch, which is abaft the engine-room structure and bridge deck. One of the crew, an engine-room wiper, Louis Rodock, who wears glasses and has been at sea for twenty-five years, told of "a roaring explosion," and a sixty-foot fissure

Here we may revert to what we can call the psychological by-products of the adventure, its effect on the minds of men. The people of Europe and America were suffering from the frustration of the Korean business. They were unhappy because international tensions, the shadow of atomic war, and the apparent impossibility of any understanding of the Asiatic enigma which is the Kremlin, were producing a mental fatigue which made them search for something relatively human and warm, some evidence that the old heroic virtues still existed somewhere in the world. They were ready for miracles, for great deeds which would uplift their hearts, show them man making a clean fight against odds, and winning gloriously. They were ready to magnify everything connected with such an episode. They wanted something bigger than themselves.

It is shyly suggested here that this feeling, so to speak, was "in the air" and inspired everyone, from engine wiper to journalist, to speak or write in superlatives. All, that is, except the star actor in the play, the actor cast in the rôle of hero. And so we have waves sixty feet high; we have nightmares in *Queen Mary's* dining saloons; we have the wiper with his "roaring explosion" and his sixty-foot fissures in the ship's hull; we have the ship lying over at sixty degrees. And we hear presently that "the most powerful tug in the world" would be on hand to render succor when she had rescued S.S. *Mactra*. We were in a wonderful world. Did not Captain Carlsen report that one of his passengers, Mr. Nikola Bundjakowsky, had expired?

The tired public, nauseated with denunciations, countercharges, international double-talk, and the ringing emptiness of political oratory, turned with pleasure and excitement to watch one man against the sea. Ships gathered around the stricken vessel to save life. Captain Carlsen, making his decisions promptly, ordered his crew of forty and his ten passengers to leave at once. S.S. *Southland* took off fifteen, and on Sunday, December thirtieth, the U.S. troop carrier *General A. W. Greeley* reported that all on board had been transferred except Captain Carlsen, who not only refused to abandon his ship, but expressed confidence that she could be towed to safety.

When it was learned that he lived in a small place, Woodbridge in New Jersey, with his Danish-born wife and two little girls, Sonja and Karen, the public was charmed and took him to its bosom. The idea of that lonely figure clinging to his ship in such a position that the bulkhead became a deck, put everything else out of mind for a few days. An American navy ship, the *Weeks*, was standing by, and in addition to a fine portrait of the captain himself, a handsome man if there ever was one, we had in the papers pictures of Captain Parker of the *General Greeley* and Captain Thompson of the *Weeks*. Soon these three were holding three-way conversations over the radio. Carlsen had a small emergency apparatus and was using it to tell us how things were going with him and how he proposed to have the tow made. He was still in command. This was on January fourth.

On December twenty-seventh, he said, there was a wind of Force 12 on the Beaufort Scale, which is hurricane weather, sixty-five miles an hour. On the twenty-eighth he was in another cyclonic storm, in which one wave knocked the ship off her course, and she split across number three hatch. Number three hatch, remember, is abaft the engine room. That hold was full of water. Which is what you get when a welded ship meets with Force 12 in a disabled condition. One of the features of a welded hull is that when a crack starts it cannot stop. Rivets hold on, each of them giving a little, but holding on. With a welded joint there is no give. Once a weld breaks, the ship is in danger of opening up like a wet paper bag.

Some of his personnel, two of the engineers and one or two seamen, wanted to stay with the captain, but he wouldn't have it. This was not captiousness or vainglory, the noble captain going down with his ship and all the rest of it. It was plain common sense. There was almost no food and no sanitation. They would have been in each other's road on that steeply sloping deck. He had not foreseen getting food and flasks of hot coffee by line from the other ships, and it might have been wisdom to have kept his mate with him. That is hindsight. When the towline first came aboard, he was unable to hold it single-handed and it fell away. As for going down with his ship, he proposed to save her. He nearly did, too. Old Man Western Ocean beat him, but he nearly did.

On January fourth, hopes were high. "The most powerful tug in the world," *Turmoil,* 1136 tons, 4,000 horsepower, came surging upon the scene. Captain Carlsen had an anxiety. Would the tremendous pull of such a tug make his ship turn turtle? Great care would be needed. She was precarious. Her reserve buoyancy had been diminishing daily. The wind had risen again; another storm was coming. This was the sixth day of Carlsen's solitary vigil. The public was almost holding its breath. The papers were now loaded with "fillers," odds and ends of news about the Carlsens, about salvage and insurance. Prayers were being offered for the captain's safety and success. Pictures of Mrs. Carlsen in her Woodbridge home with Sonja and Karen appeared, and the captain's parents, Mr. and Mrs. Martin Carlsen in their cottage in Bagovaerd, Denmark, waiting for news of their son. Salvage experts, suddenly and unexpectedly popular, had to dispel some romantic nonsense newspapermen and the public had picked up from fiction read in youth. It was true, of course, that so long as the captain remained on board, *Flying Enterprise* was not technically a derelict. She could not be salvaged by any passing ship, supposing a passing ship had no business of her own, no schedule to keep, no cargo rating demurrage, no passengers who wanted to reach their destination. The owners were employing *Turmoil,* and a French tug, *Abeille,* was also standing by now. The position was very much as when a car has broken down and the owner has telephoned for a tow. The old romantic conditions of the sea existed now only in the minds of landsmen and fiction writers who do not read technical journals.

The pictures of *Flying Enterprise* now being printed in the papers (on January fourth) give us a vivid impression of Carlsen's predicament. The text refers constantly to a list of sixty degrees. Not fifty-nine degrees; sixty. Careful study of the pictures puts the actual list at forty-five, which is enough to bring one's heart into the mouth, surely. But the public appetite had been whetted and it was sixty. We read of sixty-foot waves (an impossibility) sixty-mile-an-hour winds, sixty-foot cracks in the hull, and a sixty-degree list. Events are inevitably shaped to moods, so everything had to go like sixty . . .

Except, we may venture, on the *Flying Enterprise,* where "the New Jersey man," moving slowly, carefully, and painfully, half on the deck, half on the bulkhead of his stricken vessel, or wedging himself into a corner of the charthouse settee for an hour or so of uneasy slumber, waited through the long days and longer nights for the weather to make a tow possible. The strain, bodily and mental, must have been heavy. After the great decision, and he had seen the last of his passengers and crew safe into the boats, there would be a reaction. He had accepted the burden. He had time, ample time, to reflect on what it meant for himself. He might be outwardly confident, but he must have entertained some doubts of the outcome.

He had thought of the lives of others, he had assumed responsibility for his ship and her owners. As the nights closed around him, and the weather, instead of moderating, worsened, as though sunshine and calm blue seas had left the Atlantic forever, he would think of the anxiety imposed on his wife at home in New Jersey. Mrs. Carlsen, of course, had long been adjusted and disciplined to the long absences which are the lot of sailors' wives everywhere. She had confidence in her husband's judgment. But she was not in the position of the old-time women of Salem and Martha's Vineyard. She could not, like them, cultivate stoicism and leave the future in the hands of God. She was getting the news every day over the radio and in the newspapers. She was sharing in thought his weary vigil on a ship which was on the point of foundering. She was answering the telephone, receiving curious newspapermen and photographers, meeting questions which must have kept her nerves jumping. Captain Carlsen would be a very unimaginative man if he had not sensed what his family was enduring while he clung to his heaving, rolling charge on the grey Atlantic. It would step up his own anxiety a hundredfold. And he would suffer many a twinge, too, when he thought of Sonja and Karen, and what might happen to them if he did not pull it off.

There was another thing. It is impossible to maintain

an imperturbable demeanor when a ship lists more than a few degrees. When she is lying literally on her beam ends, when, instead of rolling buoyantly, she just lies there and never comes up, a feeling of dread and exasperation saps a man's courage when he needs it most. And he is assailed by minor annoyances. He is sodden with sea water, he is bruised and worn out by incessant collisions with metal fittings and the struggle to keep his balance on the sloping surfaces. He cannot wash, he cannot bathe or shave. He cannot perform the most ordinary functions of hygiene in any comfort. As for sleeping, although we have his word for it that he did sleep, it was more likely an unrestful drowse. To quote an ancient English writer, "he slumbered rather than slept."

He becomes an affront to his normal, decent self. He is outwardly a pariah who would be arrested as a vagrant in his home town. Yet all the while he has to steel his mind and heart, to be alert to the weather and the ships standing by.

So far as one may judge, Captain Carlsen remained in full command of himself as well as his ship. There must have been excitement and alarm when he realized the noise he was making in the world. It would be something of which he not only had no experience, but for which he had no guiding lights, no previous warning. He passed some of the time, as we shall see, reading a book, a useful professional volume, *The Seaman and the Law*. But what about the seaman and the public? No one seems to have written a book about that. Shipowners supply instructions to their masters for use in special circumstances. But no shipowner sends out instructions on what to do in case of sudden fame. He would have to rely on himself. He must have felt appallingly inadequate, as he contemplated himself, an unshaven, shabby limpet clinging to a plunging, waterlogged derelict in a wintry sea. But he need have had no fear. He had reserves of character and nerve even for this.

Suddenly, on January fifth, there was a new thrill. Enter, by a violent leap from the most powerful tug in the world, which had gotten alongside, Mr. Kenneth R. Dancy, age twenty-seven, mate of *Turmoil*, who had become mysteriously identified in the public mind as a lover of classical music and an amateur knitter. There is nothing unusual in a seaman knitting his own socks. I have had shipmates, generally Scotchmen, who were very good at it. It fascinated the public, though, to find one of the mariners of England affecting such a ladylike hobby. It was gratifying and augmented the interest. Captain Carlsen would be able to get the towline fast next time, surely. The public could hardly wait. Promoters, advertising men, publishers, radio men, refused to wait. Obviously Captain Carlsen was their meat. Fantastic offers to endorse deodorants, soaps, and other goods poured into the line's offices, offers for radio and television broadcasts and appearances, to lecture to women's clubs, to write articles and books piled up, while the object of their pursuit, the Danish-born shipmaster and his new colleague, who liked classical music, were finally getting a towline made fast to the forecastle bitts. Asked what he thought of the situation, the captain who hadn't had a dry stitch on him for a week, and who was living on cake, sandwiches, and coffee, still refused to leave his ship and gave his chances as seventy-five per cent good. They were moving at three knots towards Falmouth.

By January eighth, they had made two-thirds of the

distance and speed was increased to three and a half
knots. More prayers at Woodbridge, New Jersey. Next
day the towline parted fifty miles from port. To make
matters worse, the shackle, which had held the broken
steel wire, had jammed. Carlsen and Dancy had to release it with a hacksaw, almost plunging overboard as
they clung to the upended forecastle. On January tenth,
the bridge of *Flying Enterprise* was under water. Naval
vessels signalled that night that they must wait for daylight to have another go. *Flying Enterprise* was drifting,
helpless, off Falmouth.

By January eleventh, it was plain that neither prayers
nor tugs could do much for her. The list was now sixty-
five degrees, which meant she was about to go. Carlsen
and Dancy were perched perilously on the practically
horizontal funnel of the ship. The other ships closed in
on her. The two men jumped into the boiling sea and
swam for the *Weeks.* Dancy, ten years younger and
much fresher physically and mentally, gave the captain
some assistance. They were hauled on board in time to
see *Flying Enterprise* plunge to the bottom of the English Channel.

Two people back home were in tears. Hans Isbrandtsen, the owner, tolling a bell in his office for the death of
a fine ship, and Mrs. Carlsen, weeping for joy in Woodbridge because her husband was saved and alive. Lloyds
of London did not weep, although the dénouement was
a financial reverse. On the contrary, they welcomed
Captain Carlsen when he reached London and gave him
a citation for his plucky attempt to save his ship.

Now Falmouth, in Cornwall, population fourteen
thousand, a parliamentary borough and a nice little fishing port once known as Pennycomequick, with a yacht

club, a Saturday market and a tourist trade in summer, suddenly became the cynosure of the western world. Trains, cars, and planes brought in swarms of newspapermen, photographers, officials and the aforementioned promoters, who proposed to take over Captain Carlsen in the modern commercial manner. For sums aggregating over a hundred thousand dollars he was to lend his name and fame and his reputation for sanity to various undertakings which had nothing to do with *Flying Enterprise,* to lay his personal probity on the altar of Mammon.

In the midst of this uproar, having been hastily furnished with a hot bath, a room for rest, and some fresh clothing, Captain Carlsen maintained his accustomed imperturbable dignity and good humor. He declined the commercial propositions and, although he would probably have preferred to concentrate on his professional problems, he consented to face the ranks of interviewers and tell them, to the best of his ability, what they wanted to know.

Space is lacking to report all they wanted to know. Captain Carlsen confesses that he "was scared of the press business" even before he jumped from his ship into a raging sea of publicity. One of the first legends he promptly disposed of was that Mrs. Carlsen had sent a message begging him to leave the ship. He knew nothing of any such message. He thought it extremely unlikely that Mrs. Carlsen would have done anything so out of character. Then, would he now quit going to sea to go lecturing and broadcasting? "No," he said, "I have no intention of changing my profession." Questions veered to what he did while alone on the ship. What did he live on? Mostly, he said, he lived on cake. Cake? Yes, pound cake. This was almost as sensational as Mr. Dancy's knitting and classical music. What else? they wanted to know. Well, he read a book. What book? He said he was reading *The Seaman and the Law*. He handled their occasionally inappropriate interrogations with such cool skill that he might have been studying a treatise on the psychology of newspapermen and women.

No doubt his reply to the questions of what he had been reading was a dead end. Nobody had ever heard of the book. An inspired questioner, who sounds feminine, but we have no information about that, shot out the query: "Captain, are you a religious man?" Some men, driven beyond endurance, might have said it was none of their business. Not Carlsen. He had an answer to that one, too. "I am not exactly a heathen," he said pleasantly. It was the perfect answer. It covered everything.

But to the insistent curiosity of those who, knowing of those rich, juicy offers of pecuniary reward, he responded with an unmistakable negative. "The thought of commercial or financial advantage has never entered my mind at all." That was that. Period.

Looking back nostalgically at some of the sea adventures in recent years, the barnstorming "heroes" of the burning *Morro Castle* and the rescuers of a shipwrecked crew gallantly smoking "Luckies" while pulling oars in a gale of wind, this behavior of Carlsen must have appeared very peculiar. The man seemed clad in an impenetrable armor of honesty and sober common sense. Cynics might doubt its permanence. They might wonder whether it would not melt when the roar of New York crowds hailed the returning hero to the land of his adoption. Very few celebrities were able to keep their heads when they moved up the canyon of Broadway under descending clouds of ticker tape.

Even when he realized that the public, the many-headed monster, was not to be denied its human sacrifice, Captain Carlsen introduced an original, revolutionary notion into the traditional ceremony. He would, he said, *walk* up Broadway to City Hall. He had often walked up Broadway and knew how to do it. To sit on the rear end of an open car, to grin and wave vacuously while thousands cheered, was repugnant to him. He knew his own value all right, but it was not that kind of value.

But it was not to be. He who had faced the peril of the storm unflinching could not alter the great tradition. He could not induce Mr. Grover Whalen, the celebrated greeter of celebrities, to walk up Broadway. This was perhaps the most serious test of all. He had brushed off the offers of commercial promoters. He had yet to run the gantlet of the luncheons, the tributes, the plaques, and the anonymous gatecrashers with their expensive presents.

It is a pleasure to report that he survived them all. Not even the unexpected appearance of an extravagantly costly wrist watch from a total stranger could catch the captain unaware. Grover Whalen was even on the point of making the presentation when, in a whisper, the captain explained that he could not accept material rewards for doing his duty. So the watch returned to its obscure and generous donor. It was a matter of principle.

Citations, plaques, scrolls, and so on, symbols of public appreciation, the reluctant hero took in his stride. He even posed kissing his wife, although we may be confident that they both regarded such an antic as kissing before a camera as exquisite torture, an invasion of domestic privacy. It was something to be endured, put behind them, before they could resume their rôles as private citizens. Some sure instinct told the captain that the quickest way out of the intolerable limelight was to accede to anything compatible with honor and probity. But he never deviated from what he deemed honorable and honest by a fraction of an inch. He had done his duty, and if it was now his duty to answer thousands of letters pouring in from admirers all over the world, he would read them and, so far as he could, he would acknowledge them. He may have had a suspicion that the writers would soon be activated by other emotions and be taken up with some fresh sensation. By January nineteenth, he had vanished temporarily from the news columns. The Right Honorable Winston Churchill, Britain's Prime Minister, was leaving the country. This was news. Then, on January twenty-third, a plane crashed into Elizabeth, New Jersey, killing an ex-secretary of war, and deflected attention from Woodbridge, where Captain Carlsen was coping heroically with "ten thousand letters" and reading a highly emotional account of how he came home from sea. "The two had been apart for a long time," chanted one reporter, a person of exquisite sensibility, but not prone to read his, or her, own paper on the marine page. According to schedule Captain Carlsen had sailed from New York in November, forty-six days before. To a man accustomed to the sea from the age of fourteen, as the captain was, this would appear overwrought.

He had said: "I don't want my attempt cheapened. It is a matter of principle." There he had them. It was a matter of principle. We used to have a phrase in the

British Merchant Navy. We would say of a dependable shipmate that he had principle. "Good principle," a chief would say of a good junior. It was an accolade much prized. So Captain Carlsen had his principle. But someone, a master of diplomacy in the Produce Exchange, when they had Captain Carlsen to luncheon to present him with a scroll, produced two one-thousand dollar bonds, one each for Sonja and Karen. Would the captain accept *them*? This was the Achilles heel of the hero. He couldn't refuse those two kids. His flawless conception of principle detected no sinister commercialism in this gracious and delicate tribute to a father's courage. And when the Propeller Club gave him a ship's clock with an inscription, with a citation from the Maritime Commission; when the Seamen's Church Mission came along with a sextant and the inevitable scroll (you will remember he described himself as "not exactly a heathen"), he accepted them in the spirit in which they were offered. They were in the tradition he understood.

This is a success story because Captain Carlsen, having kept his honor and principle untarnished, finally achieved his ambition, which was to get another ship and go to sea. Far away on the oceans, accompanied, we like to think, by his sextant and his ship's clock, by the scrolls and citations and the pictures of his wife and Sonja and Karen, he is free once again to live the life he prefers. Free also to contemplate, from a safe distance, that fantastic world of promoters, photographers, sob sisters and flashlight bulbs, from which he had escaped. Is not this success? To have principle, which is a start, and to follow it? To be shown the kingdoms of the bright lights of flashy financial notoriety, and to reject them with firmness? How can we grudge him his peace of mind, his professional ethics, his personal record, his unbroken home life? He has given us something intangible in return, something of great value, the inspiration of a noble career.

SOME "Q" SHIPS

By "Bartimeus"

World War One seems a long way off now, hull down on the horizon, and the mood of that time is not always easy to recapture. It was a very different kind of war from those we have now, and in some ways they were a different kind of men. But it was a war: let us not fool ourselves. Dying was as messy as it is today, and courage was matched against cunning, then as now.

The present reader may inquire, who is "Bartimeus?" The pen name conceals Paymaster Captain Lewis Ritchie, K.C.V.O. of the Royal Navy, former Press Secretary to King George VI. Entering the training ship Britannia *in 1901, he started a career as a fighting officer. This was terminated by a bout of Malta Fever, which affected his eyesight. So he transferred to the Paymaster's Department.*

When the war came in 1914 there arose the problem of how to bring home to the civilians of Britain the life of a service which had established a firm tradition of avoiding publicity. The Royal Navy took a grim pride in the title "The Silent Service." True, Kipling had written "A Fleet In Being" and a number of comic short stories about naval ratings. But that was peacetime maneuver stuff; now it was war. "Der Tag," so the Germans called it, The Day, had come when the Kaiser's new and untried fleet would attempt to destroy Britain's "Sure Shield." The public wanted to know about "the lively little lads in Navy Blue" as the song called them.

Reprinted by permission of the author from *An Awfully Big Adventure.* Courtesy of A. P. Watt & Son.

Paymaster Ritchie was the man who turned this trick. He called himself "Bartimeus" after the son of Timaeus, who by faith received his sight when Christ was in Jericho.

Writing an introduction to one of the "Bartimeus" books, I made the point that a paymaster is in a much better position to know the personnel of a battleship or a cruiser than any other officer. He comes in direct contact with everybody on board. He knows their financial and matrimonial problems. He can watch them going about their business in a battle. What had been a handicap became an asset. "Bartimeus" became famous for his stories of Britain's senior service. He was the liasion officer between the men in the Navy and the man in the street.

THE METHODS OF the German submarine in its war against unarmed shipping gradually settled down to a routine which varied but little in the early phases of the conflict. It was the custom to attempt to torpedo at sight, on the principle of the least said the soonest mended. If the torpedo missed, as was not infrequently the case, the submarine broke surface a mile or so away from the ship and fired a shot across her bows. The merchantman had then two alternatives: to take to her heels and try to escape, or to heave to and abandon ship. In the latter case the submarine closed the derelict to within a few hundred yards and summoned the boats alongside. At the muzzle of a revolver the Captain was ordered into the submarine with his papers, and the crew of his boat directed to row a party of German sailors, bearing bombs, back to the ship. In due course the bombs exploded and the ship disappeared. It was an economical method, since bombs cost less than torpedoes.

For a while the Navy noted these methods in silence.

Then it drew a deep breath and made its plans accordingly. It argued that a man-of-war could be disguised as a tramp steamer and carry concealed armament. Such a vessel, by plying on the trade routes, must inevitably meet a submarine in time, and in her character of peaceful merchantman be ordered to abandon ship. The ship might be abandoned to all outward appearances, but still retain sufficient men concealed on board to fight the hidden guns when the moment came for her to cast disguise to the winds and hoist the White Ensign. Certain risks had to be taken for granted, of course; the almost inevitable torpedo sooner or later, the probability of a little indiscriminate shelling while the submarine approached, the possibility of being ultimately sunk before assistance could arrive. Yet the odds were on the submarine being sunk first, and the rest was on the knees of the gods.

An old collier of some 2,000 tons was selected from among the shipping at the disposal of the Admiralty and taken to a Dockyard port, where she unostentatiously underwent certain structural alterations. These included disappearing mountings for guns concealed beneath hatchway covers, and masked by deck-houses which collapsed like cards at a jerk of a lever. From the host of volunteers, among whom were retired admirals, captains, commanders, and lieutenants of the Royal Navy, a young lieutenant-commander was selected and appointed in command. His officers were volunteers from the Royal Naval Reserve, ex-merchant seamen, familiar enough with the rôle they were required to play, and in some cases with little mental scores of their own which required adjustment when the time came. The crew was mostly from the West Country, men of Devon with one or two traditions to uphold in the matter of brave adventure. It also included Welshmen and Irish with a pretty taste for a fight, and a few Scots, of the dour type, hard to frighten. They were picked from the Royal Navy, Fleet and Royal Reserves—merchant seamen and fishermen the last, many of whom had formed a nodding acquaintance with Death long before they received this invitation to a closer intimacy. Their ages ranged between 17 and 52.

They sailed from Queenstown under the Red Ensign; but before they left some of the crew trudged, as pilgrims to a shrine, and stood awhile among the mounds in that pathetic God's acre where the women and children of the *Lusitania* rest. They were then but freshly turned, those mounds, in their eloquent diversity of lengths, and men had not begun to forget. . . .

For five weary months they endured the winter gales of the Atlantic, wallowing to and fro along the trade routes, outwardly a scallywag tramp, but behind her untidy bulwarks observing, with certain necessary modifications, the discipline and customs of his Majesty's Navy. With paint pot and sailcloth they improved the ship's disguise from time to time, and whiled away the heartbreaking monotony of the days by inventing fresh devices to conceal their character.

The ship's steward's assistant, when not engaged upon his office as "dusty boy," was ordered to don female attire over his uniform and recline in a prominent position on the poop in a deck chair. This allurement was calculated to prove an irresistible bait. The navigator, whose action station was the abandonment of the ship in the rôle of distracted master, fashioned the effigy of a stuffed parrot and fastened it inside a cage which he proposed to take away with him in the boat, thus heightening the pathos of the scene.

From time to time watchful patrols swooped down upon them, exchanged a few curt signals in the commercial code, and bade them pass on their imaginary occasions. Once a cruiser, less easily satisfied than the remainder, bade the rusty-sided collier heave to, and sent an officer to board her; he climbed inboard at the head of armed men to find himself confronted, in the person of the "master," with a term-mate of *Britannia* days and a grin he is not likely to forget. Then, early one spring morning, when the daylight was stealing out of grey skies across the Atlantic waste, the track of a torpedo bubbled across the bows and passed ahead of the ship. The moment for which they had waited five weary months had come.

In accordance with her rôle of tramp steamer in the early days of the war, the ship held steadily on her way. Inboard, however, the alarm rang along the mess-decks and saloons, and men crawled into hen-coops and deck houses to man the hidden guns. A few minutes later the submarine broke surface half a mile astern of the ship, and fired a shot across her bows. Whereupon the supposed collier stopped her engines, and lay rolling in the trough of the seas with steam pouring from her exhausts, while the crew, who had rehearsed this moment to a perfection never yet realized on the boards of legitimate drama, rushed to and fro with every semblance of panic. The captain danced from one end of the bridge to the other, waving his arms and shouting; boats were turned out and in again amid a deliberate confusion that brought blushes to the cheeks of the ex-merchant seamen called upon to play the part.

In the meantime the submarine had approached at full speed to within about seven hundred yards, and, evidently not satisfied with the speed at which the ship was being abandoned, fired another shot, which pitched fifty yards short of the engine room. There was apparently nothing further to be gained by prolonging the performance for this impatient audience, and the lieutenant-commander on the bridge, cap in hand, and breathless with his pantomimic exertions, blew a shrill blast on his whistle. Simultaneously the White Ensign fluttered to the masthead, deck-houses and screens clattered down, and three minutes later the submarine sank under a rain of shells and Maxim bullets. As she disappeared beneath the surface the avenger reached the spot, and dropped a depth charge over her. A moment after the explosion the submarine appeared in a perpendicular position alongside the ship, denting the bilging-keel as she rolled drunkenly among the waves. The after gun put five more rounds into the shattered hull at point-blank range, and, as she sank for the last time, two more depth-charges were dropped to speed her passing.

The lieutenant-commander in command had personally been superintending the administering of the *coup de grâce* from the stern, and, as he turned to make his way forward to the bridge, for a few brief moments the bonds of naval discipline relaxed. His men surged round him in a wildly cheering throng, struggling to be the first to wring him by the hand. They then mustered in the saloon, standing bareheaded while their Captain read the Prayers of Thanksgiving for Victory, and called for three cheers for his Majesty the King. They cheered as only men can cheer in the first exultant flush of victory. But as the vessel gathered way and resumed her grim quest, each man realized, deep down in his heart, that far sterner ordeals lay ahead.

II

Because man is mortal, not infallible, and Fortune at her brightest a fickle jade, it was inevitable that sooner or later a day must come when a crippled German submarine would submerge beneath a hail of shells, miraculously succeed in patching up her damaged hull, and, under cover of darkness, crawl back to port. Word would then go out from Wilhelmshaven of a British-man-of-war disguised as a lumbering tramp, with such and such a marking on her funnel, with stumpy masts and rusty deck-houses, who carried guns concealed in wheel-house and hen-coops, whose bulwarks collapsed, and whose bridge screens masked quick-firers and desperate men. German submarines would be warned that to approach such a vessel was to enter a death trap, unless every precaution was first taken to ensure she had been abandoned.

Such a day came in due course; misty, windless, with the aftermath of a great storm rolling eastward beneath a sullen swell. A vessel with the outward appearance of a merchantman (the fruits of whose labours for the past six months had doubtless perplexed that section of the Wilhelmshaven bureaucracy concerned with the non-return of U-boats) sighted towards evening the periscope and conning tower of a submarine a mile away on her beam.

The figure on the bridge of the tramp, who carried, among other papers in his charge, his commission as a commander of the Royal Navy, laughed as Drake might have laughed when the sails of a Spanish galleon broke the horizon. A tangle of flags appeared at the periscope of the submarine, and the tramp stopped obediently, blowing off steam in great clouds. Her commander turned over the pages of the International Signal Code, smiling still. "Hoist: 'Cannot understand your signal,'" he said to the signalman, "I want to waste a few minutes," and moved to the engine-room voice-pipe. Obedient to his directions, the screws furtively jogged ahead under cover of the escaping steam, edging the steamer towards the watching enemy. The latter, however, promptly manned her foremost gun, turned, and slowly steamed towards them; she opened fire at a range of half a mile, the shell passing over the funnel of the disguised man-of-war.

In the tense excitement of that moment, when men's nerves and faculties were stretched like banjo-strings, the report of the submarine's gun rang loud through the still air. One of the man-of-war's gunlayers, lying concealed within his collapsible deck-house, heard the report, and, thinking that the ship herself had opened fire without the customary warning gongs, flung down the screens which masked his weapon. Any further attempt at concealment was useless. The fire-gongs rang furiously at every gun position, the White Ensign was triced up to the masthead in the twinkling of an eye, and the action started. After the first few hits the submarine lay motionless, with her bows submerged and her stern in the air for upwards of five minutes, while shells burst all about her. The heavy swell made shooting difficult, but eventually she sank in a great commotion of the water and dense clouds of vapor that hung over the surface for some minutes. Two depth charges were dropped

over her, and if ever men had cause for modest self-con-
gratulation on having ridded the seas of yet another
scourge, it would seem that the officers and crew of the
King's ship might have laid claim to their share. Yet, by
ways unknown and incredible, it was claimed by the
enemy that the submarine contrived to return, with
shot-holes plugged, to tell the tale.

Once the cat was out of the bag, it was obvious that
in the future the enemy would not rise to the surface
until his torpedo had found its mark, and it became part
of this grim game of bluff for the victim to ensure that
she was hit. Then, when the "panic party" had abandoned the ship, the remainder must wait concealed and
unresponsive beside their hidden guns, while the submarine rose to the surface and either closed within range
or shelled them with sufficient thoroughness to convince
him—who judged endurance and self-control by no
mean standards—that the limit of human courage had
been reached; that there could be no one concealed on
board, and that he might with safety approach to loot
and burn. Now this, as Mr. Kipling would put it, "was
a damned tough bullet to chew." They were no demi-
gods, nor yet fanatics, these three-score or so sailormen.
They were just ordinary human beings, with the aver-
age man's partiality for life and a whole skin, and the
love of wife and bairn or sweetheart plucking at the
heart-strings of most of them. But they shared what is
not given to all men in this world of human frailty—a
whole-souled confidence in a fellow-man, which would
have carried them at his lightest nod through the gates
of hell.

Under his command, then, they sailed with a cargo
of timber in each hold, and in due course, about 9.45 one

morning, a torpedo was seen approaching the starboard beam. Observing his rôle as master of a careless tramp, with poor look-outs, the commander held on his course. At the last moment, however, the helm was imperceptibly altered to ensure the ship being struck abaft the engine-room, where the torpedo might do least damage. Those whom fate has afforded the opportunity of studying the trail of an approaching torpedo will, if they recall their sensations, appreciate to some extent the iron nerve requisite to such a manœuvre. The torpedo burst abreast No. 3 hold, hurling a wall of water and wreckage to the height of the mast, and blowing a hole in the ship's side 40 feet wide. Half-stunned and deafened by the concussion, the commander raised himself on his hands and knees, where he had been flung, and shouted to the navigator: "They've got us this time!" The navigator, who was inside the chart house, thrust his head out for a moment, moistening a lead pencil with his lips. "I reckon I've got time to finish working out this sight, sir," he replied with a grin, and withdrew his head.

The alarm gongs had already sent the guns' crews to their invisible guns, and immediately after the explosion "Panic stations" was ordered, followed in due course by "Abandon ship." The navigator, having finished his "sight," and now acting as "master," abandoned ship with the "panic party." No sooner had the boats been lowered and shoved off from the ship's side, however, than the chief engineer rang up from below and reported that the after bulkhead had gone and that the engine room was filling fast. Peering, on all-fours, through a slit in the bridge screen, waiting for the inevitable periscope to appear, the commander bade him hold on as long as he could and keep enough steam to work the pumps; when the water had extinguished the fires, and then only, the engines were abandoned and the staff remained concealed. This they did, crawling eventually on to the cylinders to escape from the rising flood.

Shortly after the torpedo struck the ship the periscope of a submarine broke the surface a couple of hundred yards distant, evidently watching proceedings with a deliberate, cautious scrutiny. Moving slowly through the water, like the fin of a waiting shark, the sinister object came gradually down the ship's side, within five yards of the breathless boats, and not ten yards from where the commander lay beside the voice-pipes that connected him with the assistant-paymaster, R.N.R., who, concealed in the gun control position, was awaiting the order to open fire. From the altitude of the bridge, the submerged whale-back hull was plainly visible to the figure crouched behind the bridge screens, and the temptation to yield to the impulse of the moment, to open fire and end the suspense, shook even his iron nerves. A lucky shot might pierce the lead-grey shadow that moved fifteen feet beneath the surface; but water plays strange tricks with projectiles, deflecting them at unexpected ricochets, at angles no man can foretell; moreover, the submarine was in diving trim. The odds against a broadside overwhelming her before she could plunge into the depths and escape were too great. So the commander waited, with self-control that was almost superhuman, and, prone beside their guns, unseeing and unseen, his men waited too.

The ship had then sunk by the stern until it was awash, and the crew of the gun masked by the wheelhouse were crouched up to their knees in water. A black cat, the ship's mascot, that had been blown off the fore-castle by the explosion of the torpedo, swam aft and in over the stern, whose counter rose normally twenty feet above the surface. Still the periscope continued its un-hurried observation; it travelled past the ship, across the bow, and then slowly moved away, as if content that the task was done. For the space of nearly a minute bitter disappointment and mortification rose in the com-mander's heart. His ship had been torpedoed and was sinking. Their quarry had all but been within their grasp, and was now going to escape unscathed. Then, when hope was flickering to extinction, the submarine rose to the surface three hundred yards on the port bow, and came slowly back towards the ship.

Up to this juncture, although the ship was settling deeper every moment, the commander had purposely refrained from summoning assistance by wireless, lest interruption should come before his grim work was done. Now, however, he saw at one quick glance that the Lord had indeed "placed the enemy upon his lee bow," and the rest was only a matter of a few bloody moments. Accordingly he gave orders for an urgent wireless signal to be sent out forthwith summoning as-sistance, and waited until the submarine was on a line when all his guns would bear. She reached the desired spot at the moment when the German commander was complacently emerging from the conning tower; up went the White Ensign, and the first shot beheaded him; he dropped back into the interior of the submarine, and his wholly unexpected reappearance imparted a shock of surprise to the remainder of the inmates from which they never recovered. The submarine lay motionless as a dead whale, while the avenging broadside shattered the hull, and the grizzled pensioner inside a hen-coop scientifically raked her deck with a Maxim to prevent her gun from being manned. She finally sank with her conning tower open.

From the swirling vortex in which the majority vanished, two prisoners were rescued by the exultant "panic party" in the boats, and brought back to the ship. Once on board, however, the imperious necessities of the moment overwhelmed even the elation of victory. Bulkheads were shored in all compartments still accessible, confidential documents destroyed in anticipation of the worst, and all but the commander and a handful of men took to the boats and awaited succour. It came at noon in the guise of a congratulatory and businesslike destroyer, and was augmented later by a couple of sloops. By 5 P.M. the water had ceased to gain and the ship was in tow, heading for port; there she arrived, and was safely beached after dark the following day.

Thus her crew, emerging triumphant from the ordeal, added at the last a feat of seamanship which saved the ship. It required no great power of imagination to foretell what lay ahead; yet, when the time came for a fresh venture under the command of the man who had brought them victorious through the ordeals that were past, they sailed again with light hearts.

III

The disguise adopted by such of his Majesty's ships as were selected to cope with the U-boat menace varied according to the changing fashions. In the early days of the war the rôle of care-free tramp, steering a steady course, and *minus* look-outs or gun, was sufficient to lure the enemy to close quarters on the surface. But as the methods of warfare adopted by the German Government altered, so the custom of the seas reverted to the arming of merchantmen for defensive purposes.

For purpose of offence against the enemy, with which this story of a King's ship is concerned, a dummy gun sufficed; at all events for preliminaries. It was mounted prominently aft, attended by a conspicuously vigilant gunner. To outward appearances the ship was then an armed British merchant vessel, steering a zigzag course for home at a good speed, conscious that she was in the danger zone, and, by virtue of her unmistakable gun and position, liable to be torpedoed at sight. Torpedoed at sight she was, at eight o'clock of a misty summer morning, in a blinding rain storm and heavy sea. The torpedo was fired at apparently close range, since it jumped out of the water when one hundred yards from the ship; it struck the engine-room near the water-line, flooding the boiler room, engine room, and adjacent hold. The stoker petty officer on duty in the engine room was killed outright by the explosion, and the third engineer, who held a commission as engineer sub-lieutenant in the Naval Reserve, was half-stunned and badly wounded by flying spinters and fragments of coal. Despite the inrush of water, he contrived to reach the hatchway, and arrived on deck, half-flayed, to stagger to his post in the second act of the grim drama.

One of the lifeboats had been blown to smithereens, fragments of it being lodged even in the wires of the aerial between the masts, so great was the force of the explosion. Under the command of the navigator, acting the part of master, the "panic party" abandoned the ship in the remaining three boats as the ship settled deeper in the water. The officers and men whose station was on board were already motionless at their invisible guns; in the majority of cases they were concealed by screens, but the crew of the foremost gun were compelled to lie prone on their faces on the exposed forecastle, unable to stir a muscle until the order came to open fire.

Then, for thirty-five leaden minutes, followed the savage ordeal of waiting for the unknown. For aught these motionless figures knew, the submarine might torpedo them again at any moment, might break surface and shell them at extreme range till they sank, or, an even more nerve-racking possibility, might set off in pursuit of a fresh victim and escape. Withal was the consciousness that a single movement on board, so much as a finger raised above screen or coaming, would betray their true character and bring the game of bluff to a swift and tragic conclusion. The periscope of the submarine had broken surface a quarter of an hour after the torpedo struck, about four hundred yards distant on the port beam. It turned after a while and steered towards the ship, but the captain and signalman, prone at each end of the bridge, with their eyes glued to the observation slits, alone were aware of their quarry's movements. It was in the tense stillness of those movements, a stillness disturbed only by the lapping of the waves round the waterlogged hull, and by the hiss of escaping steam, that from the little group of prostrate figures round the foremost gun rose a man's whistle, executing a gay, if somewhat tremulous, ditty of the sea. For a moment those in the immediate vicinity of the performer listened to the eerie music without comment. Then a motionless officer, moved by a sense of what was seemly at such a time and what was not, rebuked the minstrel. "I dursn't stop, sir," said the boy—he was only seventeen—"cos if I stops whistlin' I gits scared."

As the submarine drew nearer to the ship the commander on the bridge of the disguised man-of-war cast a swift glance round to see that all was well, and saw the old and trusted quartermaster lying face downwards beside the wheel. "For God's sake," he called, "don't show yourself, he's nibbling. . . ." "Aye, aye, sir," said the faithful seaman. And then, so ingrained apparently had become the habit of disguise on board, he furtively dragged a lifebelt over the most prominent portion of his anatomy.

When fifty yards off the ship the periscope vanished, to reappear a few minutes later directly astern. Very deliberately, as a cat plays with a mouse before dealing the last stroke, the periscope travelled on to the starboard quarter, turned, and came back round the stem to the port beam, where the boats were lying. The stage management of the drama then passed into the hands of the navigator in charge of the boats. His task was not lightened by a disposition on the part of the "panic party" to regard the affair in the light of high comedy, despite the cold scrutiny of the periscope. In no measured terms he reminded them that they were presumed by the Teutonic intelligence beneath the waves to be terrified mariners, not a boatload of grinning buffoons; and then, mindful of the shortness of the visibility, he began pulling towards the ship. As he had foreseen, the submarine promptly rose to the surface and followed in pursuit, closing to within a few yards of the masked guns on board.

The prospect of being shot by either party at this juncture of the performance was none too remote. Yet the boat continued pulling as if manned by deaf mutes until the submarine had been lured into the desired position. Then suddenly the eagerly awaited White Ensign shot up to the masthead. Screens clattered down along the length of the ship's side, and a broadside of flame leaped out over their heads. The submarine was suddenly plastered by bursting shell and half hidden by watersprouts, as she slowly listed over to her side, with oil spouting from the rents in her hull. Her crew scrambled out of the conning tower and waved their hands above their heads in token of surrender. Fire instantly ceased on board the British man-of-war, when unexpectedly the crippled enemy, her stern submerged, shot ahead and made off at high speed. Those on her deck were swept into the sea by her last wild rush through the water, and the British guns broke out again. Fire was continued until she blew up and sank.

In spite of the heavy sea, the boats succeeded in rescuing two prisoners from the water before returning to the ship. An American destroyer arrived a few hours later, accompanied by two sloops. With their assistance the ship was brought safely into port.

By command of His Majesty the King, one officer and one man were selected by ballot for the honor of the Victoria Cross from among the ship's company, in recognition of the fact that, where all played so valiant a part, the distinction was earned by the ship rather than by the individual. Yet their task was still unfinished. They sailed again in another ship, knowing full well that they alone could never accomplish it entirely. But the name of that ship, H.M.S. *Dunraven*, should be a household word wherever the English tongue is spoken, because of the ordeal these men endured behind her shattered bulwarks for England's sake.

THE BOAT JOURNEY

By Sir Ernest Shackleton

Sir Ernest Shackelton, who died in 1922, was a merchant marine officer whose passion for adventure led him into polar exploration. Leaving Dulwich College, where he must have been a contemporary of P. G. Wodehouse, he was apprenticed in the old White Star Company's schoolship. Eventually commanding one of the Shire Line steamers, he left the Union Castle Line in 1901 to join Captain Scott's expedition to the Antarctic as navigator.

Shackleton's first expedition in command took him within a hundred miles of the Pole. The second voyage, in the Erebus, was one of the most important, scientifically, in Antarctic history. He and his men ascended Mount Erebus, an immense and active volcano with a crater nine hundred feet deep, and they also reached the South Magnetic Pole. A heroic journey over the mountains at eleven thousand feet took them within two degrees of the Pole.

Shackleton's next voyage, which he described in his book, South! from which the following chapters are taken, was disastrous. His ship, Endurance, was crushed in the ice. With some companions, Shackleton made an incredible voyage of seven hundred and fifty miles in a twenty-two-foot boat to South Georgia. He then returned to Elephant Island and rescued all his men.

His last voyage, in 1921–1922, ended for him in South

Reprinted from *South!* published by the Macmillan Company. By permission of Thompson, Quarrell & Megaw, as agents for Sir Leonard Lucas-Tooth, deceased.

Georgia, where he is buried. He was one of the great adventurers.

THE INCREASING SEA made it necessary for us to drag the boats further up the beach. This was a task for all hands, and after much labour we got the boats into safe positions among the rocks and made fast the painters to big boulders. Then I discussed with Wild and Worsley the chances of reaching South Georgia before the winter locked the seas against us. Some effort had to be made to secure relief. Privation and exposure had left their mark on the party, and the health and mental condition of several men were causing me serious anxiety. Blackborrow's feet, which had been frost-bitten during the boat journey, were in a bad way, and the two doctors feared that an operation would be necessary. They told me that the toes would have to be amputated unless animation could be restored within a short period. Then the food-supply was a vital consideration. I decided that the party must be limited to one hot meal a day.

A boat journey in search of relief was necessary and must not be delayed. That conclusion was forced upon me. The nearest port where assistance could certainly be secured was Port Stanley, in the Falkland Islands, 540 miles away, but we could scarcely hope to beat up against the prevailing north-westerly wind in a frail and weakened boat with a small sail area. South Georgia was over 800 miles away, but lay in the area of the west winds, and I could count upon finding whalers at any of the whaling-stations on the east coast. A boat party might make the voyage and be back with relief within a month, provided that the sea was clear of ice and the boat survive the great seas. It was not difficult to decide that South Georgia must be the objective, and I proceeded to plan ways and means. The hazards of a boat journey across 800 miles of stormy sub-Antarctic Ocean were obvious, but I calculated that at worst the venture would add nothing to the risks of the men left on the island. There would be fewer mouths to feed during the winter and the boat would not require to take more than one month's provisions for six men, for if we did not make South Georgia in that time we were sure to go under. A consideration that had weight with me was that there was no chance at all of any search being made for us on Elephant Island.

The case required to be argued in some detail, since all hands knew that the perils of the proposed journey were extreme. The risk was justified solely by our urgent need of assistance. The ocean south of Cape Horn in the middle of May is known to be the most tempestuous storm-swept area of water in the world. The weather then is unsettled, the skies are dull and overcast, and the gales are almost unceasing. We had to face these conditions in a small and weather-beaten boat, already strained by the work of the months that had passed. Worsley and Wild realized that the attempt must be made, and they both asked to be allowed to accompany me on the voyage. I told Wild at once that he would have to stay behind. I relied upon him to hold the party together while I was away and to make the best of his way to Deception Island with the men in the spring in the event of our failure to bring help. Worsley I would take with me, for I had a very high opinion of his accuracy and quickness as a navigator, and especially in the snapping and working out of positions in difficult circumstances—an opinion that was only enhanced during the actual journey. Four other men would be required, and I decided to call for volunteers, although, as a matter of fact, I pretty well knew which of the people I would select. Crean I proposed to leave on the island as a right-hand man for Wild, but he begged so hard to be allowed to come in the boat that, after consultation with Wild, I promised to take him. I called the men together, explained my plan, and asked for volunteers. Many came forward at once. I finally selected McNeish, McCarthy, and Vincent in addition to Worsley and Crean. The crew seemed a strong one, and as I looked at the men I felt confidence increasing.

The decision made, I walked through the blizzard with Worsley and Wild to examine the *James Caird*. The twenty-foot boat had never looked big; she appeared to have shrunk in some mysterious way when I viewed her in the light of our new undertaking. She was an ordinary ship's whaler, fairly strong, but showing signs of the strains she had endured since the crushing of the *Endurance*. Where she was holed in leaving the pack was, fortunately, about the water-line and easily patched. Standing beside her, we glanced at the fringe of the storm-swept, tumultuous sea that formed our path. Clearly, our voyage would be a big adventure. I called the carpenter and asked him if he could do anything to make the boat more seaworthy. He first inquired if he was to go with me, and seemed quite pleased when I said "Yes." He was over fifty years of age and not altogether fit, but he had a good knowledge of sailing-boats and was very quick. McCarthy said that he could contrive some sort of covering for the *James Caird* if he might use the lids of the cases and the four sledge-runners that we had lashed inside the boat for use in the event of a landing on Graham Land at Wilhelmina Bay. This bay, at one time the goal of our desire, had been left behind in the course of our drift, but we had retained the runners. The carpenter proposed to complete the covering with some of our canvas, and he set about making his plans at once.

Noon had passed and the gale was more severe than ever. We could not proceed with our preparations that day. The tents were suffering in the wind and the sea was rising. We made our way to the snow-slope at the shoreward end of the spit, with the intention of digging a hole in the snow large enough to provide shelter for the party. I had an idea that Wild and his men might camp there during my absence, since it seemed impossible that the tents could hold together for many more days against the attacks of the wind; but an examination of the spot indicated that any hole we could dig probably would be filled quickly by the drift. At dark, about 5 p. m., we all turned in, after a supper consisting of a pannikin of hot milk, one of our precious biscuits, and a cold penguin leg each.

The gale was stronger than ever on the following morning (April 20). No work could be done. Blizzard and snow, snow and blizzard, sudden lulls and fierce returns. During the lulls we could see on the far horizon to the north-east bergs of all shapes and sizes driving along before the gale, and the sinister appearance of the swift-moving masses made us thankful indeed that, instead of battling with the storm amid the ice, we were required only to face the drift from the glaciers and the inland heights. The gusts might throw us off our feet, but at least we fell on solid ground and not on the rocking floes. Two seals came up on the beach that day, one of them within ten yards of my tent. So urgent was our need of food and blubber that I called all hands and organized a line of beaters instead of simply walking up to the seal and hitting it on the nose. We were prepared to fall upon this seal *en masse* if it attempted to escape. The kill was made with a pick-handle, and in a few minutes five days' food and six days' fuel were stowed in a place of safety among the boulders above high-water mark. During this day the cook, who had worked well on the floe and throughout the boat journey, suddenly collapsed. I happened to be at the galley at the moment and saw him fall. I pulled him down the slope to his tent and pushed him into its shelter with orders to his tent-mates to keep him in his sleeping-bag until I allowed him to come out or the doctors said he was fit enough. Then I took out to replace the cook one of the men who had expressed a desire to lie down and die. The task of keeping the galley fire alight was both difficult and strenuous, and it took his thoughts away from the chances of immediate dissolution. In fact, I found him a little later gravely concerned over the drying of a naturally not over-clean pair of socks which were hung up in close proximity to our evening milk. Occupation had brought his thoughts back to the ordinary cares of life.

There was a lull in the bad weather on April 21, and the carpenter started to collect material for the decking of the *James Caird*. He fitted the mast of the *Stancomb Wills* fore and aft inside the *James Caird* as a hogback and thus strengthened the keel with the object of preventing our boat "hogging"—that is, buckling in heavy seas. He had not sufficient wood to provide a deck, but by using the sledge-runners and box-lids he made a frame-work extending from the forecastle aft to a well. It was a patched-up affair, but it provided a base for a canvas covering. We had a bolt of canvas frozen stiff, and this material had to be cut and then thawed out over the blubber-stove, foot by foot, in order that it might be sewn into the form of a cover. When it had been nailed and screwed into position it certainly gave an appearance of safety to the boat, though I had an uneasy feeling that it bore a strong likeness to stage scenery, which may look like a granite wall and is in fact nothing better than canvas and lath. As events proved, the covering served its purpose well. We certainly could not have lived through the voyage without it.

Another fierce gale was blowing on April 22, interfering with our preparations for the voyage. The cooker from No. 5 tent came adrift in a gust, and, although it was chased to the water's edge, it disappeared for good. Blackborrow's feet were giving him much pain, and Mellroy and Macklin thought it would be necessary for them to operate soon. They were under the impression then that they had no chloroform, but they found some subsequently in the medicine-chest after we had left. Some cases of stores left on a rock off the spit on the day of our arrival were retrieved during this day. We were setting aside stores for the boat journey and choosing the essential equipment from the scanty stock at our disposal. Two ten-gallon casks had to be filled with water melted down from ice collected at the foot of the glacier. This was a rather slow business. The blubber-stove was kept going all night, and the watchman emptied the water into casks from the pot in which the ice was melted. A working party started to dig a hole in the snow-slope about forty feet above sea-level with the object of providing a site for a camp. They made fairly good progress at first, but the snow drifted down unceasingly from the inland ice, and in the end the party had to give up the project.

The weather was fine on April 23, and we hurried forward our preparations. It was on this day I decided finally that the crew for the *James Caird* should consist of Worsley, Crean, McNeish, McCarthy, Vincent, and myself. A storm came on about noon, with driving snow and heavy squalls. Occasionally the air would clear for a few minutes, and we could see a line of pack-ice, five miles out, driving across from west to east. This sight increased my anxiety to get away quickly. Winter was advancing, and soon the pack might close completely round the island and stay our departure for days or even for weeks. I did not think that ice would remain around Elephant Island continuously during the winter, since the strong winds and fast currents would keep it in motion. We had noticed ice and bergs going past at the rate of four or five knots. A certain amount of ice was held up about the end of our spit, but the sea was clear where the boat would have to be launched.

Worsley, Wild, and I climbed to the summit of the seaward rocks and examined the ice from a better vantage-point than the beach offered. The belt of pack outside appeared to be sufficiently broken for our purposes, and I decided that, unless the conditions forbade it, we would make a start in the *James Caird* on the following morning. Obviously the pack might close at any time. This decision made, I spent the rest of the day looking over the boat, gear, and stores, and discussing plans with Worsley and Wild.

Our last night on the solid ground of Elephant Island was cold and uncomfortable. We turned out at dawn and had breakfast. Then we launched the *Stancomb Wills* and loaded her with stores, gear, and ballast, which would be transferred to the *James Caird* when the heavier boat had been launched. The ballast consisted of bags made from blankets and filled with sand, making a total weight of about 1000 lbs. In addition we had gathered a number of boulders and about 250 lbs. of ice, which would supplement our two casks of water.

The swell was slight when the *Stancomb Wills* was launched and the boat got under way without any difficulty; but half an hour later, when we were pulling down the *James Caird,* the swell increased suddenly. Apparently the movement of the ice outside had made an opening and allowed the sea to run in without being blanketed by the line of pack. The swell made things difficult. Many of us got wet to the waist while dragging the boat out—a serious matter in that climate. When the *James Caird* was afloat in the surf she nearly capsized among the rocks before we could get her clear, and Vincent and the carpenter, who were on the deck, were thrown into the water. This was really bad luck, for the two men would have small chance of drying their clothes after we had got under way. Hurley, who had the eye of the professional photographer for "incidents," secured a picture of the upset, and I firmly believe that he would have liked the two unfortunate men to remain in the water until he could get a "snap" at close quarters; but we hauled them out immediately, regardless of his feelings.

The *James Caird* was soon clear of the breakers. We used all the available ropes as a long painter to prevent her drifting away to the north-east, and then the *Stancomb Wills* came alongside, transferred her load, and went back to the shore for more. As she was being beached this time the sea took her stern and half filled her with water. She had to be turned over and emptied before the return journey could be made. Every member of the crew of the *Stancomb Wills* was wet to the skin. The water-casks were towed behind the *Stancomb Wills* on this second journey, and the swell, which was increasing rapidly, drove the boat on to the rocks, where one of the casks was slightly stove in. This accident proved later to be a serious one, since some sea-water had entered the cask and the contents were now brackish.

By midday the *James Caird* was ready for the voyage. Vincent and the carpenter had secured some dry clothes by exchange with members of the shore party (I heard afterwards that it was a full fortnight before the soaked garments were finally dried), and the boat's crew was standing by waiting for the order to cast off. A moderate westerly breeze was blowing. I went ashore in the *Stancomb Wills* and had a last word with Wild, who was remaining in full command, with directions as to his course of action in the event of our failure to bring relief, but I practically left the whole situation and scope of action and decision to his own judgment, secure in the knowledge that he would act wisely. I told him that I trusted the party to him and said good-bye to the men. Then we pushed off for the last time, and within a few minutes I was aboard the *James Caird*. The crew of the *Stancomb Wills* shook hands with us as the boats bumped together and offered us the last good wishes. Then, setting our jib, we cut the painter and moved away to the north-east. The men who were staying behind made a pathetic little group on the beach, with the grim heights of the island behind them and the sea seething at their feet, but they waved to us and gave three hearty cheers. There was hope in their hearts and they trusted us to bring the help that they needed.

I had all sails set, and the *James Caird* quickly dipped the beach and its line of dark figures. The westerly wind took us rapidly to the line of pack, and as we entered it I stood up with my arm around the mast, directing the steering, so as to avoid the great lumps of ice that were flung about in the heave of the sea. The pack thickened and we were forced to turn almost due east, running before the wind towards a gap I had seen in the morning from the high ground. I could not see the gap now, but we had come out on its bearing and I was prepared to find that it had been influenced by the easterly drift. At four o'clock in the afternoon we found the channel, much narrower than it had seemed in the morning but still navigable. Dropping sail, we rowed through without touching the ice anywhere, and by 5.30 p. m. we were clear of the pack with open water before us. We passed one more piece of ice in the darkness an hour later, but the pack lay behind, and with a fair wind swelling the sails we steered our little craft through the night, our hopes centered on our distant goal. The swell was very heavy now, and when the time came for our first evening meal we found great difficulty in keeping the Primus lamp alight and preventing the hoosh splashing out of the pot. Three men were needed to attend to the cooking, one man holding the lamp and two men guarding the aluminum cooking-pot, which had to be lifted clear of the Primus whenever the movement of the boat threatened to cause a disaster. Then the lamp had to be protected from water, for sprays were coming over the bows and our flimsy decking was by no means water-tight. All these operations were conducted in the confined space under the decking, where the men lay or knelt and adjusted themselves as best they could to the angles of our cases and ballast. It was uncomfortable, but we found consolation in the reflection that without the decking we could not have used the cooker at all.

The tale of the next sixteen days is one of supreme strife amid heaving waters. The sub-Antarctic Ocean lived up to its evil winter reputation. I decided to run north for at least two days while the wind held and so get into warmer weather before turning to the east and laying a course for South Georgia. We took two-hourly spells at the tiller. The men who were not on watch crawled into the sodden sleeping-bags and tried to forget their troubles for a period; but there was no comfort in the boat. The bags and cases seemed to be alive in the unfailing knack of presenting their most uncomfortable angles to our rest-seeking bodies. A man might imagine for a moment that he had found a position of ease, but always discovered quickly that some unyielding point was impinging on muscle or bone. The first night aboard the boat was one of acute discomfort for us all, and we were heartily glad when the dawn came and we could set about the preparation of a hot breakfast.

This record of the voyage to South Georgia is based upon scanty notes made day by day. The notes dealt usually with the bare facts of distances, positions, and weather, but our memories retained the incidents of the passing days in a period never to be forgotten. By running north for the first two days I hoped to get warmer weather and also to avoid lines of pack that might be extending beyond the main body. We needed all the advantage that we could obtain from the higher latitude for sailing on the great circle, but we had to be cautious regarding possible ice-streams. Cramped in our narrow quarters and continually wet by the spray, we suffered severely from cold throughout the journey. We fought the seas and the winds and at the same time had a daily struggle to keep ourselves alive. At times we were in dire peril. Generally we were upheld by the knowledge that we were making progress towards the land where we would be, but there were days and nights when we lay hove to, drifting across the storm-whitened seas and watching with eyes interested rather than apprehensive the uprearing masses of water, flung to and fro by Nature in the pride of her strength. Deep seemed the valleys when we lay between the reeling seas. High were the hills when we perched momentarily on the tops of giant combers. Nearly always there were gales. So small was our boat and so great were the seas that often our sail flapped idly in the calm between the crests of two waves. Then we would climb the next slope and catch the full fury of the gale where the wool-like whiteness of the breaking water surged around us. We had our moments of laughter—rare, it is true, but hearty enough. Even when cracked lips and swollen mouths checked the outward and visible signs of amusement we could see a joke of the primitive kind. Man's sense of humour is always most easily stirred by the petty misfortunes of his neighbours, and I shall never forget Worsley's efforts

on one occasion to place the hot aluminum stand on top
of the Primus stove after it had fallen off in an extra
heavy roll. With his frost-bitten fingers he picked it up,
dropped it, picked it up again, and toyed with it gingerly
as though it were some fragile article of lady's wear. We
laughed, or rather gurgled with laughter.

The wind came up strong and worked into a gale from
the north-west on the third day out. We stood away to
the east. The increasing seas discovered the weaknesses
of our decking. The continuous blows shifted the box-
lids and sledge-runners so that the canvas sagged
down and accumulated water. Then icy trickles, distinct
from the driving sprays, poured fore and aft into the
boat. The nails that the carpenter had extracted from
cases at Elephant Island and used to fasten down the
battens were too short to make firm the decking. We did
what we could to secure it, but our means were very
limited, and the water continued to enter the boat at a
dozen points. Much bailing was necessary, and nothing
that we could do prevented our gear from becoming sodden. The searching runnels from the canvas were really
more unpleasant than the sodden definite douches of
the sprays. Lying under the thwarts during watches below, we tried vainly to avoid them. There were no dry
places in the boat, and at last we simply covered our
heads with our Burberrys and endured the all-pervading
water. The bailing was work for the watch. Real rest we
had none. The perpetual motion of the boat made repose
impossible; we were cold, sore, and anxious. We moved
on hands and knees in the semi-darkness of the day
under the decking. The darkness was complete by 6
P.M., and not until 7 A.M. of the following day could we
see one another under the thwarts. We had a few scraps

of candle, and they were preserved carefully in order that we might have light at meal-times. There was one fairly dry spot in the boat, under the solid original decking at the bows, and we managed to protect some of our biscuit from the salt water; but I do not think any of us got the taste of salt out of our mouths during the voyage.

The difficulty of movement in the boat would have had its humorous side if it had not involved us in so many aches and pains. We had to crawl under the thwarts in order to move along the boat, and our knees suffered considerably. When a watch turned out it was necessary for me to direct each man by name when and where to move, since if all hands had crawled about at the same time the result would have been dire confusion and many bruises. Then there was the trim of the boat to be considered. The order of the watch was four hours on and four hour off, three men to the watch. One man had the tiller-ropes, the second man attended to the sail, and the third bailed for all he was worth. Sometimes when the water in the boat had been reduced to reasonable proportions, our pump could be used. This pump, which Hurley had made from the Flinder's bar case of our ship's standard compass, was quite effective, though its capacity was not large. The man who was attending the sail could pump into the big outer cooker, which was lifted and emptied overboard when filled. We had a device by which the water could go direct from the pump into the sea through a hole in the gunwale, but this hole had to be blocked at an early stage of the voyage, since we found that it admitted water when the boat rolled.

While a new watch was shivering in the wind and spray, the men who had been relieved groped hurriedly among the soaked sleeping-bags and tried to steal a little of the warmth created by the last occupants; but it was not always possible for us to find even this comfort when we went off watch. The boulders that we had taken aboard for ballast had to be shifted continually in order to trim the boat and give access to the pump, which became choked with hairs from the moulting sleeping-bags and finneskoe. The four reindeer-skin sleeping-bags shed their hair freely owing to the continuous wetting, and soon became quite bald in appearance. The moving of the boulders was weary and painful work. We came to know every one of the stones by sight and touch, and I have vivid memories of their angular peculiarities even to-day. They might have been of considerable interest as geological specimens to a scientific man under happier conditions. As ballast they were useful. As weights to be moved about in cramped quarters they were simply appalling. They spared no portion of our poor bodies. Another of our troubles, worth mention here, was the chafing of our legs by our wet clothes, which had not been changed now for seven months. The insides of our thighs were rubbed raw, and the one tube of Hazeline cream in our medicine-chest did not go far in alleviating our pain, which was increased by the bite of the salt water. We thought at the time that we never slept. The fact was that we would doze off uncomfortably, to be aroused quickly by some new ache or another call to effort. My own share of the general unpleasantness was accentuated by a finely developed bout of sciatica. I had become possessor of this originally on the floe several months earlier.

Our meals were regular in spite of the gales. Attention to this point was essential, since the conditions of the voyage made increasing calls upon our vitality. Breakfast, at 8 A.M., consisted of a pannikin of hot hoosh made from Bovril sledging ration, two biscuits, and some lumps of sugar. Lunch came at 1 P.M., and comprised Bovril sledging ration, eaten raw, and a pannikin of hot milk for each man. Tea, at 5 P.M., had the same menu. Then during the night we had a hot drink, generally of milk. The meals were the bright beacons in those cold and stormy days. The glow of warmth and comfort produced by the food and drink made optimists of us all. We had two tins of Virol, which we were keeping for an emergency; but, finding ourselves in need of an oil-lamp to eke out our supply of candles, we emptied one of the tins in the manner that most appealed to us, and fitted it with a wick made by shredding a bit of canvas. When this lamp was filled with oil it gave a certain amount of light, though it was easily blown out, and was of great assistance to us at night. We were fairly well off as regarded fuel, since we had 6½ gallons of petroleum.

A severe south-westerly gale on the fourth day out forced us to heave to. I would have liked to have run before the wind, but the sea was very high and the *James Caird* was in danger of broaching to and swamping. The delay was vexatious, since up to that time we had been making sixty or seventy miles a day, good going with our limited sail area. We hove to under double-reefed mainsail and our little jigger, and waited for the gale to blow itself out. During that afternoon we saw bits of wreckage, the remains probably of some unfortunate vessel that had failed to weather the strong gales south of Cape Horn. The weather conditions did not improve, and on the fifth day out the gale was so fierce that we were compelled to take in the double-reefed mainsail and hoist our small jib instead. We put out a sea-anchor to keep the *James Caird's* head up to the sea. This anchor consisted of a triangular canvas bag fastened to the end of the painter and allowed to stream out from the bows. The boat was high enough to catch the wind, and, as she drifted to leeward, the drag of the anchor kept her head to windward. Thus our boat took most of the seas more or less end on. Even then the crests of the waves often would curl right over us and we shipped a great deal of water, which necessitated unceasing bailing and pumping. Looking out abeam, we would see a hollow like a tunnel formed as the crest of a big wave toppled over on to the swelling body of water. A thousand times it appeared as though the *James Caird* must be engulfed; but the boat lived. The south-westerly gale had its birthplace above the Antarctic Continent, and its freezing breath lowered the temperature far towards zero. The sprays froze upon the boat and gave bows, sides, and decking a heavy coat of mail. This accumulation of ice reduced the buoyancy of the boat, and to that extent was an added peril; but it possessed a notable advantage from one point of view. The water ceased to drop and trickle from the canvas, and the spray came in solely at the well in the after part of the boat. We could not allow the load of ice to grow beyond a certain point, and in turns we crawled about the decking forward, chipping and picking at it with the available tools.

When daylight came on the morning of the sixth day out we saw and felt that the *James Caird* had lost her resiliency. She was not rising to the oncoming seas. The weight of the ice that had formed in her and upon her during the night was having its effect, and she was becoming more like a log than a boat. The situation called for immediate action. We first broke away the spare oars, which were encased in ice and frozen to the sides of the boat, and threw them overboard. We retained two oars for use when we got inshore. Two of the fur sleeping-bags went over the side; they were thoroughly wet, weighing probably 40 lbs. each, and they had frozen stiff during the night. Three men constituted the watch below, and when a man went down it was better to turn into the wet bag just vacated by another man than to thaw out a frozen bag with the heat of his unfortunate body. We now had four bags, three in use and one for emergency use in case a member of the party should break down permanently. The reduction of weight relieved the boat to some extent, and vigorous chipping and scraping did more. We had to be very careful not to put axe or knife through the frozen canvas of the decking as we crawled over it, but gradually we got rid of a lot of ice. The *James Caird* lifted to the endless waves as though she lived again.

About 11 A.M. the boat suddenly fell off into the trough of the sea. The painter had parted and the sea-anchor had gone. This was serious. The *James Caird* went away to leeward, and we had no chance at all of recovering the anchor and our valuable rope, which had been our only means of keeping the boat's head up to the seas without the risk of hoisting sail in a gale. Now we had to set the sail and trust to its holding. While the *James Caird* rolled heavily in the trough, we beat the frozen canvas until the bulk of the ice had cracked off it and then hoisted it. The frozen gear worked protestingly, but after a struggle our little craft came up to the wind again, and we breathed more freely. Skin frostbites were troubling us, and we had developed large blisters on our fingers and hands. I shall always carry the scar of one of these frost-bites on my left hand, which became badly inflamed after the skin had burst and the cold had bitten deeply.

We held the boat up to the gale during that day, enduring as best we could discomforts that amounted to pain. The boat tossed interminably on the big waves under grey, threatening skies. Our thoughts did not embrace much more than the necessities of the hour. Every surge of the sea was an enemy to be watched and circumvented. We ate our scanty meals, treated our frost-bites, and hoped for the improved conditions that the morrow might bring. Night fell early, and in the lagging hours of darkness we were cheered by a change for the better in the weather. The wind dropped, the snow-squalls became less frequent, and the sea moderated. When the morning of the seventh day dawned there was not much wind. We shook the reef out of the sail and laid our course once more for South Georgia. The sun came out bright and clear, and presently Worsley got a snap for longitude. We hoped that the sky would remain clear until noon, so that we could get the latitude. We had been six days out without an observation, and our dead reckoning naturally was uncertain. The boat must have presented a strange appearance that morning. All hands basked in the sun. We hung our sleeping-bags to the mast and spread our socks and other gear all over the deck. Some of the ice had melted off the *James Caird* in the early morning after the gale began to slacken, and dry patches were appearing in the decking. Porpoises came blowing round the boat, and Cape pigeons wheeled and swooped within a few feet of us. These little black-and-white birds have an air of friendliness that is not possessed by the great circling albatross. They had looked grey against the swaying sea during the storm as they darted about over our heads and uttered their plaintive cries. The albatrosses, of the black or sooty variety, had watched with hard, bright eyes, and seemed to have a quite impersonal interest in our struggle to keep afloat amid the battering seas. In addition to the Cape pigeons an occasional stormy petrel flashed overhead. Then there was a small bird, unknown to me, that appeared always to be in a fussy, bustling state, quite out of keeping with the surroundings. It irritated me. It had practically no tail, and it flitted about vaguely as though in search of the lost member. I used to find myself wishing it would find its tail and have done with the silly fluttering.

We revelled in the warmth of the sun that day. Life was not so bad, after all. We felt we were well on our way. Our gear was drying, and we could have a hot meal in comparative comfort. The swell was still heavy, but it was not breaking and the boat rode easily. At noon Worsley balanced himself on the gunwale and clung with one hand to the stay of the mainmast while he got a snap of the sun. The result was more than encouraging. We had done over 380 miles and were getting on for half-way to South Georgia. It looked as though we were going to get through.

The wind freshened to a good stiff breeze during the afternoon, and the *James Caird* made satisfactory progress. I had not realized until the sunlight came how small our boat really was. There was some influence in the light and warmth, some hint of happier days, that made us revive memories of other voyages, when we had stout decks beneath our feet, unlimited food at our command, and pleasant cabins for our ease. Now we clung to a battered little boat, "alone, alone—all, all alone; alone on a wide, wide sea." So low in the water were we that each succeeding swell cut off our view of the sky-line. We were a tiny speck in the vast vista of the sea—the ocean that is open to all and merciful to none, that threatens even when it seems to yield, and that is pitiless always to weakness. For a moment the consciousness of the forces arrayed against us would be almost overwhelming. Then hope and confidence would rise again as our boat rose to a wave and tossed aside the crest in a sparkling shower like the play of prismatic colours at the foot of a waterfall. My double-barrelled gun and some cartridges had been stowed aboard the boat as emergency precautions against a shortage of food, but we were not disposed to destroy our little neighbours, the Cape pigeons, even for the sake of fresh meat. We might have shot an albatross, but the wandering king of the ocean aroused in us something of the feeling that inspired, too late, the Ancient Mariner. So the gun remained among the stores and sleeping-bags in the narrow quarters beneath our leaking deck, and the birds followed us unmolested.

The eighth, ninth, and tenth days of the voyage had few features worthy of special note. The wind blew hard during those days, and the strain of navigating the boat was unceasing; but always we made some advance towards our goal. No bergs showed on our horizon, and we knew that we were clear of the ice-fields. Each day brought its little round of troubles, but also compensation in the form of food and growing hope. We felt that we were going to succeed. The odds against us had been great, but we were winning through. We still suffered severely from the cold, for, though the temperature was rising, our vitality was declining owing to shortage of food, exposure, and the necessity of maintaining our cramped positions day and night. I found that it was now absolutely necessary to prepare hot milk for all hands during the night, in order to sustain life till dawn. This meant lighting the Primus lamp in the darkness and involved an increased drain on our small store of matches. It was the rule that one match must serve when the Primus was being lit. We had no lamp for the compass and during the early days of the voyage we would strike a match when the steersman wanted to see the course at night; but later the necessity for strict economy impressed itself upon us, and the practice of striking matches at night was stopped. We had one water-tight tin of matches. I had stowed away in a pocket, in readiness for a sunny day, a lens from one of the telescopes, but this was of no use during the voyage. The sun seldom shone upon us. The glass of the compass got broken one night, and we contrived to mend it with adhesive tape from the medicine-chest. One of the memories that comes to me from those days is of Crean singing at the tiller. He always sang while he was steering, and nobody ever discovered what the song was. It was devoid of tune and as monotonous as the chanting of a Buddhist monk at his prayers; yet somehow it was cheerful. In moments of inspiration Crean would attempt "The Wearing of the Green."

On the tenth night Worsley could not straighten his body after his spell at the tiller. He was thoroughly cramped, and we had to drag him beneath the decking and massage him before he could unbend himself and get into a sleeping-bag. A hard north-westerly gale came up on the eleventh day (May 5) and shifted to the south-

west in the late afternoon. The sky was overcast and occasional snow-squalls added to the discomfort produced
by a tremendous cross-sea—the worst, I thought, that we
had experienced. At midnight I was at the tiller and
suddenly noticed a line of clear sky between the south
and south-west. I called to the other men that the sky
was clearing, and then a moment later I realized that
what I had seen was not a rift in the clouds but the white
crest of an enormous wave. During twenty-six years'
experience of the ocean in all its moods I had not encountered a wave so gigantic. It was a mighty upheaval
of the ocean, a thing quite apart from the big white-
capped seas that had been our tireless enemies for many
days. I shouted "For God's sake, hold on! It's got us."
Then came a moment of suspense that seemed drawn
out into hours. White surged the foam of the breaking
sea around us. We felt our boat lifted and flung forward
like a cork in breaking surf. We were in a seething chaos
of tortured water; but somehow the boat lived through
it, half full of water, sagging to the dead weight and
shuddering under the blow. We bailed with the energy
of men fighting for life, flinging the water over the sides
with every receptacle that came to our hands, and after
ten minutes of uncertainty we felt the boat renew her
life beneath us. She floated again and ceased to lurch
drunkenly as though dazed by the attack of the sea.
Earnestly we hoped that never again would we encounter such a wave.

The conditions in the boat, uncomfortable before,
had been made worse by the deluge of water. All our
gear was thoroughly wet again. Our cooking-stove had
been floating about in the bottom of the boat, and por-
tions of our last hoosh seemed to have permeated every-

thing. Not until 3 A.M., when we were all chilled almost
to the limit of endurance, did we manage to get the
stove alight and make ourselves hot drinks. The carpenter was suffering particularly, but he showed grit
and spirit. Vincent had for the past week ceased to be
an active member of the crew, and I could not easily
account for his collapse. Physically he was one of the
strongest men in the boat. He was a young man, he had
served on North Sea trawlers, and he should have been
able to bear hardships better than McCarthy, who, not
so strong, was always happy.

The weather was better on the following day (May
6), and we got a glimpse of the sun. Worsley's observation showed that we were not more than a hundred
miles from the north-west corner of South Georgia. Two
more days with a favourable wind and we would sight
the promised land. I hoped that there would be no delay, for our supply of water was running very low. The
hot drink at night was essential, but I decided that the
daily allowance of water must be cut down to half a pint
per man. The lumps of ice we had taken aboard had
gone long ago. We were dependent upon the water we
had brought from Elephant Island, and our thirst was
increased by the fact that we were now using the brackish water in the breaker that had been slightly stove in in
the surf when the boat was being loaded. Some sea-water
had entered at that time.

Thirst took possession of us. I dared not permit the
allowance of water to be increased since an unfavorable
wind might drive us away from the island and lengthen
our voyage by many days. Lack of water is always the
most severe privation that men can be condemned to en-
dure, and we found, as during our earlier boat voyage,

that the salt water in our clothing and the salt spray that lashed our faces made our thirst grow quickly to a burning pain. I had to be very firm in refusing to allow any one to anticipate the morrow's allowance, which I was sometimes begged to do. We did the necessary work dully and hoped for the land. I had altered the course to the east so as to make sure of our striking the island, which would have been impossible to regain if we had run past the northern end. The course was laid on our scrap of chart for a point some thirty miles down the coast. That day and the following day passed for us in a sort of nightmare. Our mouths were dry and our tongues were swollen. The wind was still strong and the heavy sea forced us to navigate carefully, but any thought of our peril from the waves was buried beneath the consciousness of our raging thirst. The bright moments were those when we each received our one mug of hot milk during the long, bitter watches of the night. Things were bad for us in those days, but the end was coming. The morning of May 8 broke thick and stormy, with squalls from the north-west. We searched the waters ahead for a sign of land, and though we could see nothing more than had met our eyes for many days, we were cheered by a sense that the goal was near at hand. About ten o'clock that morning we passed a little bit of kelp, a glad signal of the proximity of land. An hour later we saw two shags sitting on a big mass of kelp, and knew then that we must be within ten or fifteen miles of the shore. These birds are as sure an indication of the proximity of land as a lighthouse is, for they never venture far to sea. We gazed ahead with increasing eagerness, and at 12.30 P.M., through a rift in the clouds, McCarthy caught a glimpse of the black cliffs of South Georgia, just fourteen days after our departure from Elephant Island. It was a glad moment. Thirst-ridden, chilled, and weak as we were, happiness irradiated us. The job was nearly done.

We stood in towards the shore to look for a landing-place, and presently we could see the green tussock-grass on the ledges above the surf-beaten rocks. Ahead of us and to the south, blind rollers showed the presence of uncharted reefs along the coast. Here and there the hungry rocks were close to the surface, and over them the great waves broke, swirling viciously and spouting thirty and forty feet into the air. The rocky coast appeared to descend sheer to the sea. Our need of water and rest was well-nigh desperate, but to have attempted a landing at that time would have been suicidal. Night was drawing near, and the weather indications were not favourable. There was nothing for it but to haul off till the following morning, so we stood away on the starboard tack until we had made what appeared to be a safe offing. Then we hove to in the high westerly swell. The hours passed slowly as we waited the dawn, which would herald, we fondly hoped, the last stage of our journey. Our thirst was a torment and we could scarcely touch our food; the cold seemed to strike right through our weakened bodies. At 5 A.M. the wind shifted to the northwest and quickly increased to one of the worst hurricanes any of us had ever experienced. A great cross-sea was running, and the wind simply shrieked as it tore the tops off the waves and converted the whole seascape into a haze of driving spray. Down into valleys, up to tossing heights, straining until her seams opened, swung our little boat, brave still but labouring heavily. We knew that the wind and set of the sea was driving us ashore, but we could do nothing. The dawn showed us a storm-torn ocean, and the morning passed without bringing us a sight of the land; but at 1 P.M., through a rift in the flying mists, we got a glimpse of the huge crags of the island and realized that our position had become desperate. We were on a dead lee shore, and we could gauge our approach to the unseen cliffs by the roar of the breakers against the sheer walls of rock. I ordered the double-reefed mainsail to be set in the hope that we might claw off, and this attempt increased the strain upon the boat. The *Caird* was bumping heavily, and the water was pouring in everywhere. Our thirst was forgotten in the realization of our imminent danger, as we bailed unceasingly, and adjusted our weights from time to time; occasional glimpses showed that the shore was nearer. I knew that Annewkow Island lay to the south of us, but our small and badly marked chart showed uncertain reefs in the passage between the island and the mainland, and I dared not trust it, though as a last resort we could try to lie under the lee of the island. The afternoon wore away as we edged down the coast, with the thunder of the breakers in our ears. The approach of evening found us still some distance from Annewkow Island, and, dimly in the twilight, we could see a snow-capped mountain looming above us. The chance of surviving the night, with the driving gale and the implacable sea forcing us on to the lee shore, seemed small. I think most of us had a feeling that the end was very near. Just after 6 P.M., in the dark, as the boat was in the yeasty backwash from the seas flung from this iron-bound coast, then, just when things looked their worst, they changed for the best. I have marvelled often at the thin line that divides success from failure and the sudden turn that leads from apparently certain disaster to comparative safety. The wind suddenly shifted, and we were free once more to make an offing. Almost as soon as the gale eased, the pin that locked the mast to the thwart fell out. It must have been on the point of doing this throughout the hurricane, and if it had gone nothing could have saved us; the mast would have snapped like a carrot. Our backstays had carried away once before when iced up and were not too strongly fastened now. We were thankful indeed for the mercy that had held that pin in its place throughout the hurricane.

We stood off shore again, tired almost to the point of apathy. Our water had long been finished. The last was about a pint of hairy liquid, which we strained through a bit of gauze from the medicine-chest. The pangs of thirst attacked us with redoubled intensity, and I felt that we must make a landing on the following day at almost any hazard. The night wore on. We were very tired. We longed for day. When at last the dawn came on the morning of May 10 there was practically no wind, but a high cross-sea was running. We made slow progress towards the shore. About 8 A.M. the wind backed to the north-west and threatened another blow. We had sighted in the meantime a big indentation which I thought must be King Haakon Bay, and I decided that we must land there. We set the bows of the boat towards the bay and ran before the freshening gale. Soon we had angry reefs on either side. Great glaciers came down to the sea and offered no landing-place. The sea spouted on the reefs and thundered against the shore. About noon we sighted a line of jagged reef, like blackened teeth, that seemed to bar the entrance to the bay. Inside, comparatively smooth water stretched eight or nine miles to the head of the bay. A gap in the reef appeared, and we made for it. But the fates had another rebuff for us. The wind shifted and blew from the east right out of the bay. We could see the way through the reef, but we could not approach it directly. That afternoon we bore up, tacking five times in the strong wind. The last tack enabled us to get through, and at last we were in the wide mouth of the bay. Dusk was approaching. A small cove, with a boulder-strewn beach guarded by a reef, made a break in the cliffs on the south side of the bay, and we turned in that direction. I stood in the bows directing the steering as we ran through the kelp and made the passage of the reef. The entrance was so narrow that we had to take in the oars, and the swell was piling itself right over the reef into the cove; but in a minute or two we were inside, and in the gathering darkness the *James Caird* ran in on a swell and touched the beach. I sprang ashore with the short painter and held on when the boat went out with the backward surge. When the *James Caird* came in again three of the men got ashore, and they held the painter while I climbed some rocks with another line. A slip on the wet rocks twenty feet up nearly closed my part of the story just at the moment when we were achieving safety. A jagged piece of rock held me and at the same time bruised me sorely. However, I made fast the line, and in a few minutes we were all safe on the beach, with the boat floating in the surging water just off the shore. We heard a gurgling sound that was sweet music in our ears, and, peering around, found a stream of fresh water almost at our feet. A moment later we were down on our knees drinking the pure ice-cold water in long draughts that put new life into us. It was a splendid moment.

The next thing was to get the stores and ballast out of the boat, in order that we might secure her for the night. We carried the stores and gear above high-water mark and threw out the bags of sand and the boulders that we knew so well. Then we attempted to pull the empty boat up the beach, and discovered by this effort how weak we had become. Our united strength was not sufficient to get the *James Caird* clear of the water. Time after time we pulled together, but without avail. I saw that it would be necessary to have food and rest before we beached the boat. We made fast a line to a heavy boulder and set a watch to fend the *James Caird* off the rocks of the beach. Then I sent Crean round to the left side of the cove, about thirty yards away, where I had noticed a little cave as we were running in. He could not see much in the darkness, but reported that the place certainly promised some shelter. We carried the sleeping-bags round and found a mere hollow in the rock-face, with a shingle-floor sloping at a steep angle to the sea. There we prepared a hot meal, and when the food was finished I ordered the men to turn in. The time was now about 8 P.M., and I took the first watch beside the *James Caird*, which was still afloat in the tossing water just off the beach.

Fending the *James Caird* off the rocks in the darkness was awkward work. The boat would have bumped dangerously if allowed to ride in with the waves that drove into the cove. I found a flat rock for my feet, which were in a bad way owing to cold, wetness, and lack of exercise in the boat, and during the next few hours I laboured to keep the *James Caird* clear of the beach. Occasionally I had to rush into the seething water. Then, as a wave receded, I let the boat out on the alpine rope so as to avoid a sudden jerk. The heavy painter had been lost when the sea-anchor went adrift. The *James Caird* could be seen but dimly in the cove, where the high black cliffs made the darkness almost complete, and the strain upon one's attention was great. After several hours had passed I found that my desire for sleep was becoming irresistible, and at 1 A.M. I called Crean. I could hear him groaning as he stumbled over the sharp rocks on his way down the beach. While he was taking charge of the *James Caird* she got adrift, and we had some anxious moments. Fortunately, she went across towards the cave and we secured her unharmed. The loss or destruction of the boat at this stage would have been a very serious matter, since we probably would have found it impossible to leave the cove except by sea. The cliffs and glaciers around offered no practicable path towards the head of the bay. I arranged for one-hour watches during the remainder of the night and then took Crean's place among the sleeping men and got some sleep before the dawn came.

The sea went down in the early hours of the morning (May 11), and after sunrise we were able to set about getting the boat ashore, first bracing ourselves for the task with another meal. We were all weak still. We cut off the topsides and took out all the movable gear. Then we waited for Byron's "great ninth wave," and when it lifted the *James Caird* in we held her and, by dint of great exertion, worked her round broadside to the sea. Inch by inch we dragged her up until we reached the fringe of the tussock-grass and knew that the boat was above high-water mark. The rise of the tide was about five feet, and at spring tide the water must have reached almost to the edge of the tussock-grass. The completion of this job removed our immediate anxieties, and we were free to examine our surroundings and plan the next move. The day was bright and clear.

King Haakon Bay is an eight-mile sound penetrating the coast of South Georgia in an easterly direction. We had noticed that the northern and southern sides of the sound were formed by steep mountain-ranges, their flanks furrowed by mighty glaciers, the outlets of the great ice-sheet of the interior. It was obvious that these glaciers and the precipitous slopes of the mountains barred our way inland from the cove. We must sail to the head of the sound. Swirling clouds and mist-wreaths had obscured our view of the sound when we were entering, but glimpses of snow-slopes had given us hope that an overland journey could be begun from that point. A few patches of very rough tussocky land, dotted with little tarns, lay between the glaciers along the foot of the mountains, which were heavily scarred with scree-slopes. Several magnificent peaks and crags gazed out across their snowy domains to the sparkling waters of the sound.

Our cove lay a little inside the southern headland of King Haakon Bay. A narrow break in the cliffs, which were about a hundred feet high at this point, formed the entrance to the cove. The cliffs continued inside the cove on each side and merged into a hill which descended at a steep slope to the boulder-beach. The slope, which carried tussock-grass, was not continuous. It eased at two points into little peaty swamp terraces dotted with frozen pools and drained by two small streams. Our cave was a recess in the cliff on the left-hand end of the beach. The rocky face of the cliff was undercut at this point, and the shingle thrown up by the waves formed a steep slope, which we reduced to about one in six by scraping the stones away from the inside. Later we strewed the rough floor with the dead, nearly dry, underleaves of the tussock-grass, so as to form a slightly soft bed for our sleeping-bags. Water had trickled down the face of the cliff and formed long icicles, which hung down in front of the cave to the length of about fifteen feet. These icicles provided shelter, and when we had spread our sails below them, with the assistance of oars, we had quarters that, in the circumstances, had to be regarded as reasonably comfortable. The camp at least was dry, and we moved our gear there with confidence. We built a fireplace and arranged our sleeping-bags and blankets around it. The cave was about 8 ft. deep and 12 ft. wide at the entrance.

While the camp was being arranged Crean and I climbed the tussock slope behind the beach and reached the top of a headland overlooking the sound. There we found the nests of albatrosses, and, much to our delight, the nests contained young birds. The fledgelings were fat and lusty, and we had no hesitation about deciding that they were destined to die at an early age. Our most pressing anxiety at this stage was a shortage of fuel for the cooker. We had rations for ten more days, and we knew now that we could get birds for food; but if we were to have hot meals we must secure fuel. The store of petroleum carried in the boat was running very low, and it seemed necessary to keep some quantity for use on the overland journey that lay ahead of us. A sea-elephant or a seal would have provided fuel as well as food, but we could see none in the neighbourhood. During the morning we started a fire in the cave with wood from the topsides of the boat, and though the dense smoke from the damp sticks inflamed our tired eyes, the warmth and the prospect of hot food were ample compensation. Crean was cook that day, and I suggested to him that he should wear his goggles, which he happened to have brought with him. The goggles helped him a great deal as he bent over the fire and tended the stew. And what a stew it was! The young albatrosses weighed about fourteen pounds each, fresh killed, and we estimated that they weighed at least six pounds each when cleaned and dressed for the pot. Four birds went into the pot for six men, with a Bovril ration for thickening. The flesh was white and succulent, and the bones, not fully formed, almost melted in our mouths. That was a memorable meal. When we had eaten our fill, we dried our tobacco in the embers of the fire and smoked contentedly. We made an attempt to dry our clothes, which were soaked with salt water, but did not meet with much success. We could not afford to have a fire except for cooking purposes until blubber or driftwood had come our way.

The final stage of the journey had still to be attempted. I realized that the condition of the party generally, and particularly of McNeish and Vincent, would prevent us putting to sea again except under pressure of dire necessity. Our boat, moreover, had been weakened by the cutting away of the topsides, and I doubted if we could weather the island. We were still 150 miles away from Stromness whaling-station by sea. The alternative was to attempt the crossing of the island. If we could not get over, then we must try to secure enough food and fuel to keep us alive through the winter, but this possibility was scarcely thinkable. Over on Elephant Island twenty-two men were waiting for the relief that we alone could secure for them. Their plight was worse than ours. We must push on somehow. Several days must elapse before our strength would be sufficiently recovered to allow us to row or sail the last nine miles up to the head of the bay. In the meantime we could make what preparations were possible and dry our clothes by taking advantage of every scrap of heat from the fires we lit for the cooking our our meals. We turned in early that night, and I remember that I dreamed of the great wave and aroused my companions with a shout of warning as I saw with half-awakened eyes the towering cliff on the opposite side of the cove.

Shortly before midnight a gale sprang up suddenly from the north-east with rain and sleet showers. It brought quantities of glacier-ice into the cove, and by 2 A.M. (May 12) our little harbour was filled with ice, which surged to and fro in the swell and pushed its way on to the beach. We had solid rock beneath our feet and could watch without anxiety. When daylight came rain was falling heavily, and the temperature was the highest we had experienced for many months. The icicles over-hanging our cave were melting down in streams, and we had to move smartly when passing in and out lest we should be struck by falling lumps. A fragment weighing fifteen or twenty pounds crashed down while we were having breakfast. We found that a big hole had been burned in the bottom of Worsley's reindeer sleeping-bag during the night. Worsley had been awakened by a burn-ing sensation in his feet, and had asked the men near him if his bag was all right; they looked and could see noth-ing wrong. We were all superficially frost-bitten about the feet, and this condition caused the extremities to burn painfully, while at the same time sensation was lost in the skin. Worsley thought that the uncomfortable heat of his feet was due to the frost-bites, and he stayed in his bag and presently went to sleep again. He discovered when he turned out in the morning that the tussock-grass which we had laid on the floor of the cave had smouldered outwards from the fire and had actually burned a large hole in the bag beneath his feet. Fortunately, his feet were not harmed.

Our party spent a quiet day, attending to clothing and gear, checking stores, eating and resting. Some more of the young albatrosses made a noble end in our pot. The birds were nesting on a small plateau above the right-hand end of our beach. We had previously discovered that when we were landing from the boat on the night of May 10 we had lost the rudder. The *James Caird* had been bumping heavily astern as we were scrambling ashore, and evidently the rudder was then knocked off. A careful search of the beach and the rocks within our reach failed to reveal the missing article. This was a serious loss, even if the voyage to the head of the sound could be made in good weather. At dusk the ice in the cove was rearing and crashing on the beach. It had forced up a ridge of stones close to where the *James Caird* lay at the edge of the tussock-grass. Some pieces of ice were driven right up to the canvas wall at the front of our cave. Fragments lodged within two feet of Vincent, who had the lowest sleeping-place, and within four feet of our fire. Crean and McCarthy had brought down six more of the young albatrosses in the afternoon, so we were well supplied with fresh food. The air temperature that night probably was not lower than 38° or 40° Fahr., and we were rendered uncomfortable in our cramped sleeping quarters by the unaccustomed warmth. Our feelings towards our neighbours underwent a change. When the temperature was below 20° Fahr. we could not get too close to one another—every man wanted to cuddle against his neighbour; but let the temperature rise a few degrees and the warmth of another man's body ceased to be a blessing. The ice and the waves had a voice of menace that night, but I heard it only in my dreams.

The bay was still filled with ice on the morning of Saturday, May 13, but the tide took it all away in the afternoon. Then a strange thing happened. The rudder, with all the broad Atlantic to sail in and the coasts of two continents to search for a resting-place, came bobbing into our cove. With anxious eyes we watched it as it advanced, receded again, and then advanced once more under the capricious influence of wind and wave. Nearer and nearer it came as we waited on the shore, oars in hand, and at last we were able to seize it. Surely a remarkable salvage! The day was bright and clear; our clothes were drying and our strength was returning. Running water made a musical sound down the tussock slope and among the boulders. We carried our blankets up the hill and tried to dry them in the breeze 300 ft. above sea-level. In the afternoon we began to prepare the *James Caird* for the journey to the head of King Haakon Bay. A noon observation on this day gave our latitude as 54° 10′ 47″ S., but according to the German chart the position should have been 54° 12′ S. Probably Worsley's observation was the more accurate. We were able to keep the fire alight until we went to sleep that night, for while climbing the rocks above the cove I had seen at the foot of a cliff a broken spar, which had been thrown up by the waves. We could reach this spar by climbing down the cliff, and with a reserve supply of fuel thus in sight we could afford to burn the fragments of the *James Caird's* topsides more freely.

During the morning of this day (May 13) Worsley and I tramped across the hills in a north-easterly direction with the object of getting a view of the sound and possibly gathering some information that would be useful to us in the next stage of our journey. It was exhausting work, but after covering about 2½ miles in two hours, we were able to look east, up the bay. We could not see very much of the country that we would have to cross in order to reach the whaling station on the other side of the island. We had passed several brooks and frozen tarns, and at a point where we had to take to the beach on the shore of the sound we found some wreckage—an 18-ft. pine-spar (probably part of a ship's topmast), several pieces of timber, and a little model of a ship's hull, evidently a child's toy. We wondered what tragedy that pitiful little plaything indicated. We encountered also some gentoo penguins and a young sea-elephant, which Worsley killed.

When we got back to the cave at 3 P.M., tired, hungry, but rather pleased with ourselves, we found a splendid meal of stewed albatross chicken waiting for us. We had carried a quantity of blubber and the sea-elephant's liver in our blouses, and we produced our treasures as a surprise for the men. Rough climbing on the way back to camp had nearly persuaded us to throw the stuff away, but we had held on (regardless of the condition of our already sorely tried clothing), and had our reward at the camp. The long bay had been a magnificent sight, even to eyes that had dwelt on grandeur long enough and were hungry for the simple, familiar things of everyday life. Its green-blue waters were being beaten to fury by the north-westerly gale. The mountains, "stern peaks that dared the stars," peered through the mists, and between them huge glaciers poured down from the great ice-slopes and fields that lay behind. We counted twelve glaciers and heard every few minutes the reverberating roar caused by masses of ice calving from the parent streams.

On May 14 we made our preparations for an early start on the following day if the weather held fair. We expected to be able to pick up the remains of the sea-elephant on our way up the sound. All hands were recovering from the chafing caused by our wet clothes during the boat journey. The insides of our legs had suffered severely, and for some time after landing in the cove we found movement extremely uncomfortable. We paid our last visit to the nests of the albatrosses, which were situated on a little undulating plateau above the cave amid tussocks, snow-patches, and little frozen tarns. Each nest consisted of a mound over a foot high of tussock-grass, roots, and a little earth. The albatross lays one egg and very rarely two. The chicks, which are hatched in January, are fed on the nest by the parent birds for almost seven months before they take to sea and fend for themselves. Up to four months of age the chicks are beautiful white masses of downy fluff, but when we arrived on the scene their plumage was almost complete. Very often one of the parent birds was on guard near the nest. We did not enjoy attacking these birds, but our hunger knew no law. They tasted so very good and assisted our recuperation to such an extent that each time we killed one of them we felt a little less remorseful.

May 15 was a great day. We made our hoosh at 7.30
A.M. Then we loaded up the boat and gave her a flying
launch down the steep beach into the surf. Heavy rain
had fallen in the night and a gusty north-westerly wind
was now blowing, with misty showers. The *James Caird*
headed to the sea as if anxious to face the battle of the
waves once more. We passed through the narrow mouth
of the cove with the ugly rocks and waving kelp close
on either side, turned to the east, and sailed merrily up
the bay as the sun broke through the mists and made the
tossing waters sparkle around us. We were a curious-
looking party on that bright morning, but we were feeling happy. We even broke into song, and, but for our
Robinson Crusoe appearance, a casual observer might
have taken us for a picnic party sailing in a Norwegian
fiord or one of the beautiful sounds of the west coast of
New Zealand. The wind blew fresh and strong, and a
small sea broke on the coast as we advanced. The surf
was sufficient to have endangered the boat if we had attempted to land where the carcass of the sea-elephant
was lying, so we decided to go on to the head of the bay
without risking anything, particularly as we were likely
to find sea-elephants on the upper beaches. The big
creatures have a habit of seeking peaceful quarters protected from the waves. We had hopes, too, of finding
penguins. Our expectation as far as the sea-elephants
were concerned was not at fault. We heard the roar of
the bulls as we neared the head of the bay, and soon
afterwards saw the great unwieldy forms of the beasts
lying on a shelving beach towards the bay-head. We
rounded a high, glacier-worn bluff on the north side,
and at 12.30 P.M. we ran the boat ashore on a low beach
of sand and pebbles, with tussock growing above high-

water mark. There were hundreds of sea-elephants lying about, and our anxieties with regard to food disappeared. Meat and blubber enough to feed our party for years was in sight. Our landing-place was about a mile and a half west of the north-east corner of the bay. Just east of us was a glacier-snout, ending on the beach but giving a passage towards the head of the bay except at high water or when a very heavy surf was running. A cold, drizzling rain had begun to fall, and we provided ourselves with shelter as quickly as possible. We hauled the *James Caird* up above high-water mark and turned her over just to the lee or east side of the bluff. The spot was separated from the mountain-side by a low morainic bank, rising twenty or thirty feet above sea-level. Soon we had converted the boat into a very comfortable cabin *à la* Peggotty, turfing it round with tussocks, which we dug up with knives. One side of the *James Caird* rested on stones so as to afford a low entrance, and when we had finished she looked as though she had grown there. McCarthy entered into this work with great spirit. A sea-elephant provided us with fuel and meat, and that evening found a well-fed and fairly contented party at rest in Peggotty Camp.

Our camp, as I have said, lay on the north side of King Haakon Bay near the head. Our path towards the whaling-stations led round the seaward end of the snouted glacier on the east side of the camp and up a snow-slope that appeared to lead to a pass in the great Allardyce Range, which runs north-west and south-east and forms the main backbone of South Georgia. The range dipped opposite the bay into a well-defined pass from east to west. An ice-sheet covered most of the interior, filling the valleys and disguising the configuration of the land, which, indeed, showed only in big rocky ridges, peaks, and nunataks. When we looked up the pass from Peggotty Camp the country to the left appeared to offer two easy paths through to the opposite coast, but we knew that the island was uninhabited at that point (Possession Bay). We had to turn our attention further east, and it was impossible from the camp to learn much of the conditions that would confront us on the overland journey. I planned to climb to the pass and then be guided by the configuration of the country in the selection of a route eastward to Stromness Bay, where the whaling-stations were established in the minor bays, Leith, Huvik, and Stromness. A range of mountains with precipitous slopes, forbidding peaks, and large glaciers, lay immediately to the south of King Haakon Bay and seemed to form a continuation of the main range. Between this secondary range and the pass above our camp a great snow-upland sloped up to the inland ice-sheet and reached a rocky ridge that stretched athwart our path and seemed to bar the way. This ridge was a right-angled offshoot from the main ridge. Its chief features were four rocky peaks with spaces between that looked from a distance as though they might prove to be passes.

The weather was bad on Tuesday, May 16, and we stayed under the boat nearly all day. The quarters were cramped but gave full protection from the weather, and we regarded our little cabin with a great deal of satisfaction. Abundant meals of sea-elephant steak and liver increased our contentment. McNeish reported during the day that he had seen rats feeding on the scraps, but this interesting statement was not verified. One would not expect to find rats at such a spot, but there was a bare possibility that they had landed from a wreck and managed to survive the very rigorous conditions.

A fresh west-south-westerly breeze was blowing on

the following morning (Wednesday, May 17), with misty squalls, sleet, and rain. I took Worsley with me on a pioneer journey to the west with the object of examining the country to be traversed at the beginning of the overland journey. We went round the seaward end of the snouted glacier, and after tramping about a mile over stony ground and snow-coated debris, we crossed some big ridges of scree and moraines. We found that there was good going for a sledge as far as the north-east corner of the bay, but did not get much information regarding the conditions further on owing to the view becoming obscured by a snow-squall. We waited a quarter of an hour for the weather to clear but were forced to turn back without having seen more of the country. I had satisfied myself, however, that we could reach a good snow-slope leading apparently to the inland ice. Worsley reckoned from the chart that the distance from our camp to Huvik, on an east magnetic course, was seventeen geographical miles, but we could not expect to follow a direct line. The carpenter started making a sledge for use on the overland journey. The materials at his disposal were limited in quantity and scarcely suitable in quality.

We overhauled our gear on Thursday, May 18, and hauled our sledge to the lower edge of the snouted glacier. The vehicle proved heavy and cumbrous. We had to lift it empty over bare patches of rock along the shore, and I realized that it would be too heavy for three men to manage amid the snow-plains, glaciers, and peaks of the interior. Worsley and Crean were coming with me, and after consultation we decided to leave the sleeping-bags behind us and make the journey in very light marching order. We would take three days' provisions for each man in the form of sledging ration and biscuit. The food was to be packed in three socks, so that each member of the party could carry his own supply. Then we were to take the Primus lamp filled with oil, the small cooker, the carpenter's adze (for use as an ice-axe), and the alpine rope, which made a total length of fifty feet when knotted. We might have to lower ourselves down steep slopes or cross crevassed glaciers. The filled lamp would provide six hot meals, which would consist of sledging ration boiled up with biscuit. There were two boxes of matches left, one full and the other partially used. We left the full box with the men at the camp and took the second box, which contained forty-eight matches. I was unfortunate as regarded footgear, since I had given away my heavy Burberry boots on the floe, and had now a comparatively light pair in poor condition. The carpenter assisted me by putting several screws in the sole of each boot with the object of providing a grip on the ice. The screws came out of the *James Caird.*

We turned in early that night, but sleep did not come to me. My mind was busy with the task of the following day. The weather was clear and the outlook for an early start in the morning was good. We were going to leave a weak party behind us in the camp. Vincent was still in the same condition, and he could not march. McNeish was pretty well broken up. The two men were not capable of managing for themselves and McCarthy must stay to look after them. He might have a difficult task if we failed to reach the whaling-station. The distance to Huvik, according to the chart, was no more than seventeen geographical miles in a direct line, but we had very scanty knowledge of the conditions of the interior. No man had ever penetrated a mile from the coast of South Georgia at any point, and the whalers, I knew, regarded the country as inaccessible. During that day, while we were walking to the snouted glacier, we had seen three wild duck flying towards the head of the bay from the eastward. I hoped that the presence of these birds indicated tussock-land and not snow-fields and glaciers in the interior, but the hope was not a very bright one.

We turned out at 2 A.M. on the Friday morning and had our hoosh ready an hour later. The full moon was shining in a practically cloudless sky, its rays reflected gloriously from the pinnacles and crevassed ice of the adjacent glaciers. The huge peaks of the mountains stood in bold relief against the sky and threw dark shadows on the waters of the sound. There was no need for delay, and we made a start as soon as we had eaten our meal. McNeish walked about 200 yds. with us; he could do no more. Then we said good-bye and he turned back to the camp. The first task was to get round the edge of the snouted glacier, which had points like fingers projecting towards the sea. The waves were reaching the points of these fingers, and we had to rush from one recess to another when the waters receded. We soon reached the east side of the glacier and noticed its great activity at this point. Changes had occurred within the preceding twenty-four hours. Some huge pieces had broken off, and the masses of mud and stone that were being driven before the advancing ice showed movement. The glacier was like a gigantic plough driving irresistibly towards the sea.

Lying on the beach beyond the glacier was wreckage that told of many ill-fated ships. We noticed stanchions of teakwood, liberally carved, that must have come from ships of the older type; iron-bound timbers with the iron almost rusted through; battered barrels, and all the usual debris of the ocean. We had difficulties and anxieties of our own, but as we passed that graveyard of the sea we thought of the many tragedies written in the wave-worn fragments of lost vessels. We did not pause, and soon we were ascending a snow-slope, headed due east on the last lap of our long trail.

The snow-surface was disappointing. Two days before we had been able to move rapidly on hard, packed snow; now we sank over our ankles at each step and progress was slow. After two hours' steady climbing we were 2500 ft. above sea-level. The weather continued fine and calm, and as the ridges drew nearer and the western coast of the island spread out below, the bright moonlight showed us that the interior was broken tremendously. High peaks, impassable cliffs, steep snow-slopes, and sharply descending glaciers were prominent features in all directions, with stretches of snow-plain overlaying the ice-sheet of the interior. The slope we were ascending mounted to a ridge and our course lay direct to the top. The moon, which proved a good friend during this journey, threw a long shadow at one point and told us that the surface was broken in our path. Warned in time, we avoided a huge hole capable of swallowing an army. The bay was now about three miles away, and the continued roaring of a big glacier at the head of the bay came to our ears. This glacier, which we had noticed during the stay at Peggotty Camp, seemed to be calving almost continuously.

I had hoped to get a view of the country ahead of us from the top of the slope, but as the surface became more level beneath our feet, a thick fog drifted down.

The moon became obscured and produced a diffused light that was more trying than darkness, since it illuminated the fog without guiding our steps. We roped ourselves together as a precaution against holes, crevasses, and precipices, and I broke trail through the soft snow. With almost the full length of the rope between myself and the last man we were able to steer an approximately straight course, since, if I veered to the right or the left when marching into the blank wall of the fog, the last man on the rope could shout a direction. So, like a ship with its "port," "starboard," "steady," we tramped through the fog for the next two hours.

Then, as daylight came, the fog thinned and lifted, and from an elevation of about 3000 ft. we looked down on what seemed to be a huge frozen lake with its further shores still obscured by the fog. We halted there to eat a bit of biscuit while we discussed whether we would go down and cross the flat surface of the lake, or keep on the ridge we had already reached. I decided to go down, since the lake lay on our course. After an hour of comparatively easy travel through the snow we noticed the thin beginnings of crevasses. Soon they were increasing in size and showing fractures, indicating that we were travelling on a glacier. As the daylight brightened the fog dissipated; the lake could be seen more clearly, but still we could not discover its east shore. A little later the fog lifted completely, and then we saw that our lake stretched to the horizon, and realized suddenly that we were looking down upon the open sea on the east coast of the island. The slight pulsation at the shore showed that the sea was not even frozen; it was the bad light that had deceived us. Evidently we were at the top of Possession Bay, and the island at that point could not be more than five miles across from the head of King Haakon Bay. Our rough chart was inaccurate. There was nothing for it but to start up the glacier again. That was about seven o'clock in the morning, and by nine o'clock we had more than recovered our lost ground. We regained the ridge and then struck south-east, for the chart showed that two more bays indented the coast before Stromness. It was comforting to realize that we would have the eastern water in sight during our journey, although we could see there was no way around the shore-line owing to steep cliffs and glaciers. Men lived in houses lit by electric light on the east coast. News of the outside world waited us there, and, above all, the east coast meant for us the means of rescuing the twenty-two men we had left on Elephant Island.

THREE SKELETON KEY

George G. Toudouze

Probably few readers in America had ever heard of the author of this story when it appeared in Esquire. *However, George G. Toudouze, who is now seventy-six, is a well-known playwright and man of letters in France. In 1917 he wrote* Gloire et Drame de la Mer. *In 1934 he collaborated with Rene Lefebre in a history of the French Navy. He is also an illustrator.*

Just how he came to hear the tale on which he has based his hair-raising yarn of a lighthouse beseiged by rats, we do not know, but the old convict settlement at Cayenne, in French Guiana, is an integral part of the nation's history and literature.

As Arnold Gingrich remarks, in his introduction to The Bedside Esquire, *out of which I exhumed "Three Skeleton Key," this is no story for ladies. It is nonetheless an excellent example of the French way of telling a tale. It reminds me at once of Prosper Merrimée's method, of a man sitting after dinner, peeling a walnut and drinking a cognac, and telling his companions, in easy conversational style, some interesting anecdote. There are no redundancies in such a method. It is the precise opposite of the Henry James technique, for example, or the William Faulkner trick of loading a simple story down with psychoanalytical implications. There is nothing literary about it at all. It has the impact of a powerful man at a fair who, for the fun of it, takes the hammer and at one blow sends the machine to the top, rings the bell, and walks off.*

Reprinted by permission of *Esquire—The Magazine for Men*.

My MOST TERRIFYING experience? Well, one does have a few in thirty-five years of service in the Lights, although it's mostly monotonous routine work—keeping the light in order, making out the reports.

When I was a young man, not very long in the service, there was an opening in a lighthouse newly built off the coast of Guiana, on a small rock twenty miles or so from the mainland. The pay was high, so in order to reach the sum I had set out to save before I married, I volunteered for service in the new light.

Three Skeleton Key, the small rock on which the light stood, bore a bad reputation. It earned its name from the story of the three convicts who, escaping from Cayenne in a stolen dugout canoe, were wrecked on the rock during the night, managed to escape the sea but eventually died of hunger and thirst. When they were discovered, nothing remained but three heaps of bones, picked clean by the birds. The story was that the three skeletons, gleaming with phosphorescent light, danced over the small rock, screaming. . . .

But there are many such stories and I did not give the warnings of the old-timers at the *Isle de Sein* a second thought. I signed up, boarded ship and in a month I was installed at the light.

Picture a grey, tapering cylinder, welded to the solid black rock by iron rods and concrete, rising from a small island twenty odd miles from land. It lay in the midst of the sea, this island, a small, bare piece of stone, about one hundred fifty feet long, perhaps forty, wide. Small, barely large enough for a man to walk about and stretch his legs at low tide.

This is an advantage one doesn't find in all lights,

however, for some of them rise sheer from the waves, with no room for one to move save within the light itself. Still, on our island, one must be careful, for the rocks were treacherously smooth. One misstep and down you would fall into the sea—not that the risk of drowning was so great, but the waters about our island swarmed with huge sharks who kept an eternal patrol around the base of the light.

Still, it was a nice life there. We had enough provisions to last for months, in the event that the sea should become too rough for the supply ship to reach us on schedule. During the day we would work about the light, cleaning the rooms, polishing the metalwork and the lens and reflector of the light itself, and at night we would sit on the gallery and watch our light, a twenty thousand candlepower lantern, swinging its strong, white bar of light over the sea from the top of its hundred twenty foot tower. Some days, when the air would be very clear, we could see the land, a thread-like line to the west. To the east, north and south stretched the ocean. Landsmen, perhaps, would soon have tired of that kind of life, perched on a small island off the coast of South America for eighteen weeks, until one's turn for leave ashore came around. But we liked it there, my two fellow-tenders and myself—so much so that, for twenty-two months on end with the exception of shore leaves, I was greatly satisfied with the life on Three Skeleton Key.

I had just returned from my leave at the end of June, that is to say mid-winter in that latitude, and had settled down to the routine with my two fellow-keepers, a Breton by the name of Le Gleo and the head-keeper Itchoua, a Basque some dozen years or so older than either of us.

Eight days went by as usual, then on the ninth night after my return, Itchoua, who was on night duty, called Le Gleo and me, sleeping in our rooms in the middle of the tower, at two in the morning. We rose immediately and, climbing the thirty or so steps that led to the gallery, stood beside our chief.

Itchoua pointed, and following his finger, we saw a big three-master, with all sail set, heading straight for the light. A queer course, for the vessel must have seen us, our light lit her with the glare of day each time it passed over her.

Now, ships were a rare sight in our waters for our light was a warning of treacherous reefs, barely hidden under the surface and running far out to sea. Consequently we were always given a wide berth, especially by sailing vessels, which cannot maneuver as readily as steamers.

No wonder that we were surprised at seeing this three-master heading dead for us in the gloom of early morning. I had immediately recognized her lines, for she stood out plainly, even at the distance of a mile, when our light shone on her.

She was a beautiful ship of some four thousand tons, a fast sailer that had carried cargoes to every part of the world, plowing the seas unceasingly. By her lines she was identified as Dutch-built, which was understandable as Paramaribo and Dutch Guiana are very close to Cayenne.

Watching her sailing dead for us, a white wave boiling under her bows, Le Gleo cried out:

"What's wrong with her crew? Are they all drunk or insane? Can't they see us?"

Itchoua nodded soberly, looked at us sharply as he remarked: "See us? No doubt—if there *is* a crew aboard!"

"What do you mean, chief?" Le Gleo had started,

turned to the Basque, "Are you saying that she's the 'Flying Dutchman'?"

His sudden fright had been so evident that the older man laughed:

"No, old man, that's not what I meant. If I say that no one's aboard, I mean she's a derelict."

Then we understood her queer behavior. Itchoua was right. For some reason, believing her doomed, her crew had abandoned her. Then she had righted herself and sailed on, wandering with the wind.

The three of us grew tense as the ship seemed about to crash on one of our numerous reefs, but she suddenly lurched with some change of the wind, the yards swung around and the derelict came clumsily about and sailed dead away from us.

In the light of our lantern she seemed so sound, so strong, that Itchoua exclaimed impatiently:

"But why the devil was she abandoned? Nothing is smashed, no sign of fire—and she doesn't sail as if she were taking water."

Le Gleo waved to the departing ship:

"*Bon voyage!*" he smiled at Itchoua and went on. "She's leaving us, chief, and now we'll never know what——"

"No she's not!" cried the Basque. "Look! She's turning!"

As if obeying his words, the derelict three-master stopped, came about and headed for us once more. And for the next four hours the vessel played around us—zigzagging, coming about, stopping, then suddenly lurching forward. No doubt some freak of current and wind, of which our island was the center, kept her near us.

Then suddenly, the tropic dawn broke, the sun rose and it was day, and the ship was plainly visible as she sailed past us. Our light extinguished, we returned to the gallery with our glasses and inspected her.

The three of us focused our glasses on her poop, saw standing out sharply, black letters on the white background of a life-ring, the stenciled name:

"Cornelius-de-Witt, Rotterdam."

We had read her lines correctly, she was Dutch. Just then the wind rose and the *Cornelius de Witt* changed course, leaned to port and headed straight for us once more. But this time she was so close that we knew she would not turn in time.

"Thunder!" cried Le Gleo, his Breton soul aching to see a fine ship doomed to smash upon a reef, "she's going to pile up! She's gone!"

I shook my head:

"Yes, and a shame to see that beautiful ship wreck herself. And we're helpless."

There was nothing we could do but watch. A ship sailing with all sail spread, creaming the sea with her forefoot as she runs before the wind, is one of the most beautiful sights in the world—but this time I could feel the tears stinging in my eyes as I saw this fine ship headed for her doom.

All this time our glasses were riveted on her and we suddenly cried out together:

"The rats!"

Now we knew why this ship, in perfect condition, was sailing without her crew aboard. They had been driven out by the rats. Not those poor specimens of rats you see ashore, barely reaching the length of one foot from their trembling noses to the tip of their skinny tails, wretched creatures that dodge and hide at the mere sound of a footfall.

No, these were ships' rats, huge, wise creatures, born on the sea, sailing all over the world on ships, transferring to other, larger ships as they multiply. There is as much difference between the rats of the land and these maritime rats as between a fishing smack and an armored cruiser.

The rats of the sea are fierce, bold animals. Large, strong and intelligent, clannish and seawise, able to put the best of mariners to shame with their knowledge of the sea, their uncanny ability to foretell the weather.

And they are brave, the rats, and vengeful. If you so much as harm one, his sharp cry will bring hordes of his fellows to swarm over you, tear you and not cease until your flesh has been stripped from the bones.

The ones on this ship, the rats of Holland, are the worst, superior to other rats of the sea as their brethren are to the land rats. There is a well-known tale about these animals.

A Dutch captain, thinking to protect his cargo, brought aboard his ship—not cats—but two terriers, dogs trained in the hunting, fighting and killing of vicious rats. By the time the ship, sailing from Rotterdam, had passed the Ostend light, the dogs were gone and never seen again. In twenty-four hours they had been overwhelmed, killed, and eaten by the rats.

At times, when the cargo does not suffice, the rats attack the crew, either driving them from the ship or eating them alive. And studying the *Cornelius de Witt*, I turned sick, for her small boats were all in place. She had not been abandoned.

Over her bridge, on her deck, in the rigging, on every

visible spot, the ship was a writhing mass—a starving army coming towards us aboard a vessel gone mad!

Our island was a small spot in that immense stretch of sea. The ship could have grazed us, passed to port or starboard with its ravening cargo—but no, she came for us at full speed, as if she were leading the regatta at a race, and impaled herself on a sharp point of rock.

There was a dull shock as her bottom stove in, then a horrible crackling as the three masts went overboard at once, as if cut down with one blow of some gigantic sickle. A sighing groan came as the water rushed into the ship, then she split in two and sank like a stone.

But the rats did not drown. Not these fellows! As much at home in the sea as any fish, they formed ranks in the water, heads lifted, tails stretched out, paws paddling. And half of them, those from the forepart of the ship, sprang along the masts and onto the rocks in the instant before she sank. Before we had time even to move, nothing remained of the three-master save some pieces of wreckage floating on the surface and an army of rats covering the rocks left bare by the receding tide.

Thousands of heads rose, felt the wind and we were scented, seen! To them we were fresh meat, after possible weeks of starving. There came a scream, composed of innumerable screams, sharper than the howl of a saw attacking a bar of iron, and in the one motion, every rat leaped to attack the tower!

We barely had time to leap back, close the door leading onto the gallery, descend the stairs and shut every window tightly. Luckily the door at the base of the light, which we never could have reached in time, was of bronze set in granite and was tightly closed.

The horrible band, in no measurable time, had

swarmed up and over the tower as if it had been a tree, piled on the embrasures of the windows, scraped at the glass with thousands of claws, covered the lighthouse with a furry mantle and reached the top of the tower, filling the gallery and piling atop the lantern.

Their teeth grated as they pressed against the glass of the lantern-room, where they could plainly see us, though they could not reach us. A few millimeters of glass, luckily very strong, separated our faces from their gleaming, beady eyes, their sharp claws and teeth. Their odor filled the tower, poisoned our lungs and rasped our nostrils with a pestilential, nauseating smell. And there we were, sealed alive in our own light, prisoners of a horde of starving rats.

That first night, the tension was so great that we could not sleep. Every moment, we felt that some opening had been made, some window given away, and that our horrible besiegers were pouring through the breach. The rising tide, chasing those of the rats which had stayed on the bare rocks, increased the numbers clinging to the walls, piled on the balcony—so much so that clusters of rats clinging to one another hung from the lantern and the gallery.

With the coming of darkness we lit the light and the turning beam completely maddened the beasts. As the light turned, it successively blinded thousands of rats crowded against the glass, while the darkside of the lantern-room gleamed with thousands of points of light, burning like the eyes of jungle beasts in the night.

All the while we could hear the enraged scraping of claws against the stone and glass, while the chorus of cries was so loud that we had to shout to hear one another. From time to time, some of the rats fought among themselves and a dark cluster would detach itself, fall-ing into the sea like a ripe fruit from a tree. Then we would see phosphorescent streaks as triangular fins slashed the water—sharks, permanent guardians of our rock, feasting on our jailors.

The next day we were calmer, and amused ourselves teasing the rats, placing our faces against the glass which separated us. They could not fathom the invisible barrier which separated them from us and we laughed as we watched them leaping against the heavy glass.

But the day after that, we realized how serious our position was. The air was foul, even the heavy smell of oil within our stronghold could not dominate the fetid odor of the beasts massed around us. And there was no way of admitting fresh air without also admitting the rats.

The morning of the fourth day, at early dawn, I saw the wooden framework of my window, eaten away from the outside, sagging inwards. I called my comrades and the three of us fastened a sheet of tin in the opening, sealing it tightly. When we had completed the task, Itchoua turned to us and said dully:

"Well—the supply boat came thirteen days ago, and she won't be back for twenty-nine." He pointed at the white metal plate sealing the opening through the gran-ite—"If that gives way—" he shrugged—"they can change the name of this place to Six Skeletons Key."

The next six days and seven nights, our only distrac-tion was watching the rats whose holds were insecure, fall a hundred and twenty feet into the maws of the sharks—but they were so many that we could not see any diminution in their numbers.

Thinking to calm ourselves and pass the time, we attempted to count them, but we soon gave up. They moved incessantly, never still. Then we tried identifying them, naming them.

One of them, larger than the others, who seemed to lead them in their rushes against the glass separating us, we named "Nero"; and there were several others whom we had learned to distinguish through various peculiarities.

But the thought of our bones joining those of the convicts was always in the back of our minds. And the gloom of our prison fed these thoughts, for the interior of the light was almost completely dark, as we had to seal every window in the same fashion as mine, and the only space that still admitted daylight was the glassed-in lantern-room at the very top of the tower.

Then Le Gleo became morose and had nightmares in which he would see the three skeletons dancing around him, gleaming coldly, seeking to grasp him. His maniacal, raving descriptions were so vivid that Itchoua and I began seeing them also.

It was a living nightmare, the raging cries of the rats as they swarmed over the light, mad with hunger; the sickening, strangling odor of their bodies——

True, there is a way of signaling from lighthouses. But to reach the mast on which to hang the signal we would have to go out on the gallery where the rats were.

There was only one thing left to do. After debating all of the ninth day, we decided not to light the lantern that night. This is the greatest breach of our service, never committed as long as the tenders of the light are alive; for the light is something sacred, warning ships of danger in the night. Either the light gleams, a quarter hour after sundown, or no one is left alive to light it.

Well, that night, Three Skeleton Light was dark, and

all the men were alive. At the risk of causing ships to crash on our reefs, we left it unlit, for we were worn out—going mad!

At two in the morning, while Itchoua was dozing in his room, the sheet of metal sealing his window gave way. The chief had just time enough to leap to his feet and cry for help, the rats swarming over him.

But Le Gleo and I, who had been watching from the lantern-room, got to him immediately, and the three of us battled with the horde of maddened rats which flowed through the gaping window. They bit, we struck them down with our knives—and retreated.

We locked the door of the room on them, but before we had time to bind our wounds, the door was eaten through, and gave way and we retreated up the stairs, fighting off the rats that leaped on us from the knee deep swarm.

I do not remember, to this day, how we ever managed to escape. All I can remember is wading through them up the stairs, striking them off as they swarmed over us; and then we found ourselves, bleeding from innumerable bites, our clothes shredded, sprawled across the trapdoor in the floor of the lantern-room—without food or drink. Luckily, the trapdoor was metal set into the granite with iron bolts.

The rats occupied the entire light beneath us, and on the floor of our retreat lay some twenty of their fellows, who had gotten in with us before the trapdoor closed, and whom we had killed with our knives. Below us, in the tower, we could hear the screams of the rats as they devoured everything edible that they found. Those on the outside squealed in reply, and writhed in a horrible curtain as they stared at us through the glass of the lantern-room.

Itchoua sat up, stared silently at his blood trickling from the wounds on his limbs and body, and running in thin streams on the floor around him. Le Gleo, who was in as bad a state (and so was I, for that matter) stared at the chief and me vacantly, started as his gaze swung to the multitude of rats against the glass, then suddenly began laughing horribly:

"Hee! Hee! The Three Skeletons! Hee! Hee! The Three Skeletons are now *six* skeletons! *Six* skeletons!"

He threw his head back and howled, his eyes glazed, a trickle of saliva running from the corners of his mouth and thinning the blood flowing over his chest. I shouted to him to shut up, but he did not hear me, so I did the only thing I could to quiet him—I swung the back of my hand across his face.

The howling stopped suddenly, his eyes swung around the room, then he bowed his head and began weeping softly, like a child.

Our darkened light had been noticed from the mainland, and as dawn was breaking the patrol was there, to investigate the failure of our light. Looking through my binoculars, I could see the horrified expression on the faces of the officers and crew when, the daylight strengthening, they saw the light completely covered by a seething mass of rats. They thought, as I afterwards found out, that we had been eaten alive.

But the rats had also seen the ship, or had scented the crew. As the ship drew nearer, a solid phalanx left the light, plunged into the water and, swimming out, attempted to board her. They would have succeeded, as the ship was hove to, but the engineer connected his steam to hose on the deck and scalded the head of the attacking column, which slowed them up long enough for the ship to get underway and leave the rats behind.

Then the sharks took part. Belly up, mouths gaping, they arrived in swarms and scooped up the rats, sweeping through them like a sickle through wheat. That was one day that sharks really served a useful purpose.

The remaining rats turned tail, swam to the shore and emerged dripping. As they neared the light, their comrades greeted them with shrill cries, with what sounded like a derisive note predominating. They answered angrily and mingled with their fellows. From the several tussles that broke out, they resented being ridiculed for their failure to capture the ship.

But all this did nothing to get us out of our jail. The small ship could not approach, but steamed around the light at a safe distance, and the tower must have seemed fantastic, some weird, many-mouthed beast hurling defiance at them.

Finally, seeing the rats running in and out of the tower through the door and the windows, those on the ship decided that we had perished and were about to leave when Itchoua, regaining his senses, thought of using the light as a signal. He lit it and, using a plank placed and withdrawn before the beam to form the dots and dashes, quickly sent out our story to those on the vessel.

Our reply came quickly. When they understood our position, how we could not get rid of the rats, Le Gleo's mind going fast, Itchoua and myself covered with bites; cornered in the lantern-room without food or water, they had a signal-man send us their reply.

His arms, swinging like those of a windmill, he quickly spelled out:

"Don't give up, hang on a little longer! We'll get you out of this!"

Then she turned and steamed at top speed for the coast, leaving us little reassured.

She was back at noon, accompanied by the supply ship, two small coast guard boats, and the fire boat—a small squadron. At twelve-thirty the battle was on.

After a short reconnaissance, the fire boat picked her way slowly through the reefs until she was close to us, then turned her powerful jet of water on the rats. The heavy stream tore the rats from their places, hurled them screaming into the water where the sharks gulped them down. But for every ten that were dislodged, seven swam ashore, and the stream could do nothing to the rats within the tower. Furthermore, some of them, instead of returning to the rocks, boarded the fire boat and the men were forced to battle them hand to hand. They were true rats of Holland, fearing no man, fighting for the right to live!

Nightfall came, and it was as if nothing had been done, the rats were still in possession. One of the patrol boats stayed by the island, the rest of the flotilla departed for the coast. We had to spend another night in our prison. Le Gleo was sitting on the floor, babbling about skeletons and as I turned to Itchoua, he fell unconscious from his wounds. I was in no better shape and could feel my blood flaming with fever.

Somehow the night dragged by, and the next afternoon I saw a tug, accompanied by the fire boat, come from the mainland with a huge barge in tow. Through my glasses, I saw that the barge was filled with meat.

Risking the treacherous reefs, the tug dragged the barge as close to the island as possible. To the last rat, our besiegers deserted the rock, swam out and boarded the barge reeking with the scent of freshly cut meat. The tug dragged the barge about a mile from shore, where the fire boat drenched the barge with gasoline. A well placed incendiary shell from the patrol boat set her on fire. The barge was covered with flames immediately and the rats took to the water in swarms, but the patrol boat bombarded them with shrapnel from a safe distance, and the sharks finished off the survivors.

A whaleboat from the patrol boat took us off the island and left three men to replace us. By nightfall we were in the hospital in Cayenne. What became of my friends?

Well, Le Gleo's mind had cracked and he was raving mad. They sent him back to France and locked him up in an asylum, the poor devil; Itchoua died within a week; a rat's bite is dangerous in that hot, humid climate, and infection sets in rapidly.

As for me—when they fumigated the light and repaired the damage done by the rats, I resumed my service there. Why not? No reason why such an incident should keep me from finishing out my service there, is there?

Besides—I told you I liked the place—to be truthful, I've never had a post as pleasant as that one, and when my time came to leave it forever, I tell you that I almost wept as Three Skeleton Key disappeared below the horizon.

RESCUER EXTRAORDINARY

By J. Campbell Bruce

Here is what I call a human interest sea story. J. Campbell Bruce, a newspaperman on The San Francisco Chronicle, *became interested in the fate of a fisherman named John Napoli, who had performed a feat demanding wide publicity. John was involved, in August of 1950, in one of those disasters which occur with unhappy regularity in all the seas of the world. A brand new navy hospital ship, out on her trials outside San Francisco, returned home in the fog which is all too common in those parts, and was rammed by an outward-bound freighter and sunk. The hospital ship, as is usual on trials, carried a double crew of navy and civilian personnel. John Napoli, homeward bound with a load of fish, found himself in a sea covered with fog and cluttered with human beings. For hours he toiled to haul them into his little boat. He jettisoned his load of fish and took on more and more survivors. He even towed a bunch of sailors to another rescue boat. Seventy people owe their lives to John's tremendous exertions. Those efforts were so serious that he was hospitalized when he got ashore. He lost his fish and his health, and eventually was forced to sell his boat to continue to eat.*

Mr. Bruce took the matter up and the result was that the public sent in subscriptions. Eventually, the navy paid John compensation for his losses. The Board of Supervisors sent him a scroll, his fellow Italian-Americans gave him a banquet, and we may be sure some of those seventy rescued men and women did not forget their savior. It seems likely that both

Reprinted by permission of the author and the publishers from *The Reader's Digest*, March, 1951.

John Napoli and his survivors will live happily for the rest of their lives.

ONE DAY not long ago John Napoli, a fisherman in San Francisco, made a deal to sell his crab traps. He had paid $3200 for them; he let them go for $1000. His reason: "I gotta eat."

When word of the transaction got out, the people of San Francisco were furious. For John Napoli is a hero. What he did was incredible, but he did it. Singlehanded, he saved 70 lives and in so doing, made himself a cripple.

The U.S.S. *Benevolence*, a Navy hospital ship, was returning from a trial run in a blinding fog one day last August when, two miles off the Golden Gate, she collided with an outbound freighter, the *Mary Luckenbach*. Because it was a trial, the *Benevolence* carried two full crews—Navy and civilian—so that there were 526 persons aboard. She sank within half an hour.

At two o'clock in the morning of August 25, Napoli had eased his 34-foot *Flora* out of her mooring at Fisherman's Wharf. He still had seven weeks to go in salmon, then a month of the rich albacore run. After that, if he hauled high boat again in the crab season, he could pay off the $400 he owed on a recent overhaul job on the *Flora*, and maybe he could even whittle down the mortgage on his new home.

At the fishing grounds 30 miles out the fog hung on all day. Napoli worked hard watching his trolling course and hauling in the salmon, some of them 60 pounds of lashing fight. By late afternoon he had caught 550 pounds of fish, and he headed home.

About two miles off the Gate he saw what he thought was a turtle. And then, a minute or so later—

"All a sudden I see a big black spot. Jeez, I got a-scared! I thought I was on wrong side the channel."

It was the towering steel wall of the *Mary Luckenbach*. Abruptly a Coast Guard boat slid out of the mist and a megaphoned voice boomed: "We need your assistance."

He thought they said something about a body overboard. He remembered the turtle and shouted, "Follow me." He went directly to the spot and hauled his first survivor aboard.

"I notice he is wearin' a Navy suit. Must be a shipwreck, but I can't get nuttin' outa that man. His mouth is all cut and bleedin' from chatterin', he's so froze.

"What happens then it's a miracle, like God pressed a button and lifts the fog. You could see a three-block area. God Almighty, those heads bobbin' all round, like seagulls sittin' on the water. My hair stands up, my eyes get fulla tears. And then the fog comes down, like God said, 'Now you seen 'em, go to work.'"

It was now slack water—the period between tides—and there were perhaps three hours before the swift run-out might sweep victims to sea. Napoli set the *Flora* at a trolling crawl and began scouting for survivors. When he spotted a head and shoulders nesting in a life jacket he would throw out a line, then put the *Flora* in neutral.

Now came the real job—incredibly difficult for one man. The survivors had been in the numbing water an hour and a half; they were sea-soaked, helpless. And the stretch from the *Flora's* rail to the water was better than three feet.

"I put my knees against the rail, then stoop down and grab 'em over the shoulders and under the arms. Wait for a wave, pull up, then grab 'em more by the seat of the pants. Two hands ain't enough sometimes so I use my teeth like a horse, bite his shirt or pants, then pull more, till his belly's over the rail. Soon as a body gets there, boy, he's safe. I grab a good hold on his leg and heave 'em. I have to make plenty room so they don't hurt the other guys when they flop down. So I throw three of my four big boxes of fish overboard and push the other one back outa the way.

"Pretty soon I got a full boat. I figure these people need first aid quick. They all got shocked from standin' around in the cold water."

He came alongside the *Mary Luckenbach* and shouted for assistance. Two men slid down the *Flora's* mast, and one of them shoved the last box of fish over the stern. "Don't worry," he assured Napoli, "Luckenbach will pay for it."

They transferred the eighteen survivors in wire-basket stretchers—a slow, dangerous business. The little boat bobbed and lurched and banged against the steel plates of the freighter. Her rail got chewed up and her turn-buckles busted.

After that Napoli went trolling for more. He was worried. This was taking too long; the run-out tide would catch up with them.

"All my life I don't work so hard. My arms ache like I got a charley horse. And alla time I keep sayin' in Italian, 'God give me strength to pull these people in.'"

A priest, Chaplain John J. Reardon of the *Benevolence*, was now aboard. He understood and spoke up, "Don't you worry, signor. God will give you the strength."

It startled Napoli. "Him answerin' like that—I thought it was God. I almost jump outa the boat."

The scene was like a painting of doom by an old master. Dark-gray shapes of rescue craft prowled in the gloomy mists. The shifting fog at times revealed the submerged *Benevolence;* the great red cross freshly painted on her white hull shimmered in the liquid-glass wash of the waves. The green combers were sown with litter and upstretched arms. And over all dinned an unearthly tumult—the watery throb of motors, the shouting of the crews, the piercing cries from throats filled with fear.

"The noise was somethin' terrible. When I get to thinkin' about it in my sleep it jumps me outa bed and I'm done for the night. You hear 500 people hollerin', you never get it outa the system."

Napoli's muscles were beginning to flame with fatigue. His throat was parched, but he kept on.

Napoli grabbed one survivor under the arms, pulled up, then reached farther for a chest hold.

"And I think, that's funny. He's all soft there. When I get him up I say to myself, 'Sonofagun, this is a woman!' She was barefeet and walks by herself up in the bow and sit down. She's purple like everybody so I give her my coat and say, 'You want my underwears, too?' She tole me, 'No, thanks, I'm okay now.' And she smile at me, she's that happy to be save."

This was Ensign Helen Wallis, a Navy nurse. Napoli beams as he recalls her pluckiness. "There's a brave soldier! She don't complain one bit, not even a word. She tole me, 'I'm gonna give these fellas respiration.' And all soakin' wet herself. She got guts, that woman."

He was transferring his last batch when night suddenly settled into the fog. In all he had pulled 54 survivors out of the water. As he finished unloading he heard with relief that "everythin' was underneath control," for the tide was beginning to ebb fast.

The *Flora*, battered and wobbly, had crawled about a city block when she plowed into a cluster of plasma boxes. Above the crunching noise came a solitary cry.

"I stop and run up forward to get away from the *purp-purp* of the exhaust and I yell, 'Holler again, fella, holler again!'"

He heard nothing more and started back to the pilot house. And then he saw them, about 12 feet off midships.

"There they was on a big lazy swell, 16 Navy fellas— just kids, all huggin' each other like a ring. Another stroke of the propeller and I'd a run by and maybe they'd a gone out to sea. I get 'em to the boat but I just ain't got the strength left to pull 'em up. I stood there and cried. I couldn't help it; I bawl like a baby. I tole 'em, 'Take it easy. I get you saved somehow.'"

He made them fast to the rail and carefully towed them until he found another rescue craft.

Complete tally next day showed that only 23 lives were lost, because eventually 30 rescue craft had gathered at the scene.

It was well past midnight when Napoli climbed the stairs to his home. His wife, Flora, after whom the boat was christened, took one look and almost fainted.

"I was so cold she give me two hot baths but I don't even feel it. Next day I have a time gettin' outa bed. I can't straighten out. Arms, legs, neck, everything's stiff. When I cough I hurt all over, specially the chest and back. I try to tie my shoes but I can't stoop so good. And when I'm stooped it clicks here"—indicating the small of the back—"and it won't let me up."

Despite his aches, Napoli went down to the Lucken-bach Steamship Line to ask about that last box of fish pushed overboard. The claims agent suggested he see their attorneys. "Why do I got to see attorneys?" Napoli demanded. "I ain't committed no crime."

The sinking of the *Benevolence* was of course a big story for the San Francisco papers but somehow Napoli's exploit received only a brief mention and was quickly forgotten.

As a reporter for the *Chronicle* I happened to tele-phone him on a news-quiet Sunday afternoon two months later, to ask how things were going.

"Oh, fine," he said. "Everything comin' along fine."

No particular story there. I was about to hang up when I remembered the fish. Had he been paid?

"The Navy says she is goin' to pay me but things like that, it takes time. But everything fine. Tomorrow a man is buyin' my crab traps."

With crab season coming on? But why?

The answer was simple: "I gotta eat. My wife got a job, first time she work since we got married, but that don't catch up with the bills."

What about his fishing?

"I can't stand standin' up, my back hurts. I got to lay down. And you can't make a livin' layin' down."

Of all the hundreds of *Benevolence* disaster pictures, none had included Napoli. So we went down to the wharf one day to take a belated shot. And there my throat tightened up. Nailed to the mast of the *Flora* was a board and on it, newly written with painful care, was the announcement: "FOR SALE. LO 4-3582. Call at 6 p.m."

Napoli, a native San Franciscan and son of an im-migrant Sicilian fisherman, had gone out with the boats for 35 years. After the disaster he had spent 22 days in the hospital—and lost 27 pounds. "I feel kinda bad," he said. "But I figure like this, no use foolin' anybody, specially myself. If I go out there alone I want to be perfect specimen. If I'm pullin' in a wild one and my back locks up maybe I stay out there."

The *Flora* bore ugly scars of her encounter with the steel-plated ships that night. It would cost $1000 to put her in shape to sell.

After Napoli's story was told, dollars poured in to the *Chronicle*, unsolicited; readers quickly contributed over $1100. Many of the letters to the editor asked why the people Napoli saved had not kicked through. Napoli explained that they tried to.

"They all come out to see me in bunches. The nurse, she looked 60 years old when I pull her outa the water; when she come to the hospital, boy, she was a real kewpie doll. And she brought me a bouquet of roses like you never seen. But what really gag me up was seein' those kids; they come to see me all together. I got so choke up I couldn't say hello, boys. Everybody's very grateful and want to pay me. One even offers $1000."

Napoli hunched his shoulders. "You save a fella's life you don't take money for it. They do the same for you."

In the days after Napoli became an outpatient at the hospital he was like a fish out of water: "I go every day to get my terrapy. Bake the back, shoot electricity through the system, massage the back—what they call terrapy. If it's a nice day I go down and bail out the *Flora;* she's leakin' water by the galore."

On the foggy, rainy days Napoli sits alone and counts his blessings. There's one trophy—a glittering sloop on a plastic base, tendered him at a banquet by Italian

Americans in Oakland. There's a resolution by the San Francisco Board of Supervisors. There's a scroll in a gilt frame: "The United States Navy recognizes with gratitude the meritorious service . . . worthy of the highest tribute from all. . . ."

The Navy's gratitude took more material form a week later: the Secretary of the Navy okayed a $4422 check for Napoli's loss of fish and damage to the *Flora*.

And there's the sheaf of letters. John Napoli sifted them through his stubby fingers. "I didn't think so many people would . . . no foolin', I feel so happy about things"—his voice thickened a little—"I feel very kind to these people."

THE SECRET SHARER

By Joseph Conrad

When Joseph Conrad was becoming known as a writer, he received a peremptory request from a Polish lady novelist to contribute to a Polish magazine, and furthermore to write in Polish, rather than in English. She charged him with lack of patriotism for this habit.

Conrad, by that time, had a long service in the British Merchant Marine, and before that had served in French ships. He had been in local vessels in the eastern seas. He had settled in England and married an English wife. He explained to his fellow Pole that he was not a political exile, but a voluntary emigrant who had chosen England and English to practice his art.

This was our good fortune. Few of us read Polish, and it is doubtful if Conrad's special genius as a writer would have carried over in translation. He really created a special kind of English to express his somber and ironical view of the world.

"The Secret Sharer," a story of the East, was the product of Conrad's supreme powers in the early years of the century, the years which produced Youth and Heart of Darkness. It appeared with two other long tales in Twixt Land and Sea in 1912. He returned to the same locale, the Gulf of Siam, in his novel, The Shadow Line.

"The Secret Sharer" is a good example of the Conrad method at its simplest. He discards the more complex mech-

Reprinted from *Twixt Land and Sea*, published by Doubleday & Co. By permission of J. M. Dent & Sons, Ltd.

anism of his Jamesian long novels (Chance, Lord Jim, and The Rescue are examples) and uses straight narrative in the first person. It is the narrator's first command, suddenly thrust upon him by one of those casualties of the sea which are always happening. He takes the anchor watch himself, with the idea of giving his officers some rest and to get acquainted with his new ship. During the night he finds the rope ladder hanging over the side and tries to pull it in. He finds an unknown swimmer holding to it in exhaustion. It is the mate of a ship just arrived, who had killed a man during a storm, and who had escaped by swimming. The captain lends him some pajamas and hides him in his bathroom.

The extreme ingenuity and simplicity of the plot, its obvious naturalness, is characteristic of Conrad. On the highest fiction level he gives you a storm, a murder, an escape, and another escape. The supposed eccentricities of their new captain conceal the fugitive from the crew until, at the moment of supreme suspense, while the ship is altering her course away from a dangerous shore, he dives through an after hatch. He leaves, as he arrives, in darkness and secrecy.

While no anthology of sea writing would be complete without one of Conrad's stories, I feel a particular pleasure in reprinting this one.

ON MY right hand there were lines of fishing-stakes resembling a mysterious system of half-submerged bamboo fences, incomprehensible in its division of the domain of tropical fishes, and crazy of aspect as if abandoned for ever by some nomad tribe of fishermen now gone to the other end of the ocean; for there was no sign of human habitation as far as the eye could reach. To the left a group of barren islets, suggesting ruins of stone walls, towers, and blockhouses, had its foundation set in a blue sea that itself looked solid, so still and stable did it lie below my feet; even the track of light from the westering sun shone smoothly, without that animated glitter which tells of an imperceptible ripple. And when I turned my head to take a parting glance at the tug which had just left us anchored outside the bar, I saw the straight line of the flat shore joined to the stable sea, edge to edge, with a perfect and unmarked closeness, in one levelled floor half brown, half blue under the enormous dome of the sky. Corresponding in their insignificance to the islets of the sea, two small clumps of trees, one on each side of the only fault in the impeccable joint, marked the mouth of the river Meinam we had just left on the first preparatory stage of our homeward journey; and, far back on the inland level, a larger and loftier mass, the grove surrounding the great Paknam pagoda, was the only thing on which the eye could rest from the vain task of exploring the monotonous sweep of the horizon. Here and there gleams as of a few scattered pieces of silver marked the windings of the great river; and on the nearest of them, just within the bar, the tug steaming right into the land became lost to my sight, hull and funnel and masts, as though the impassive earth had swallowed her up without an effort, without a tremor. My eye followed the light cloud of her smoke, now here, now there, above the plain, according to the devious curves of the stream, but always fainter and farther away, till I lost it at last behind the mitre-shaped hill of the great pagoda. And then I was left alone with my ship, anchored at the head of the Gulf of Siam.

She floated at the starting-point of a long journey, very still in an immense stillness, the shadows of her spars flung far to the eastward by the setting sun. At that moment I was alone on her decks. There was not a sound in her—and around us nothing moved, nothing lived, not a canoe on the water, not a bird in the air, not a cloud in the sky. In this breathless pause at the threshold of a long passage we seemed to be measuring our fitness for a long and arduous enterprise, the appointed task of both our existences to be carried out, far from all human eyes, with only sky and sea for spectators and for judges.

There must have been some glare in the air to interfere with one's sight, because it was only just before the sun left us that my roaming eyes made out beyond the highest ridge of the principal islet of the group something which did away with the solemnity of perfect solitude. The tide of darkness flowed on swiftly; and with tropical suddenness a swarm of stars came out above the shadowy earth, while I lingered yet, my hand resting lightly on my ship's rail as if on the shoulder of a trusted friend. But, with all that multitude of celestial bodies staring down at once, the comfort of quiet communion with her was gone for good. And there were also disturbing sounds by this time—voices, footsteps forward; the steward flitted along the maindeck, a busily ministering spirit; a hand-bell tinkled urgently under the poopdeck. . . .

I found my two officers waiting for me near the supper table, in the lighted cuddy. We sat down at once, and as I helped the chief mate, I said:

"Are you aware that there is a ship anchored inside the islands? I saw her mastheads above the ridge as the sun went down."

He raised sharply his simple face, overcharged by a terrible growth of whisker, and emitted his usual ejaculations: "Bless my soul, sir! You don't say so!"

My second mate was a round-cheeked, silent young man, grave beyond his years, I thought; but as our eyes

happened to meet I detected a slight quiver on his lips.
I looked down at once. It was not my part to encourage
sneering on board my ship. It must be said, too, that I
knew very little of my officers. In consequence of certain
events of no particular significance, except to myself, I
had been appointed to the command only a fortnight before. Neither did I know much of the hands forward. All
these people had been together for eighteen months or
so, and my position was that of the only stranger on
board. I mention this because it has some bearing on
what is to follow. But what I felt most was my being a
stranger to the ship; and if all the truth must be told, I
was somewhat of a stranger to myself. The youngest
man on board (barring the second mate), and untried as
yet by a position of the fullest responsibility, I was willing to take the adequacy of the others for granted. They
had simply to be equal to their tasks; but I wondered
how far I should turn out faithful to that ideal conception of one's own personality every man sets up for himself secretly.

Meantime the chief mate, with an almost visible effect
of collaboration on the part of his round eyes and
frightful whiskers, was trying to evolve a theory of the
anchored ship. His dominant trait was to take all things
into earnest consideration. He was of a painstaking turn
of mind. As he used to say, he "liked to account to himself" for practically everything that came in his way,
down to a miserable scorpion he had found in his cabin
a week before. The why and the wherefore of that
scorpion—how it got on board and came to select his
room rather than the pantry (which was a dark place
and more what a scorpion would be partial to), and how
on earth it managed to drown itself in the inkwell of his

writing desk—had exercised him infinitely. The ship within the islands was much more easily accounted for; and just as we were about to rise from table he made his pronouncement. She was, he doubted not, a ship from home lately arrived. Probably she drew too much water to cross the bar except at the top of spring tides. Therefore she went into that natural harbour to wait for a few days in preference to remaining in an open roadstead.

"That's so," confirmed the second mate, suddenly, in his slightly hoarse voice. "She draws over twenty feet. She's the Liverpool ship *Sephora* with a cargo of coal. Hundred and twenty-three days from Cardiff."

We looked at him in surprise.

"The tugboat skipper told me when he came on board for your letters, sir," explained the young man. "He expects to take her up the river the day after tomorrow."

After thus overwhelming us with the extent of his information he slipped out of the cabin. The mate observed regretfully that he "could not account for that young fellow's whims." What prevented him telling us all about it at once, he wanted to know.

I detained him as he was making a move. For the last two days the crew had had plenty of hard work, and the night before they had very little sleep. I felt painfully that I—a stranger—was doing something unusual when I directed him to let all hands turn in without setting an anchor-watch. I proposed to keep on deck myself till one o'clock or thereabouts. I would get the second mate to relieve me at that hour.

"He will turn out the cook and the steward at four," I concluded, "and then give you a call. Of course at the slightest sign of any sort of wind we'll have the hands up and make a start at once."

He concealed his astonishment. "Very well, sir." Outside the cuddy he put his head in the second mate's door to inform him of my unheard-of caprice to take a five hours' anchor-watch on myself. I heard the other raise his voice incredulously—"What? The Captain himself?" Then a few more murmurs, a door closed, then another. A few moments later I went on deck.

My strangeness, which had made me sleepless, had prompted that unconventional arrangement, as if I had expected in those solitary hours of the night to get on terms with the ship of which I knew nothing, manned by men of whom I knew very little more. Fast alongside a wharf, littered like any ship in port with a tangle of unrelated things, invaded by unrelated shore people, I had hardly seen her yet properly. Now, as she lay cleared for sea, the stretch of her main-deck seemed to me very fine under the stars. Very fine, very roomy for her size, and very inviting. I descended the poop and paced the waist, my mind picturing to myself the coming passage through the Malay Archipelago, down the Indian Ocean, and up the Atlantic. All its phases were familiar enough to me, every characteristic, all the alternatives which were likely to face me on the high seas—everything!
. . . except the novel responsibility of command. But I took heart from the reasonable thought that the ship was like other ships, the men like other men, and that the sea was not likely to keep any special surprises for my discomfiture.

Arrived at that comforting conclusion, I bethought myself of a cigar and went below to get it. All was still down there. Everybody at the after end of the ship was sleeping profoundly. I came out again on the quarter-deck, agreeably at ease in my sleeping-suit on that warm breathless night, barefooted, a glowing cigar in my teeth, and, going forward, I was met by the profound silence of the fore end of the ship. Only as I passed the door of the forecastle I heard a deep, quiet, trustful sigh of some sleeper inside. And suddenly I rejoiced in the great security of the sea as compared with the unrest of the land, in my choice of that untempted life presenting no disquieting problems, invested with an elementary moral beauty by the absolute straightforwardness of its appeal and by the singleness of its purpose.

The riding-light in the fore-rigging burned with a clear, untroubled, as if symbolic, flame, confident and bright in the mysterious shades of the night. Passing on my way aft along the other side of the ship, I observed that the rope side-ladder, put over, no doubt, for the master of the tug when he came to fetch away our letters, had not been hauled in as it should have been. I became annoyed at this, for exactitude in small matters is the very soul of discipline. Then I reflected that I had myself peremptorily dismissed my officers from duty, and by my own act had prevented the anchor-watch being formally set and things properly attended to. I asked myself whether it was wise ever to interfere with the established routine of duties even from the kindest of motives. My action might have made me appear eccentric. Goodness only knew how that absurdly whiskered mate would "account" for my conduct, and what the whole ship thought of that informality of their new captain. I was vexed with myself.

Not from compunction certainly, but, as it were mechanically, I proceeded to get the ladder in myself. Now a side-ladder of that sort is a light affair and comes in easily, yet my vigorous tug, which should have brought it flying on board, merely recoiled upon my body in a totally unexpected jerk. What the devil! . . . I was so astounded by the immovableness of that ladder that I remained stock-still, trying to account for it to myself like that imbecile mate of mine. In the end, of course, I put my head over the rail.

The side of the ship made an opaque belt of shadow on the darkling glassy shimmer of the sea. But I saw at once something elongated and pale floating very close to the ladder. Before I could form a guess a faint flash of phosphorescent light, which seemed to issue suddenly from the naked body of a man, flickered in the sleeping water with the elusive, silent play of summer lightning in a night sky. With a gasp I saw revealed to my stare a pair of feet, the long legs, a broad livid back immersed right up to the neck in a greenish cadaverous glow. One hand, awash, clutched the bottom rung of the ladder. He was complete but for the head. A headless corpse! The cigar dropped out of my gaping mouth with a tiny plop and a short hiss quite audible in the absolute still-ness of all things under heaven. At that I suppose he raised up his face, a dimly pale oval in the shadow of the ship's side. But even then I could only barely make out down there the shape of his black-haired head. How-ever, it was enough for the horrid, frost-bound sensation which had gripped me about the chest to pass off. The moment of vain exclamations was past, too. I only climbed on the spare spar and leaned over the rail as far as I could, to bring my eyes nearer to that mystery float-ing alongside.

As he hung by the ladder, like a resting swimmer, the sea-lightning played about his limbs at every stir; and he appeared in it ghastly, silvery, fish-like. He remained as mute as a fish too. He made no motion to get out of the water, either. It was inconceivable that he should not attempt to come on board, and strangely troubling to suspect that perhaps he did not want to. And my first words were prompted by just that troubled incertitude.

"What's the matter?" I asked in my ordinary tone, speaking down to the face upturned exactly under mine.

"Cramp," it answered, no louder. Then slightly anxious, "I say, no need to call any one."

"I was not going to," I said.

"Are you alone on deck?"

"Yes."

I had somehow the impression that he was on the point of letting go the ladder to swim away beyond my ken—mysterious as he came. But, for the moment, this being appearing as if he had risen from the bottom of the sea (it was certainly the nearest land to the ship) wanted only to know the time. I told him. And he, down there, tentatively:

"I suppose your captain's turned in?"

"I am sure he isn't," I said.

He seemed to struggle with himself, for I heard something like the low, bitter murmur of doubt. "What's the good?" His next words came out with a hesitating effort.

"Look here, my man. Could you call him out quietly?"

I thought the time had come to declare myself.

"*I* am the captain."

I heard a "By Jove!" whispered at the level of the water. The phosphorescence flashed in the swirl of the water all about his limbs, his other hand seized the ladder.

"My name's Leggatt."

The voice was calm and resolute. A good voice. The self-possession of that man had somehow induced a corresponding state in myself. It was very quietly that I remarked:

"You must be a good swimmer."

"Yes. I've been in the water practically since nine o'clock. The question for me now is whether I am to let go this ladder and go on swimming till I sink from exhaustion, or—to come on board here."

I felt this was no mere formula of desperate speech, but a real alternative in the view of a strong soul. I should have gathered from this that he was young; indeed, it is only the young who are ever confronted by such clear issues. But at the time it was pure intuition on my part. A mysterious communication was established already between us two—in the face of that silent, darkened tropical sea. I was young, too; young enough to make no comment. The man in the water began suddenly to climb up the ladder, and I hastened away from the rail to fetch some clothes.

Before entering the cabin I stood still, listening in the lobby at the foot of the stairs. A faint snore came through the closed door of the chief mate's room. The second mate's door was on the hook, but the darkness in there was absolutely soundless. He, too, was young and could sleep like a stone. Remained the steward, but he was not likely to wake up before he was called. I got a sleeping-suit out of my room and, coming back on deck, saw the naked man from the sea sitting on the main-hatch, glimmering white in the darkness, his elbows on his knees and his head in his hands. In a moment he had concealed his damp body in a sleeping-suit of the same grey-stripe pattern as the one I was wearing and followed me like my double on the poop. Together we moved right aft, barefooted, silent.

"What is it?" I asked in a deadened voice, taking the lighted lamp out of the binnacle, and raising it to his face.

"An ugly business."

He had rather regular features; a good mouth; light eyes under somewhat heavy, dark eyebrows; a smooth, square forehead; no growth on his cheeks; a small, brown moustache, and a well-shaped, round chin. His expression was concentrated, meditative, under the inspecting light of the lamp I held up to his face; such as a man thinking hard in solitude might wear. My sleeping-suit was just right for his size. A well-knit young fellow of twenty-five at most. He caught his lower lip with the edge of white, even teeth.

"Yes," I said, replacing the lamp in the binnacle. The warm, heavy tropical night closed upon his head again.

"There's a ship over there," he murmured.

"Yes, I know. The *Sephora*. Did you know of us?"

"Hadn't the slightest idea. I am the mate of her——" He paused and corrected himself. "I should say I *was*."

"Aha! Something wrong?"

"Yes. Very wrong indeed. I've killed a man."

"What do you mean? Just now?"

"No, on the passage. Weeks ago. Thirty-nine south. When I say a man——"

"Fit of temper," I suggested, confidently.

The shadowy, dark head, like mine, seemed to nod imperceptibly above the ghostly grey of my sleeping-suit. It was, in the night, as though I had been faced by my own reflection in the depths of a sombre and immense mirror.

"A pretty thing to have to own up to for a Conway boy," murmured my double, distinctly.

"You're a Conway boy?"

"I am," he said, as if startled. Then, slowly . . . . "Perhaps you too——"

It was so; but being a couple of years older I had left before he joined. After a quick interchange of dates a silence fell; and I thought suddenly of my absurd mate with his terrific whiskers and the "Bless my soul—you don't say so" type of intellect. My double gave me an inkling of his thoughts by saying: "My father's a parson in Norfolk. Do you see me before a judge and jury on that charge? For myself I can't see the necessity. There are fellows that an angel from heaven—— And I am not that. He was one of those creatures that are just simmering all the time with a silly sort of wickedness. Miserable devils that have no business to live at all. He wouldn't do his duty and wouldn't let anybody else do theirs. But what's the good of talking! You know well enough the sort of ill-conditioned snarling cur——"

He appealed to me as if our experiences had been as identical as our clothes. And I knew well enough the pestiferous danger of such a character where there are no means of legal repression. And I knew well enough also that my double there was no homicidal ruffian. I did not think of asking him for details, and he told me the story roughly in brusque, disconnected sentences. I needed no more. I saw it all going on as though I were myself inside that other sleeping-suit.

"It happened while we were setting a reefed foresail, at dusk. Reefed foresail! You understand the sort of weather. The only sail we had left to keep the ship running; so you may guess what it had been like for days.

Anxious sort of job, that. He gave me some of his cursed insolence at the sheet. I tell you I was overdone with this terrific weather that seemed to have no end to it. Terrific, I tell you—and a deep ship. I believe the fellow himself was half crazed with funk. It was not time for gentlemanly reproof, so I turned round and felled him like an ox. He up and at me. We closed just as an awful sea made for the ship. All hands saw it coming and took to the rigging, but I had him by the throat, and went on shaking him like a rat, the men above us yelling, 'Look out! look out!' Then a crash as if the sky had fallen on my head. They say that for over ten minutes hardly anything was to be seen of the ship—just the three masts and a bit of the forecastle head and of the poop all awash driving along in a smother of foam. It was a miracle that they found us, jammed together behind the forebits. It's clear that I meant business, because I was holding him by the throat still when they picked us up. He was black in the face. It was too much for them. It seems they rushed us aft together, gripped as we were, screaming 'Murder!' like a lot of lunatics, and broke into the cuddy. And the ship running for her life, touch and go all the time, any minute her last in a sea fit to turn your hair grey only a-looking at it. I understand that the skipper, too, started raving like the rest of them. The man had been deprived of sleep for more than a week, and to have this sprung on him at the height of a furious gale nearly drove him out of his mind. I wonder they didn't fling me overboard after getting the carcass of their precious ship-mate out of my fingers. They had rather a job to separate us, I've been told. A sufficiently fierce story to make an old judge and a respectable jury sit up a bit. The first thing I heard when I came to myself was the maddening howling of that endless gale, and on that the voice of the old man. He was hanging on to my bunk, staring into my face out of his sou'wester.

" 'Mr. Leggatt, you have killed a man. You can act no longer as chief mate of this ship.' "

His care to subdue his voice made it sound monotonous. He rested a hand on the end of the skylight to steady himself with, and all that time did not stir a limb, so far as I could see. "Nice little tale for a quiet tea-party," he concluded in the same tone.

One of my hands, too, rested on the end of the skylight; neither did I stir a limb, so far as I knew. We stood less than a foot from each other. It occurred to me that if old "Bless my soul—you don't say so" were to put his head up the companion and catch sight of us, he would think he was seeing double, or imagine himself come upon a scene of weird witchcraft; the strange captain having a quiet confabulation by the wheel with his own grey ghost. I became very much concerned to prevent anything of the sort. I heard the other's soothing undertone.

"My father's a parson in Norfolk," it said. Evidently he had forgotten he had told me this important fact before. Truly a nice little tale.

"You had better slip down into my stateroom now," I said, moving off stealthily. My double followed my movements; our bare feet made no sound; I let him in, closed the door with care, and, after giving a call to the second mate, returned on deck for my relief.

"Not much sign of any wind yet," I remarked when he approached.

"No, sir. Not much," he assented, sleepily, in his

hoarse voice, with just enough deference, no more, and barely suppressing a yawn.

"Well, that's all you have to look out for. You have got your orders."

"Yes, sir."

I paced a turn or two on the poop and saw him take up his position face forward with his elbow in the rat-lines of the mizzen-rigging before I went below. The mate's faint snoring was still going on peacefully. The cuddy lamp was burning over the table on which stood a vase with flowers, a polite attention from the ship's provision merchant—the last flowers we should see for the next three months at the very least. Two bunches of bananas hung from the beam symmetrically, one on each side of the rudder-casing. Everything was as before in the ship—except that two of her captain's sleeping-suits were simultaneously in use, one motionless in the cuddy, the other keeping very still in the captain's stateroom.

It must be explained here that my cabin had the form of the capital letter L, the door being within the angle and opening into the short part of the letter. A couch was to the left, the bed-place to the right; my writing-desk and the chronometers' table faced the door. But any one opening it, unless he stepped right inside, had no view of what I call the long (or vertical) part of the letter. It contained some lockers surmounted by a book-case; and a few clothes, a thick jacket or two, caps, oil-skin coat, and such like, hung on hooks. There was at the bottom of that part a door opening into my bath-room, which could be entered also directly from the sa-loon. But that way was never used.

The mysterious arrival had discovered the advantage

of this particular shape. Entering my room, lighted strongly by a big bulkhead lamp swung on gimbals above my writing-desk, I did not see him anywhere till he stepped out quietly from behind the coats hung in the recessed part.

"I heard somebody moving about, and went in there at once," he whispered.

I, too, spoke under my breath.

"Nobody is likely to come in here without knocking and getting permission."

He nodded. His face was thin and the sunburn faded, as though he had been ill. And no wonder. He had been, I heard presently, kept under arrest in his cabin for nearly seven weeks. But there was nothing sickly in his eyes or in his expression. He was not a bit like me really; yet, as we stood leaning over my bed-place, whispering side by side, with our dark heads together and our backs to the door, anybody bold enough to open it stealthily would have been treated to the uncanny sight of a double captain busy talking in whispers with his other self.

"But all this doesn't tell me how you came to hang on to our side-ladder," I inquired, in the hardly audible murmurs we used, after he had told me something more of the proceedings on board the *Sephora* once the bad weather was over.

"When we sighted Java Head I had had time to think all those matters out several times over. I had six weeks of doing nothing else, and with only an hour or so every evening for a tramp on the quarter-deck."

He whispered, his arms folded on the side of my bed-place, staring through the open port. And I could imagine perfectly the manner of this thinking out—a stubborn if not a steadfast operation; something of which I should have been perfectly incapable.

"I reckoned it would be dark before we closed with the land," he continued, so low that I had to strain my hearing, near as we were to each other, shoulder touching shoulder almost. "So I asked to speak to the old man. He always seemed very sick when he came to see me—as if he could not look me in the face. You know, that foresail saved the ship. She was too deep to have run long under bare poles. And it was I that managed to set it for him. Anyway, he came. When I had him in my cabin—he stood by the door looking at me as if I had the halter round my neck already—I asked him right away to leave my cabin door unlocked at night while the ship was going through Sunda Straits. There would be the Java coast within two or three miles, off Angier Point. I wanted nothing more. I've had a prize for swimming my second year in the Conway."

"I can believe it," I breathed out.

"God only knows why they locked me in every night. To see some of their faces you'd have thought they were afraid I'd go about at night strangling people. Am I a murdering brute? Do I look it? By Jove! If I had been he wouldn't have trusted himself like that into my room. You'll say I might have chucked him aside and bolted out, there and then—it was dark already. Well, no. And for the same reason I wouldn't think of trying to smash the door. There would have been a rush to stop me at the noise, and I did not mean to get into a confounded scrimmage. Somebody else might have got killed—for I would not have broken out only to get chucked back, and I did not want any more of that work. He refused, looking more sick than ever. He was afraid of the men,

and also of that old second mate of his who had been
sailing with him for years—a grey-headed old humbug;
and his steward, too, had been with him devil knows
how long—seventeen years or more—a dogmatic sort of
loafer who hated me like poison, just because I was the
chief mate. No chief mate ever made more than one
voyage in the *Sephora*, you know. Those two old chaps
ran the ship. Devil only knows what the skipper wasn't
afraid of (all his nerve went to pieces altogether in that
hellish spell of bad weather we had)—of what the law
would do to him—of his wife, perhaps. Oh, yes! she's on
board. Though I don't think she would have meddled.
She would have been only too glad to have me out of
the ship in any way. The 'brand of Cain' business, don't
you see. That's all right. I was ready enough to go off
wandering on the face of the earth—and that was price
enough to pay for an Abel of that sort. Anyhow, he
wouldn't listen to me. 'This thing must take its course.
I represent the law here.' He was shaking like a leaf.
'So you won't?' 'No!' 'Then I hope you will be able to
sleep on that,' I said, and turned my back on him. 'I
wonder that *you* can,' cries he, and locks the door.

"Well, after that, I couldn't. Not very well. That was
three weeks ago. We have had a slow passage through
the Java Sea; drifted about Carimata for ten days. When
we anchored here they thought, I suppose, it was all
right. The nearest land (and that's five miles) is the
ship's destination; the consul would soon set about
catching me; and there would have been no object in
bolting to these islets there. I don't suppose there's a
drop of water on them. I don't know how it was, but
to-night that steward, after bringing me my supper,
went out to let me eat it, and left the door unlocked.

And I ate it—all there was, too. After I had finished I
strolled out on the quarter-deck. I don't know that I
meant to do anything. A breath of fresh air was all I
wanted, I believe. Then a sudden temptation came over
me. I kicked off my slippers and was in the water before
I had made up my mind fairly. Somebody heard the
splash and they raised an awful hullabaloo. 'He's gone!
Lower the boats! He's committed suicide! No, he's swimming.' Certainly I was swimming. It's not so easy for a
swimmer like me to commit suicide by drowning. I
landed on the nearest islet before the boat left the ship's
side. I heard them pulling about in the dark, hailing,
and so on, but after a bit they gave up. Everything qui-
eted down and the anchorage became as still as death.
I sat down on a stone and began to think. I felt certain
they would start searching for me at daylight. There was
no place to hide on those stony things—and if there had
been, what would have been the good? But now I was
clear of that ship, I was not going back. So after a while
I took off all my clothes, tied them up in a bundle with
a stone inside, and dropped them in the deep water
on the outer side of that islet. That was suicide enough
for me. Let them think what they liked, but I didn't
mean to drown myself. I meant to swim till I sank—but
that's not the same thing. I struck out for another of
these little islands, and it was from that one that I first
saw your riding-light. Something to swim for. I went
on easily, and on the way I came upon a flat rock a foot
or two above water. In the daytime, I dare say, you
might make it out with a glass from your poop. I scrambled up on it and rested myself for a bit. Then I made
another start. That last spell must have been over a
mile."

His whisper was getting fainter and fainter, and all the time he stared straight out through the port-hole, in which there was not even a star to be seen. I had not interrupted him. There was something that made comment impossible in his narrative, or perhaps in himself; a sort of feeling, a quality, which I can't find a name for. And when he ceased, all I found was a futile whisper: "So you swam for our light?"

"Yes—straight for it. It was something to swim for. I couldn't see any stars low down because the coast was in the way, and I couldn't see the land, either. The water was like glass. One might have been swimming in a confounded thousand-feet deep cistern with no place for scrambling out anywhere; but what I didn't like was the notion of swimming round and round like a crazed bullock before I gave out; and as I didn't mean to go back . . . No. Do you see me being hauled back, stark naked, off one of these little islands by the scruff of the neck and fighting like a wild beast? Somebody would have got killed for certain, and I did not want any of that. So I went on. Then your ladder——"

"Why didn't you hail the ship?" I asked, a little louder.

He touched my shoulder lightly. Lazy footsteps came right over our heads and stopped. The second mate had crossed from the other side of the poop and might have been hanging over the rail, for all we knew.

"He couldn't hear us talking—could he?" My double breathed into my very ear, anxiously.

His anxiety was an answer, a sufficient answer, to the question I had put to him. An answer containing all the difficulty of that situation. I closed the port-hole quietly, to make sure. A louder word might have been overheard.

"Who's that?" he whispered then.

"My second mate. But I don't know much more of the fellow than you do."

And I told him a little about myself. I had been appointed to take charge while I least expected anything of the sort, not quite a fortnight ago. I didn't know either the ship or the people. Hadn't had the time in port to look about me or size anybody up. And as to the crew, all they knew was that I was appointed to take the ship home. For the rest, I was almost as much of a stranger on board as himself, I said. And at the moment I felt it most acutely. I felt that it would take very little to make me a suspect person in the eyes of the ship's company.

He had turned about meantime; and we, the two strangers in the ship, faced each other in identical attitudes.

"Your ladder—" he murmured, after a silence. "Who'd have thought of finding a ladder hanging over at night in a ship anchored out here! I felt just then a very unpleasant faintness. After the life I've been leading for nine weeks, anybody would have got out of condition. I wasn't capable of swimming round as far as your rudder-chains. And, lo and behold! there was a ladder to get hold of. After I gripped it I said to myself, 'What's the good?' When I saw a man's head looking over I thought I would swim away presently and leave him shouting—in whatever language it was. I didn't mind being looked at. I—I liked it. And then you speaking to me so quietly—as if you had expected me—made me hold on a little longer. It had been a confounded lonely time—I don't mean while swimming. I was glad to talk a little to somebody that didn't belong to the *Sephora*.

As to asking for the captain, that was a mere impulse. It could have been no use, with all the ship knowing about me and the other people pretty certain to be round here in the morning. I don't know—I wanted to be seen, to talk with somebody, before I went on. I don't know what I would have said. . . . 'Fine night, isn't it?' or something of the sort."

"Do you think they will be round here presently?" I asked with some incredulity.

"Quite likely," he said, faintly.

He looked extremely haggard all of a sudden. His head rolled on his shoulders.

"H'm. We shall see then. Meantime get into that bed," I whispered. "Want help? There."

It was a rather high bed-place with a set of drawers underneath. This amazing swimmer really needed the lift I gave him by seizing his leg. He tumbled in, rolled over on his back, and flung one arm across his eyes. And then, with his face nearly hidden, he must have looked exactly as I used to look in that bed. I gazed upon my other self for a while before drawing across carefully the two green serge curtains which ran on a brass rod. I thought for a moment of pinning them together for greater safety, but I sat down on the couch, and once there I felt unwilling to rise and hunt for a pin. I would do it in a moment. I was extremely tired, in a peculiarly intimate way, by the strain of stealthiness, by the effort of whispering and the general secrecy of this excitement. It was three o'clock by now and I had been on my feet since nine, but I was not sleepy; I could not have gone to sleep. I sat there, fagged out, looking at the curtains, trying to clear my mind of the confused sensation of being in two places at once, and greatly bothered by an exasperating knocking in my head. It was a relief to discover suddenly that it was not in my head at all, but on the outside of the door. Before I could collect myself the words "Come in" were out of my mouth, and the steward entered with a tray, bringing in my morning coffee. I had slept, after all, and I was so frightened that I shouted, "This way! I am here, steward," as though he had been miles away. He put down the tray on the table next the couch and only then said, very quietly, "I can see you are here, sir." I felt him give me a keen look, but I dared not meet his eyes just then. He must have wondered why I had drawn the curtains of my bed before going to sleep on the couch. He went out, hooking the door open as usual.

I heard the crew washing decks above me. I knew I would have been told at once if there had been any wind. Calm, I thought, and I was doubly vexed. Indeed, I felt dual more than ever. The steward reappeared suddenly in the doorway. I jumped up from the couch so quickly that he gave a start.

"What do you want here?"

"Close your port, sir—they are washing decks."

"It is closed," I said, reddening.

"Very well, sir." But he did not move from the doorway and returned my stare in an extraordinary, equivocal manner for a time. Then his eyes wavered, all his expression changed, and in a voice unusually gentle, almost coaxingly:

"May I come in to take the empty cup away, sir?"

"Of course!" I turned my back on him while he popped in and out. Then I unhooked and closed the door and even pushed the bolt. This sort of thing could not go on very long. The cabin was as hot as an oven, too. I took a peep at my double, and discovered that he had not moved, his arm was still over his eyes; but his chest heaved; his hair was wet; his chin glistened with perspiration. I reached over him and opened the port.

"I must show myself on deck," I reflected.

Of course, theoretically, I could do what I liked, with no one to say nay to me within the whole circle of the horizon; but to lock my cabin door and take the key away I did not dare. Directly I put my head out of the companion I saw the group of my two officers, the second mate barefooted, the chief mate in long india-rubber boots, near the break of the poop, and the steward half-way down the poop-ladder talking to them eagerly. He happened to catch sight of me and dived, the second ran down on the main-deck shouting some order or other, and the chief mate came to meet me, touching his cap.

There was a sort of curiosity in his eye that I did not like. I don't know whether the steward had told them that I was "queer" only, or downright drunk, but I know the man meant to have a good look at me. I watched him coming with a smile which, as he got into point-blank range, took effect and froze his very whiskers. I did not give him time to open his lips.

"Square the yards by lifts and braces before the hands go to breakfast."

It was the first particular order I had given on board that ship; and I stayed on deck to see it executed, too. I had felt the need of asserting myself without loss of time. That sneering young cub got taken down a peg or two on that occasion, and I also seized the opportunity of having a good look at the face of every foremast man as they filed past me to go to the after braces. At breakfast time, eating nothing myself, I presided with such frigid dignity that the two mates were only too glad to escape from the cabin as soon as decency permitted; and all the time the dual working of my mind distracted me almost to the point of insanity. I was constantly watching myself, my secret self, as dependent on my actions as my own personality, sleeping in that bed, behind that door which faced me as I sat at the head of the table. It was very much like being mad, only it was worse because one was aware of it.

I had to shake him for a solid minute, but when at last he opened his eyes it was in the full possession of his senses, with an inquiring look.

"All's well so far," I whispered. "Now you must vanish into the bath-room."

He did so, as noiseless as a ghost, and then I rang for the steward, and facing him boldly, directed him to tidy up my stateroom while I was having my bath—"and be quick about it." As my tone admitted of no excuses, he said, "Yes, sir," and ran off to fetch his dust-pan and brushes. I took a bath and did most of my dressing, splashing, and whistling softly for the steward's edification, while the secret sharer of my life stood drawn up bolt upright in that little space, his face looking very sunken in daylight, his eyelids lowered under the stern, dark line of his eyebrows drawn together by a slight frown.

When I left him there to go back to my room the steward was finishing dusting. I sent for the mate and engaged him in some insignificant conversation. It was, as it were, trifling with the terrific character of his whiskers; but my object was to give him an opportunity for a good look at my cabin. And then I could at last shut, with a clear conscience, the door of my stateroom and get my double back into the recessed part. There was nothing else for it. He had to sit still on a small folding stool, half smothered by the heavy coats hanging there. We listened to the steward going into the bath-room out of the saloon, filling the water-bottles there, scrubbing the bath, setting things to rights, whisk, bang, clatter—out again into the saloon—turn the key—click. Such was my scheme for keeping my second self invisible. Nothing better could be contrived under the circumstances. And there we sat; I at my writing-desk ready to appear busy with some papers, he behind me out of sight of the door. It would not have been prudent to talk in daytime; and I could not have stood the excitement of that queer sense of whispering to myself. Now and then, glancing over my shoulder, I saw him far back there, sitting rigidly on the low stool, his bare feet close together, his arms folded, his head hanging on his breast—and perfectly still. Anybody would have taken him for me.

I was fascinated by it myself. Every moment I had to glance over my shoulder. I was looking at him when a voice outside the door said:

"Beg pardon, sir."

"Well!" . . . I kept my eyes on him, and so when the voice outside the door announced, "There's a ship's boat coming our way, sir," I saw him give a start—the first movement he had made for hours. But he did not raise his bowed head.

"All right. Get the ladder over."

I hesitated. Should I whisper something to him? But

what? His immobility seemed to have been never disturbed. What could I tell him he did not know already? . . . Finally I went on deck.

II

The skipper of the *Sephora* had a thin red whisker all round his face, and the sort of complexion that goes with hair of that colour; also the particular, rather smeary shade of blue in the eyes. He was not exactly a showy figure; his shoulders were high, his stature but middling—one leg slightly more bandy than the other. He shook hands, looking vaguely around. A spiritless tenacity was his main characteristic, I judged. I behaved with a politeness which seemed to disconcert him. Perhaps he was shy. He mumbled to me as if he were ashamed of what he was saying; gave his name (it was something like Archbold—but at this distance of years I hardly am sure), his ship's name, and a few other particulars of that sort, in the manner of a criminal making a reluctant and doleful confession. He had had terrible weather on the passage out—terrible—terrible—wife aboard, too.

By this time we were seated in the cabin and the steward brought in a tray with a bottle and glasses. "Thanks! No." Never took liquor. Would have some water, though. He drank two tumblerfuls. Terrible thirsty work. Ever since daylight had been exploring the islands round his ship.

"What was that for—fun?" I asked, with an appearance of polite interest.

"No!" He sighed. "Painful duty."

As he persisted in his mumbling and I wanted my double to hear every word, I hit upon the notion of informing him that I regretted to say I was hard of hearing.

"Such a young man, too!" he nodded, keeping his smeary blue, unintelligent eyes fastened upon me. "What was the cause of it—some disease?" he inquired, without the least sympathy and as if he thought that, if so, I'd got no more than I deserved.

"Yes; disease," I admitted in a cheerful tone which seemed to shock him. But my point was gained, because he had to raise his voice to give me his tale. It is not worth while to record that version. It was just over two months since all this had happened, and he had thought so much about it that he seemed completely muddled as to its bearings, but still immensely impressed.

"What would you think of such a thing happening on board your own ship? I've had the *Sephora* for these fifteen years. I am a well-known shipmaster."

He was densely distressed—and perhaps I should have sympathized with him if I had been able to detach my mental vision from the unsuspected sharer of my cabin as though he were my second self. There he was on the other side of the bulkhead, four or five feet from us, no more, as we sat in the saloon. I looked politely at Captain Archbold (if that was his name), but it was the other I saw, in a grey sleeping-suit, seated on a low stool, his bare feet close together, his arms folded, and every word said between us falling into the ears of his dark head bowed on his chest.

"I have been at sea now, man and boy, for seven-and-thirty years, and I've never heard of such a thing happening in an English ship. And that it should be my ship. Wife on board, too."

I was hardly listening to him.

"Don't you think," I said, "that the heavy sea which, you told me, came aboard just then might have killed the man? I have seen the sheer weight of a sea kill a man very neatly, by simply breaking his neck."

"Good God!" he uttered, impressively, fixing his smeary blue eyes on me. "The sea! No man killed by the sea ever looked like that." He seemed positively scandalized at my suggestion. And as I gazed at him, certainly not prepared for anything original on his part, he advanced his head close to mine and thrust his tongue out at me so suddenly that I couldn't help starting back.

After scoring over my calmness in this graphic way he nodded wisely. If I had seen the sight, he assured me, I would never forget it as long as I lived. The weather was too bad to give the corpse a proper sea burial. So next day at dawn they took it up on the poop, covering its face with a bit of bunting; he read a short prayer, and then, just as it was, in its oilskins and long boots, they launched it amongst those mountainous seas that seemed ready every moment to swallow up the ship herself and the terrified lives on board of her.

"That reefed foresail saved you," I threw in.

"Under God—it did," he exclaimed fervently. "It was by a special mercy, I firmly believe, that it stood some of those hurricane squalls."

"It was the setting of that sail which——" I began.

"God's own hand in it," he interrupted me. "Nothing less could have done it. I don't mind telling you that I hardly dared give the order. It seemed impossible that we could touch anything without losing it, and then our last hope would have been gone."

The terror of that gale was on him yet. I let him go on for a bit, then said, casually—as if returning to a minor subject:

"You were very anxious to give up your mate to the shore people, I believe?"

He was. To the law. His obscure tenacity on that point had in it something incomprehensible and a little awful; something, as it were, mystical, quite apart from his anxiety that he should not be suspected of "countenancing any doings of that sort." Seven-and-thirty virtuous years at sea, of which over twenty of immaculate command, and the last fifteen in the *Sephora*, seemed to have laid him under some pitiless obligation.

"And you know," he went on, groping shamefacedly amongst his feelings, "I did not engage that young fellow. His people had some interest with my owners. I was in a way forced to take him on. He looked very smart, very gentlemanly, and all that. But do you know —I never liked him, somehow. I am a plain man. You see, he wasn't exactly the sort for the chief mate of a ship like the *Sephora*."

I had become so connected in thoughts and impressions with the secret sharer of my cabin that I felt as if I, personally, were being given to understand that I, too, was not the sort that would have done for the chief mate of a ship like the *Sephora*. I had no doubt of it in my mind.

"Not at all the style of man. You understand," he insisted, superfluously, looking at me.

I smiled urbanely. He seemed at a loss for a while.

"I suppose I must report a suicide."

"Beg pardon?"

"Sui-cide! That's what I'll have to write to my owners directly I get in."

"Unless you manage to recover him before to-morrow," I assented, dispassionately. . . . "I mean, alive."

He mumbled something which I really did not catch,

and I turned my ear to him in a puzzled manner. He fairly bawled:

"The land—I say, the mainland is at least seven miles off my anchorage."

"About that."

My lack of excitement, of curiosity, of surprise, of any sort of pronounced interest, began to arouse his distrust. But except for the felicitous pretense of deafness I had not tried to pretend anything. I had felt utterly incapable of playing the part of ignorance properly, and therefore was afraid to try. It is also certain that he had brought some ready-made suspicions with him, and that he viewed my politeness as a strange and unnatural phenomenon. And yet how else could I have received him? Not heartily! That was impossible for psychological reasons, which I need not state here. My only object was to keep off his inquiries. Surlily? Yes, but surliness might have provoked a point-blank question. From its novelty to him and from its nature, punctilious courtesy was the manner best calculated to restrain the man. But there was the danger of his breaking through my defense bluntly. I could not, I think, have met him by a direct lie, also for psychological (not moral) reasons. If he had only known how afraid I was of his putting my feeling of identity with the other to the test! But, strangely enough—(I thought of it only afterwards)—I believe that he was not a little disconcerted by the reverse side of that weird situation, by something in me that reminded him of the man he was seeking—suggested a mysterious similitude to the young fellow he had distrusted and disliked from the first.

However that might have been, the silence was not very prolonged. He took another oblique step.

"I reckon I had no more than a two-mile pull to your ship. Not a bit more."

"And quite enough, too, in this awful heat," I said.

Another pause full of mistrust followed. Necessity, they say, is mother of invention, but fear, too, is not barren of ingenious suggestions. And I was afraid he would ask me point-blank for news of my other self.

"Nice little saloon, isn't it?" I remarked, as if noticing for the first time the way his eyes roamed from one closed door to the other. "And very well fitted out, too. Here, for instance," I continued, reaching over the back of my seat negligently and flinging the door open, "is my bath-room."

He made an eager movement, but hardly gave it a glance. I got up, shut the door of the bath-room, and invited him to have a look round, as if I were very proud of my accommodation. He had to rise and be shown round, but he went through the business without any raptures whatever.

"And now we'll have a look at my stateroom," I declared, in a voice as loud as I dared to make it, crossing the cabin to the starboard side with purposely heavy steps.

He followed me in and gazed around. My intelligent double had vanished. I played my part.

"Very convenient—isn't it?"

"Very nice. Very comf . . ." He didn't finish and went out brusquely as if to escape from some unrighteous wiles of mine. But it was not to be. I had been too frightened not to feel vengeful; I felt I had him on the run, and I meant to keep him on the run. My polite insistence must have had something menacing in it, because he gave in suddenly. And I did not let him off a single item;

mate's room, pantry, storerooms, the very sail-locker which was also under the poop—he had to look into them all. When at last I showed him out on the quarter-deck he drew a long, spiritless sigh, and mumbled dismally that he must really be going back to his ship now. I desired my mate, who had joined us, to see to the captain's boat.

The man of whiskers gave a blast on the whistle which he used to wear hanging round his neck, and yelled, "*Sephora's* away!" My double down there in my cabin must have heard, and certainly could not feel more relieved than I. Four fellows came running out from somewhere forward and went over the side, while my own men, appearing on deck too, lined the rail. I escorted my visitor to the gangway ceremoniously, and nearly overdid it. He was a tenacious beast. On the very ladder he lingered, and in that unique, guiltily conscientious manner of sticking to the point:

"I say . . . you . . . you don't think that——"

I covered his voice loudly:

"Certainly not. . . . I am delighted. Goodbye."

I had an idea of what he meant to say, and just saved myself by the privilege of defective hearing. He was too shaken generally to insist, but my mate, close witness of that parting, looked mystified and his face took on a thoughtful cast. As I did not want to appear as if I wished to avoid all communication with my officers, he had the opportunity to address me.

"Seems a very nice man. His boat's crew told our chaps a very extraordinary story, if what I am told by the steward is true. I suppose you had it from the captain, sir?"

"Yes. I had a story from the captain."

"A very horrible affair—isn't it, sir?"

"It is."

"Beats all these tales we hear about murders in Yankee ships."

"I don't think it beats them. I don't think it resembles them in the least."

"Bless my soul—you don't say so! But of course I've no acquaintance whatever with American ships, not I, so I couldn't go against your knowledge. It's horrible enough for me. . . . But the queerest part is that those fellows seemed to have some idea the man was hidden aboard here. They had really. Did you ever hear of such a thing?"

"Preposterous—isn't it?"

We were walking to and fro athwart the quarter-deck. No one of the crew forward could be seen (the day was Sunday), and the mate pursued:

"There was some little dispute about it. Our chaps took offense. 'As if we would harbour a thing like that,' they said. 'Wouldn't you like to look for him in our coal-hole?' Quite a tiff. But they made it up in the end. I suppose he did drown himself. Don't you, sir?"

"I don't suppose anything."

"You have no doubt in the matter, sir?"

"None whatever."

I left him suddenly. I felt I was producing a bad impression, but with my double down there it was most trying to be on deck. And it was almost as trying to be below. Altogether a nerve-trying situation. But on the whole I felt less torn in two when I was with him. There was no one in the whole ship whom I dared take into my confidence. Since the hands had got to know his story, it would have been impossible to pass him off for any one else, and an accidental discovery was to be dreaded now more than ever. . . .

The steward being engaged in laying the table for dinner, we could talk only with our eyes when I first went down. Later in the afternoon we had a cautious try at whispering. The Sunday quietness of the ship was against us; the elements, the men were against us—everything was against us in our secret partnership; time itself—for this could not go on forever. The very trust in Providence was, I suppose, denied to his guilt. Shall I confess that this thought cast me down very much? And as to the chapter of accidents which counts for so much in the book of success, I could only hope that it was closed. For what favourable accident could be expected?

"Did you hear everything?" were my first words as soon as we took up our position side by side, leaning over my bed-place.

He had. And the proof of it was his earnest whisper, "The man told you he hardly dared to give the order."

I understood the reference to be to that saving foresail.

"Yes. He was afraid of it being lost in the setting."

"I assure you he never gave the order. He may think he did, but he never gave it. He stood there with me on the break of the poop after the maintopsail blew away, and whimpered about our last hope—positively whimpered about it and nothing else—and the night coming on! To hear one's skipper go on like that in such weather was enough to drive any fellow out of his mind. It worked me up into a sort of desperation. I just took it into my own hands and went away from him, boiling, and—— But what's the use telling you? *You* know!

. . . Do you think that if I had not been pretty fierce
with them I should have got the men to do anything?
Not I! The bo's'n perhaps? Perhaps! It wasn't a heavy
sea—it was a sea gone mad! I suppose the end of the
world will be something like that; and a man may have
the heart to see it coming once and be done with it—
but to have to face it day after day——— I don't blame
anybody. I was precious little better than the rest. Only
—I was an officer of that old coal-wagon, anyhow———"

"I quite understand," I conveyed that sincere assur-
ance into his ear. He was out of breath with whispering;
I could hear him pant slightly. It was all very simple.
The same strung-up force which had given twenty-four
men a chance, at least, for their lives, had, in a sort of
recoil, crushed an unworthy mutinous existence.

But I had no leisure to weigh the merits of the matter
—footsteps in the saloon, a heavy knock. "There's enough
wind to get under way with, sir." Here was the call of a
new claim upon my thoughts and even upon my feelings.

"Turn the hands up," I cried through the door. "I'll
be on deck directly."

I was going out to make the acquaintance of my ship.
Before I left the cabin our eyes met—the eyes of the
only two strangers on board. I pointed to the recessed
part where the little camp-stool awaited him and laid
my fingers on my lips. He made a gesture—somewhat
vague—a little mysterious, accompanied by a faint smile,
as if of regret.

This is not the place to enlarge upon the sensations
of a man who feels for the first time a ship move under
his feet to his own independent word. In my case they
were not unalloyed. I was not wholly alone with my
command; for there was that stranger in my cabin. Or

rather, I was not completely and wholly with her. Part
of me was absent. That mental feeling of being in two
places at once affected me physically as if the mood of
secrecy had penetrated my very soul. Before an hour
had elapsed since the ship had begun to move, having
occasion to ask the mate (he stood by my side) to take
a compass bearing of the Pagoda, I caught myself reaching up to his ear in whispers. I say I caught myself, but
enough had escaped to startle the man. I can't describe
it otherwise than by saying that he shied. A grave, preoccupied manner, as though he were in possession of
some perplexing intelligence, did not leave him henceforth. A little later I moved away from the rail to look at
the compass with such a stealthy gait that the helmsman
noticed it—and I could not help noticing the unusual
roundness of his eyes. These are trifling instances, though
it's to no commander's advantage to be suspected of
ludicrous eccentricities. But I was also more seriously
affected. There are to a seaman certain words, gestures,
that should in given conditions come as naturally, as instinctively as the winking of a menaced eye. A certain
order should spring on to his lips without thinking; a
certain sign should get itself made, so to speak, without reflection. But all unconscious alertness had abandoned me. I had to make an effort of will to recall myself back (from the cabin) to the conditions of the moment. I felt that I was appearing an irresolute commander to those people who were watching me more or
less critically.

And, besides, there were the scares. On the second
day out, for instance, coming off the deck in the afternoon (I had straw slippers on my bare feet) I stopped at
the open pantry door and spoke to the steward. He

was doing something there with his back to me. At the sound of my voice he nearly jumped out of his skin, as the saying is, and incidentally broke a cup.

"What on earth's the matter with you?" I asked, astonished.

He was extremely confused. "Beg your pardon, sir. I made sure you were in your cabin."

"You see I wasn't."

"No, sir. I could have sworn I had heard you moving in there not a moment ago. It's most extraordinary . . . very sorry, sir."

I passed on with an inward shudder. I was so identified with my secret double that I did not even mention the fact in those scanty, fearful whispers we exchanged. I suppose he had made some slight noise of some kind or other. It would have been miraculous if he hadn't at one time or another. And yet, haggard as he appeared, he looked always perfectly self-controlled, more than calm —almost invulnerable. On my suggestion he remained almost entirely in the bath-room, which, upon the whole, was the safest place. There could be really no shadow of an excuse for any one ever wanting to go in there, once the steward had done with it. It was a very tiny place. Sometimes he reclined on the floor, his legs bent, his head sustained on one elbow. At others I would find him on the camp-stool, sitting in his grey sleeping-suit and with his cropped dark hair like a patient, unmoved convict. At night I would smuggle him into my bed-place, and we would whisper together, with the regular footfalls of the officer of the watch passing and repassing over our heads. It was an infinitely miserable time. It was lucky that some tins of fine preserves were stowed in a locker in my stateroom; hard bread I could always get hold of; and so he lived on stewed chicken, paté de foie gras, asparagus, cooked oysters, sardines—on all sorts of abominable sham delicacies out of tins. My early morning coffee he always drank; and it was all I dared do for him in that respect.

Every day there was the horrible manoeuvring to go through so that my room and then the bath-room should be done in the usual way. I came to hate the sight of the steward, to abhor the voice of that harmless man. I felt that it was he who would bring on the disaster of discovery. It hung like a sword over our heads.

The fourth day out, I think (we were then working down the east side of the Gulf of Siam, tack for tack, in light winds and smooth water)—the fourth day, I say, of this miserable juggling with the unavoidable, as we sat at our evening meal, that man, whose slightest movement I dreaded, after putting down the dishes ran up on deck busily. This could not be dangerous. Presently he came down again; and then it appeared that he had remembered a coat of mine which I had thrown over a rail to dry after having been wetted in a shower which had passed over the ship in the afternoon. Sitting stolidly at the head of the table I became terrified at the sight of the garment on his arm. Of course he made for my door. There was no time to lose.

"Steward," I thundered. My nerves were so shaken that I could not govern my voice and conceal my agitation. This was the sort of thing that made my terrifically whiskered mate tap his forehead with his forefinger. I had detected him using that gesture while talking on deck with a confidential air to the carpenter. It was too far to hear a word, but I had no doubt that this pantomime could only refer to the strange new captain.

"Yes, sir," the pale-faced steward turned resignedly to me. It was this maddening course of being shouted at, checked without rhyme or reason, arbitrarily chased out of my cabin, suddenly called into it, sent flying out of his pantry on incomprehensible errands, that accounted for the growing wretchedness of his expression.

"Where are you going with that coat?"

"To your room, sir."

"Is there another shower coming?"

"I'm sure I don't know, sir. Shall I go up again and see, sir?"

"No! never mind."

My object was attained, as of course my other self in there would have heard everything that passed. During this interlude my two officers never raised their eyes off their respective plates; but the lip of that confounded cub, the second mate, quivered visibly.

I expected the steward to hook my coat on and come out at once. He was very slow about it; but I dominated my nervousness sufficiently not to shout after him. Suddenly I became aware (it could be heard plainly enough) that the fellow for some reason or other was opening the door of the bath-room. It was the end. The place was literally not big enough to swing a cat in. My voice died in my throat and I went stony all over. I expected to hear a yell of surprise and terror, and made a movement, but had not the strength to get on my legs. Everything remained still. Had my second self taken the poor wretch by the throat? I don't know what I could have done next moment if I had not seen the steward come out of my room, close the door, and then stand quietly by the sideboard.

"Saved," I thought. "But, no! Lost! Gone! He was gone!"

I laid my knife and fork down and leaned back in my chair. My head swam. After a while, when sufficiently recovered to speak in a steady voice, I instructed my mate to put the ship round at eight o'clock himself.

"I won't come on deck," I went on. "I think I'll turn in, and unless the wind shifts I don't want to be disturbed before midnight. I feel a bit seedy."

"You did look middling bad a little while ago," the chief mate remarked without showing any great concern.

They both went out, and I stared at the steward clearing the table. There was nothing to be read on that wretched man's face. But why did he avoid my eyes, I asked myself. Then I thought I should like to hear the sound of his voice.

"Steward!"

"Sir!" Startled as usual.

"Where did you hang up that coat?"

"In the bath-room, sir." The usual anxious tone. "It's not quite dry yet, sir."

For some time longer I sat in the cuddy. Had my double vanished as he had come? But of his coming there was an explanation, whereas his disappearance would be inexplicable. . . . I went slowly into my dark room, shut the door, lighted the lamp, and for a time dared not turn round. When at last I did I saw him standing bolt-upright in the narrow recessed part. It would not be true to say I had a shock, but an irresistible doubt of his bodily existence flitted through my mind. Can it be, I asked myself, that he is not visible to other eyes than mine? It was like being haunted. Motionless, with a grave face, he raised his hands slightly at me in a gesture which meant clearly, "Heavens! what a narrow escape!" Narrow indeed. I think I had come creeping quietly as near insanity as any man who has not actually gone over the border. That gesture restrained me, so to speak.

The mate with the terrific whiskers was now putting the ship on the other tack. In the moment of profound silence which follows upon the hands going to their stations I heard on the poop his raised voice: "Hard alee!" and the distant shout of the order repeated on the maindeck. The sails, in that light breeze, made but a faint fluttering noise. It ceased. The ship was coming round slowly; I held my breath in the renewed stillness of expectation; one wouldn't have thought that there was a single living soul on her decks. A sudden brisk shout, "Mainsail haul!" broke the spell, and in the noisy cries and rush overhead of the men running away with the main-brace we two, down in my cabin, came together in our usual position by the bed-place.

He did not wait for my question. "I heard him fumbling here and just managed to squat myself down in the bath," he whispered to me. "The fellow only opened the door and put his arm in to hang the coat up. All the same——"

"I never thought of that," I whispered back, even more appalled than before at the closeness of the shave, and marvelling at that something unyielding in his character which was carrying him through so finely. There was no agitation in his whisper. Whoever was being driven distracted, it was not he. He was sane. And the proof of his sanity was continued when he took up the whispering again.

"It would never do for me to come to life again."

"It was something that a ghost might have said. But what he was alluding to was his old captain's reluctant admission of the theory of suicide. It would obviously serve his turn—if I had understood at all the view which seemed to govern the unalterable purpose of his action.

"You must maroon me as soon as ever you can get amongst these islands off the Cambodge shore," he went on.

"Maroon you! We are not living in a boy's adventure tale," I protested. His scornful whispering took me up.

"We aren't indeed! There's nothing of a boy's tale in this. But there's nothing else for it. I want no more. You don't suppose I am afraid of what can be done to me? Prison or gallows or whatever they may please. But you don't see me coming back to explain such things to an old fellow in a wig and twelve respectable tradesmen, do you? What can they know whether I am guilty or not—or of *what* I am guilty, either? That's my affair. What does the Bible say? 'Driven off the face of the earth.' Very well. I am off the face of the earth now. As I came at night so I shall go."

"Impossible!" I murmured. "You can't."

"Can't? . . . Not naked like a soul on the Day of Judgment, I shall freeze on to this sleeping-suit. The Last Day is not yet—and . . . you have understood thoroughly. Didn't you?"

I felt suddenly ashamed of myself. I may say truly that I understood—and my hesitation in letting that man swim away from my ship's side had been a mere sham sentiment, a sort of cowardice.

"It can't be done now till next night," I breathed out. "The ship is on the off-shore tack and the wind may fail us."

"As long as I know that you understand," he whispered. "But of course you do. It's a great satisfaction to have got somebody to understand. You seem to have been there on purpose." And in the same whisper, as if we two whenever we talked had to say things to each other which were not fit for the world to hear, he added, "It's very wonderful."

We remained side by side talking in our secret way —but sometimes silent or just exchanging a whispered word or two at long intervals. And as usual he stared through the port. A breath of wind came now and again into our faces. The ship might have been moored in dock, so gently and on an even keel she slipped through the water, that did not murmur even at our passage, shadowy and silent like a phantom sea.

At midnight I went on deck, and to my mate's great surprise put the ship round on the other tack. His terrible whiskers flitted round me in silent criticism. I certainly should not have done it if it had been only a question of getting out of that sleepy gulf as quickly as possible. I believe he told the second mate, who relieved him, that it was a great want of judgment. The other only yawned. That intolerable cub shuffled about so sleepily and lolled against the rails in such a slack, improper fashion that I came down on him sharply.

"Aren't you properly awake yet?"

"Yes, sir! I am awake."

"Well, then, be good enough to hold yourself as if you were. And keep a look-out. If there's any current we'll be closing with some islands before daylight."

The east side of the gulf's fringed with islands, some solitary, others in groups. On the blue background of the high coast they seem to float on silvery patches of calm water, arid and grey, or dark green and rounded like clumps of evergreen bushes, with the larger ones, a mile or two long, showing the outlines of ridges, ribs of grey rock under the dank mantle of matted leafage. Unknown to trade, to travel, almost to geography, the manner of life they harbour is an unsolved secret. There must be villages—settlements of fishermen at least—on the largest of them, and some communication with the world is probably kept up by native craft. But all that forenoon, as we headed for them, fanned along by the faintest of breezes, I saw no sign of man or canoe in the field of the telescope I kept on pointing at the scattered group.

At noon I gave no orders for a change of course, and the mate's whiskers became much concerned and seemed to be offering themselves unduly to my notice. At last I said:

"I am going to stand right in. Quite in—as far as I can take her."

The stare of extreme surprise imparted an air of ferocity also to his eyes, and he looked truly terrific for a moment.

"We're not doing well in the middle of the gulf," I continued, casually. "I am going to look for the land breezes to-night."

"Bless my soul! Do you mean, sir, in the dark amongst the lot of all them islands and reefs and shoals?"

"Well—if there are any regular land breezes at all on this coast one must get close inshore to find them, mustn't one?"

"Bless my soul!" he exclaimed again under his breath. All that afternoon he wore a dreamy, contemplative appearance which in him was a mark of perplexity. After dinner I went into my stateroom as if I meant to take some rest. There we two bent our dark heads over a half-unrolled chart lying on my bed.

"There," I said. "It's got to be Koh-ring. I've been looking at it ever since sunrise. It has got two hills and a low point. It must be inhabited. And on the coast opposite there is what looks like the mouth of a biggish river—with some town, no doubt, not far up. It's the best chance for you that I can see."

"Anything. Koh-ring let it be."

He looked thoughtfully at the chart as if surveying chances and distances from a lofty height—and following with his eyes his own figure wandering on the blank land of Cochin-China, and then passing off that piece of paper clean out of sight into uncharted regions. And it was as if the ship had two captains to plan her course for her. I had been so worried and restless running up and down that I had not had the patience to dress that day. I had remained in my sleeping-suit, with straw slippers and a soft floppy hat. The closeness of the heat in the gulf had been most oppressive, and the crew were used to see me wandering in that airy attire.

"She will clear the south point as she heads now," I whispered into his ear. "Goodness only knows when, though, but certainly after dark. I'll edge her in to half a mile, as far as I may be able to judge in the dark——"

"Be careful," he murmured, warningly—and I realized suddenly that all my future, the only future for which I was fit, would perhaps go irretrievably to pieces in any mishap to my first command.

I could not stop a moment longer in the room. I motioned him to get out of sight and made my way on the poop. That unplayful cub had the watch. I walked up and down for a while thinking things out, then beckoned him over.

"Send a couple of hands to open the two quarter-deck ports," I said, mildly.

He actually had the impudence, or else so forgot himself in his wonder at such an incomprehensible order, as to repeat:

"Open the quarter-deck ports! What for, sir?"

"The only reason you need concern yourself about is because I tell you to do so. Have them opened wide and fastened properly."

He reddened and went off, but I believe made some jeering remark to the carpenter as to the sensible practice of ventilating a ship's quarter-deck. I know he popped into the mate's cabin to impart the fact to him because the whiskers came on deck, as it were by chance, and stole glances at me from below—for signs of lunacy or drunkenness, I suppose.

A little before supper, feeling more restless than ever, I rejoined, for a moment, my second self. And to find him sitting so quietly was surprising, like something against nature, inhuman.

I developed my plan in a hurried whisper.

"I shall stand in as close as I dare and then put her round. I will presently find means to smuggle you out of here into the sail-locker, which communicates with the lobby. But there is an opening, a sort of square for hauling the sails out, which gives straight on the quarter-deck and which is never closed in fine weather, so as to give air to the sails. When the ship's way is deadened in stays and all the hands are aft at the main-braces you will have a clear road to slip out and get overboard through the open quarter-deck port. I've had them both fastened up. Use a rope's end to lower yourself into the water so as to avoid a splash—you know. It could be heard and cause some beastly complication."

He kept silent for a while, then whispered, "I understand."

"I won't be there to see you go," I began with an effort. "The rest . . . I only hope I have understood, too."

"You have. From first to last"—and for the first time there seemed to be a faltering, something strained in his whisper. He caught hold of my arm, but the ringing of the supper bell made me start. He didn't, though; he only released his grip.

After supper I didn't come below again till well past eight o'clock. The faint, steady breeze was loaded with dew; and the wet, darkened sails held all there was of propelling power in it. The night, clear and starry, sparkled darkly, and the opaque, lightless patches shifting slowly against the low stars were the drifting islets. On the port bow there was a big one more distant and shadowily imposing by the great space of sky it eclipsed.

On opening the door I had a back view of my very own self looking at a chart. He had come out of the recess and was standing near the table.

"Quite dark enough," I whispered.

He stepped back and leaned against my bed with a level, quiet glance. I sat on the couch. We had nothing to say to each other. Over our heads the officer of the watch moved here and there. Then I heard him move quickly. I knew what that meant. He was making for the companion; and presently his voice was outside my door.

"We are drawing in pretty fast, sir. Land looks rather close."

"Very well," I answered. "I am coming on deck directly."

I waited till he was gone out of the cuddy, then rose. My double moved too. The time had come to exchange our last whispers, for neither of us was ever to hear each other's natural voice.

"Look here!" I opened a drawer and took out three sovereigns. "Take this anyhow. I've got six and I'd give you the lot, only I must keep a little money to buy some fruit and vegetables for the crew from native boats as we go through Sunda Straits."

He shook his head.

"Take it," I urged him, whispering desperately. "No one can tell what——"

He smiled and slapped meaningly the only pocket of the sleeping-jacket. It was not safe, certainly. But I produced a large old silk handkerchief of mine, and tying the three pieces of gold in a corner, pressed it on him. He was touched, I suppose, because he took it at last and tied it quickly round his waist under the jacket, on his bare skin.

Our eyes met; several seconds elapsed, till, our glances still mingled, I extended my hand and turned the lamp out. Then I passed through the cuddy, leaving the door of my room wide open. . . . "Steward!"

He was still lingering in the pantry in the greatness of his zeal, giving a rub-up to a plated cruet stand the last thing before going to bed. Being careful not to wake up the mate, whose room was opposite, I spoke in an undertone.

He looked round anxiously. "Sir!"

"Can you get me a little hot water from the galley?"

"I am afraid, sir, the galley fire's been out for some time now."

"Go and see."

He flew up the stairs.

"Now," I whispered, loudly, into the saloon—too loudly, perhaps, but I was afraid I couldn't make a sound. He was by my side in an instant—the double captain slipped past the stairs—through a tiny dark passage . . . a sliding door. We were in the sail-locker, scrambling on our knees over the sails. A sudden thought struck me. I saw myself wandering barefooted, bareheaded, the sun beating on my dark poll. I snatched off my floppy hat and tried hurriedly in the dark to ram it on my other self. He dodged and fended off silently. I wonder what he thought had come to me before he understood and suddenly desisted. Our hands met gropingly, lingered united in a steady, motionless clasp for a second. . . . No word was breathed by either of us when they separated.

I was standing quietly by the pantry door when the steward returned.

"Sorry, sir. Kettle barely warm. Shall I light the spirit-lamp?"

"Never mind."

I came out on deck slowly. It was now a matter of conscience to shave the land as close as possible—for now he must go overboard whenever the ship was put in stays. Must! There could be no going back for him. After a moment I walked over to leeward and my heart flew into my mouth at the nearness of the land on the bow. Under any other circumstances I would not have held on a minute longer. The second mate had followed me anxiously.

I looked on till I felt I could command my voice.

"She will weather," I said then in a quiet tone.

"Are you going to try that, sir?" he stammered out incredulously.

I took no notice of him and raised my tone just enough to be heard by the helmsman.

"Keep her good full."

"Good full, sir."

The wind fanned my cheek, the sails slept, the world was silent. The strain of watching the dark loom of the land grow bigger and denser was too much for me. I had shut my eyes—because the ship must go closer. She must! The stillness was intolerable. Were we standing still?

When I opened my eyes the second view started my heart with a thump. The black southern hill of Koh-ring seemed to hang right over the ship like a towering fragment of the everlasting night. On that enormous mass of blackness there was not a gleam to be seen, not a sound to be heard. It was gliding irresistibly towards us and yet seemed already within reach of the hand. I saw the vague figures of the watch grouped in the waist, gazing in awed silence.

"Are you going on, sir?" inquired an unsteady voice at my elbow.

I ignored it. I had to go on.

"Keep her full. Don't check her way. That won't do now," I said, warningly.

"I can't see the sails very well," the helmsman answered me, in strange, quavering tones.

Was she close enough? Already she was, I won't say in the shadow of the land, but in the very blackness of it, already swallowed up as it were, gone too close to be recalled, gone from me altogether.

"Give the mate a call," I said to the young man who stood at my elbow as still as death. "And turn all hands up."

My tone had a borrowed loudness reverberated from the height of the land. Several voices cried out together: "We are all on deck, sir."

Then stillness again, with the great shadow gliding closer, towering higher, without a light, without a sound. Such a hush had fallen on the ship that she might have been a bark of the dead floating in slowly under the very gate of Erebus.

"My God! Where are we?"

It was the mate moaning at my elbow. He was thunderstruck, and as it were deprived of the moral support of his whiskers. He clapped his hands and absolutely cried out, "Lost!"

"Be quiet," I said, sternly.

He lowered his tone, but I saw the shadowy gesture of his despair. "What are we doing here?"

"Looking for the land wind."

He made as if to tear his hair, and addressed me recklessly.

"She will never get out. You have done it, sir. I knew it'd end in something like this. She will never weather, and you are too close now to stay. She'll drift ashore before she's round. O my God!"

I caught his arm as he was raising it to batter his poor devoted head, and shook it violently.

"She's ashore already," he wailed, trying to tear himself away.

"Is she? . . . Keep good full there!"

"Good full, sir," cried the helmsman in a frightened, thin, child-like voice.

I hadn't let go the mate's arm and went on shaking

it. "Ready about, do you hear? You go forward"—shake
—"and stop there"—shake—"and hold your noise"—shake
—"and see these head-sheets properly overhauled"—
shake, shake—shake.

And all the time I dared not look towards the land
lest my heart should fail me. I released my grip at last
and he ran forward as if fleeing for dear life.

I wondered what my double there in the sail-locker
thought of this commotion. He was able to hear everything—and perhaps he was able to understand why, on
my conscience, it had to be thus close—no less. My first
order "Hard alee!" re-echoed ominously under the towering shadow of Koh-ring as if I had shouted in a mountain gorge. And then I watched the land intently. In that
smooth water and light wind it was impossible to feel
the ship coming-to. No! I could not feel her. And my
second self was making now ready to slip out and lower
himself overboard. Perhaps he was gone already . . . ?

The great black mass brooding over our very mastheads began to pivot away from the ship's side silently.
And now I forgot the secret stranger ready to depart,
and remembered only that I was a total stranger to the
ship. I did not know her. Would she do it? How was she
to be handled?

I swung the mainyard and waited helplessly. She was
perhaps stopped, and her very fate hung in the balance,
with the black mass of Koh-ring like the gate of the
everlasting night towering over her taffrail. What would
she do now? Had she way on her yet? I stepped to the
side swiftly, and on the shadowy water I could see nothing except a faint phosphorescent flash revealing the
glassy smoothness of the sleeping surface. It was impossible to tell—and I had not learned yet the feel of my
ship. Was she moving? What I needed was something

easily seen, a piece of paper, which I could throw overboard and watch. I had nothing on me. To run down for it I didn't dare. There was no time. All at once my strained, yearning stare distinguished a white object floating within a yard of the ship's side. White on the black water. A phosphorescent flash passed under it. What was that thing? . . . I recognized my own floppy hat. It must have fallen off his head . . . and he didn't bother. Now I had what I wanted—the saving mark for my eyes. But I hardly thought of my other self, now gone from the ship, to be hidden for ever from all friendly faces, to be a fugitive and a vagabond on the earth, with no brand of the curse on his sane forehead to stay a slaying hand . . . too proud to explain.

And I watched the hat—the expression of my sudden pity for his mere flesh. It had been meant to save his homeless head from the dangers of the sun. And now —behold—it was saving the ship, by serving me for a mark to help out the ignorance of my strangeness. Ha! It was drifting forward, warning me just in time that the ship had gathered sternway.

"Shift the helm," I said in a low voice to the seaman standing still like a statue.

The man's eyes glistened wildly in the binnacle light as he jumped round to the other side and spun round the wheel.

I walked to the break of the poop. On the overshadowed deck all hands stood by the forebraces waiting for my order. The stars ahead seemed to be gliding from right to left. And all was so still in the world that I heard the quiet remark, "She's round," passed in a tone of intense relief between two seamen.

"Let go and haul."

The foreyards ran round with a great noise, amidst

cheery cries. And now the frightful whiskers made themselves heard giving various orders. Already the ship was drawing ahead. And I was alone with her. Nothing! no one in the world should stand now between us, throwing a shadow on the way of silent knowledge and mute affection, the perfect communion of a seaman with his first command.

Walking to the taffrail, I was in time to make out, on the very edge of a darkness thrown by a towering black mass like the very gateway of Erebus—yes, I was in time to catch an evanescent glimpse of my white hat left behind to mark the spot where the secret sharer of my cabin and of my thoughts, as though he were my second self, had lowered himself into the water to take his punishment: a free man, a proud swimmer striking out for a new destiny.

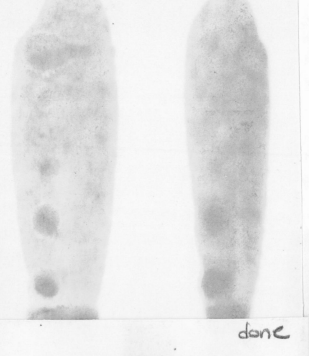

done